*Agricultural
Development
in China
1368-1968*

Dwight H. Perkins is Associate Professor of Modern China Studies and Economics and is an Associate of the East Asian Research Center at Harvard University. He is the author of Market Control and Planning in Communist China and Communist China and Arms Control (with M. H. Halperin).

Agricultural Development in China 1368-1968

By DWIGHT H. PERKINS

With the assistance of
YEH-CHIEN WANG
KUO-YING WANG HSIAO
YUNG-MING SU

ALDINE PUBLISHING COMPANY / CHICAGO

First published 1969 by
Aldine Publishing Company
529 South Wabash
Chicago, Illinois

Library of Congress Catalog Card Number 68–8644
Standard Book Number 20231005
Printed in the United States of America

Foreword

This volume summarizes the results of one of the studies sponsored by the Social Science Research Council Committee on the Economy of China. The Committee was appointed by the Council to stimulate scholarly analysis of the contemporary economic scene in China, with support provided by the Ford Foundation. Although the Committee has been concerned primarily with the developments of the past two decades, it has, on occasion, supported work covering earlier periods when there was likelihood that such work would contribute to our understanding of present trends. The critical agricultural sector is very much a case in point. The broad sweep of Professor Perkins' study yields findings of direct relevance to the problems that the Chinese Communists now face in their efforts to raise farm output and keep pace with a rapidly growing population.

The Committee tries to insure that the volumes published in its series are objective and accurate. In the final analysis, however, both the ultimate responsibility and the full credit for the finished work remain with the author.

WALTER GALENSON
DIRECTOR OF RESEARCH

Preface

Three years ago, with the encouragement of Professor Simon Kuznets, I set out to study Chinese economic history with the intention of writing a general economic history of China. It immediately became apparent to me that there was no systematic work in English that, from an economist's view, analyzed Chinese agricultural development prior to the twentieth century. Since before 1900 there was little of China's economy that was not either within the farm sector or directly connected with it, it was necessary to at least attempt to discern the broad outlines of agricultural development before proceeding with the more general study.

This book represents the fruits of that attempt. Although I alone am responsible, right or wrong, for the analysis in the text, this study could not have been undertaken without the continuing help of a number of individuals. Yeh-chien Wang, an established economic historian in his own right, was of invaluable assistance in getting the project underway and in providing guidance and key references throughout. The particular problem of combing through thousands of local histories (gazetteers) for pre-1900 data would have been a nearly impossible undertaking for me even if my knowledge of *wen-yen* (classical Chinese) were far better than it in fact is. This task has been performed admirably for me by Mrs. Kuo-ying Wang Hsiao and Miss Yung-ming Su.

Others who have been involved at one point or another in helping with the research include Lucy Lee, Thomas Kershner, and Thomas Wiens. Gloria Gerrig oversaw most of the typing and reproduction of the last two drafts of the manuscript.

I have also been particularly fortunate in the number of individuals who have been willing to read earlier drafts of this book and make extensive comments. Professor Kuznets read each draft of every chapter. Professors Ch'uan Han-sheng, Robert F. Dernberger, Robert Hartwell, and Ramon Myers each wrote lengthy comments which were really almost essays in themselves. Numerous others have read parts of the study, but special mention must be made of suggestions by Professors John Fairbank, Leo Orleans, Evelyn Sakakida Rawski, Henry Rosovsky, and Subramanian Swamy.

Finally, throughout these three years, I have received generous financial assistance from the Social Science Research Council's Committee on the Economy of China.

D.H.P.

Contents

Tables

Maps and Charts

Abbreviations and Equivalents

EQUIVALENTS

Weights

1 catty = 1.1 pounds
2 catties = 1 kilogram
100 catties = 1 *picul*
20 *piculs* = 1 metric ton
2000 catties = 1 metric ton

Area

1 *mou* = 0.1647 acre*
6 *mou* = 1 acre (approx.)
15 *mou* = 1 hectare

Capacity

1 *shih* = 100 litres*
10 *tou* = 1 *shih*
10 *sheng* = 1 *tou*

Length

1000 *cash* = 1 *tael* (approx.)
1 *tael* = 1.5 *yuan* (1930's—approx.)
1 *yuan* (1933) = US $0.26 (1933 dollars)
1 *yuan* (1952) = US $0.427 (1952 dollars)

* For pre-modern equivalents, refer to Table G.1.

*Agricultural
Development
in China
1368-1968*

Provincial Map of China

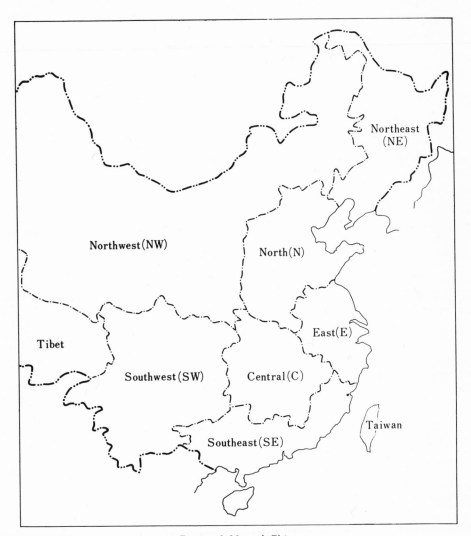

Regional Map of China

CHAPTER ONE

Introduction

China's agriculture today feeds a quarter of the world's population on 7 per cent of the globe's cultivated land. The area sown to crops in China is only 70 per cent of that in the United States, and yet it must provide for three to four times as many people.

By twentieth-century Western standards the people of China have not been well fed, but the fact remains that they have survived and multiplied many-fold during the past six centuries. The energy of Chinese peasant farmers provided the foundation for one of the world's great civilizations. Today the descendants of the men who built those foundations are providing the surplus for the industrialization and modernization of China.

Prior to the twentieth century, the agricultural sector was the economy of China virtually in its entirety. Other sectors either serviced the farm sector or drew their raw materials from it. Until the 1940's and 1950's, industry in China involved little more than the processing of cotton, grain, and other products of the land. Commerce was occupied primarily with the distribution of food and clothing. Only a small mining sector, government services, and perhaps construction were independent of agricultural raw materials (except for food for the workers).

This book is an attempt to explain how China's farm economy responded to the demands of a rising population and still was able to provide a small surplus for the rich, the arts, and industrialization. Were there always new lands to be opened up and cultivated, or did Chinese farmers have to devise ways of raising the yields on existing land? If yields were raised, how were they raised? Did new ideas come from abroad or did they derive from the scholarship of officials and the imagination of an intelligent peasantry? Were there in fact many new ideas in agriculture during the past six centuries?

The period treated in this book begins with the late fourteenth century and ends in the 1960's. Why begin with the fourteenth century, and why cover such a long time span?

The year A.D. 1368 is the founding date of the Ming dynasty. More important, it marks the end of nearly two centuries of violent destruction and loss of life primarily connected with the rise and fall of the Mongols. The Ming dynasty and its successor, the Ch'ing, were not free from war, plague, and famine, but loss of life was kept within sufficient bounds to allow for China's population to rise from a level of 65–80 million people around 1400 to approximately 400 million in the nineteenth century and over 700 million in the 1960's.

The period beginning with the fourteenth century was also one in which there were no obvious or dramatic changes in farming technique or in rural institutions. The single most important change in the entire history of Chinese rural technology was connected with the southward migration into areas suitable to the cultivation of rice.

During the Former and Later Han dynasties (206 B.C.–A.D. 220), China's population and hence its agriculture were concentrated on the North China Plain and to the west of the gorges of the Yellow River where, for reasons of military defense, the capital city was located. The principal grain crop was millet, but wheat, barley, and rice were also grown. A few major irrigation works were built by the government, but grain generally was produced by dry farming methods. The rich wore silk, the peasants were clothed in material made from coarse hemp fibers—cotton was not used for cloth until the Yuan, at least not in any significant quantity. There were also numerous varieties of vegetables and fruits; and meat was provided by hogs, chickens, fish, and dogs.

This picture of dry farming in the north, with millet as the key crop, was transformed rapidly in the centuries following the collapse of the Later Han. During the fourth and fifth centuries A.D., Chinese settlers began to migrate in large numbers into the Yangtze river valley. Initially the methods of cultivation were extremely crude and had much in common with methods employed today in parts of Laos and by the Montagnards in Vietnam. The land was cleared by fire and then flooded and eventually abandoned.

As more people moved south, however, farming became settled and wet rice cultivation as we know it today became dominant. Accompanying the expansion of rice cultivation were the development of new tools, new crop rotations, and hundreds of new seeds. Wet rice, transplanted into flooded fields, required a radically different technology from that used to grow millet and wheat on the parched land of the north.

Long before the fourteenth century, however, the key elements of the rice technology had been developed and had spread to the populated regions where rice was grown. In the six centuries that followed the founding of the Ming dynasty there were few obvious major improvements in farming technique.

Chapters Three and Four present evidence to support the view that there were, in fact, only modest changes in agricultural technology during this period.

Economists and others have long been interested in how a pre-modern rural community makes economic decisions. Some have suggested that in such communities, production moves toward an equilibrium position and then stagnates until new techniques are discovered. Since few new techniques could presumably be discovered without the methods of modern science, farm output was assumed to remain stagnant or nearly so over long periods.

China is one of the few countries in the world where the performance of a pre-modern agricultural sector can be studied over an extended length of time, and the existence of stagnation or the lack of it tested against actual events. Such testing is possible because of China's great historical tradition. For more than two millenia, Chinese scholars and officials have recorded materials relevant to the study of economic history. Many of these materials are useful only in the analysis of governmental institutions. But the requirements and responsibilities of that government were such that much had to be known about the condition of the rural population, and some of this information found its way into local and dynastic histories.

The data in these sources, however, are far from ideal for the purposes of this study. There are many key gaps in the materials available, both quantitative and qualitative, and much of the information is not particularly reliable. Reliability in a study of so long a period depends not only on the faithfulness with which information was recorded originally, but also on the ability of the modern analyst to understand the context in which that information was recorded and used. This context often is far removed from twentieth-century Chinese society, and even more from twentieth-century American society.

The analytical problems are made especially difficult by the slow pace of change in a pre-modern rural economy. When changes took place at all, they occurred over such a long period that even a sensitive contemporary observer might fail to notice them. Thus, in a study such as this, we cannot rely heavily on remarks and essays by scholar-officials of the Ming and Ch'ing periods. Instead we must attempt to piece together as complete a picture as possible from the original records, particularly the quantitative records.

The slow pace of change, the low quality of many Chinese historical statistics, and the inability to rely on contemporary observers all dictate the use of a long period of time in an analysis of China's farm economy. Small differences between one century and the next in such key indicators as per-acre crop yields can be too easily explained away as data errors rather than as real changes in productivity. Differences of 100 per cent or more cannot be dismissed so readily.

Between the fourteenth and nineteenth or twentieth centuries in China, there appear to have been changes of sufficient magnitude to make possible their verification. There may also have been substantial differences between the fifteenth or sixteenth and nineteenth centuries, but it happens that data for the fifteenth and sixteenth centuries are less complete or reliable than those for the fourteenth.

Thus there are two essential reasons for beginning the analysis with the fourteenth century. First, the subsequent five or six centuries cover a period when the basic pattern of China's pre-modern agriculture had been well established from the beginning. It was also a period when population grew slowly but substantially until by the 1950's it was eight to ten times the level prevailing in the late fourteenth century. Chinese farmers, therefore, had to increase their aggregate output even if per capita production remained constant or declined. The question is how they did it. Second, these six centuries cover a period for which useful data are available. Most important, there are reasonably reliable statistics for both the beginning and the end of the period—though not always for the years intervening.

If a study of Chinese agriculture over a period of six centuries makes it possible to discern certain characteristic features of China's pre-modern rural economy, that knowledge in turn contributes to an understanding of Chinese agriculture and Chinese Communist agricultural policies in the 1950's and 1960's. In spite of the reorganizations of rural society that accompanied the establishment of agricultural cooperatives in 1955–56 and the communes in 1958, China's farm technology in 1960 and 1961 in certain fundamental respects had changed little from what prevailed in the nineteenth or even in the fourteenth centuries. Cooperatives and communes as such had not been tried before. But rice continued to be transplanted and fertilized in ways developed long ago. Even the mass mobilization of labor to construct irrigation and flood control works, an important reason for setting up the cooperatives in the first place, was different from previous similar efforts by Chinese emperors and officials only in scale. The construction and water control techniques themselves were little changed.

It was only in the 1960's, following the crisis years of 1959 through 1961, that the Chinese government in Peking began to push a truly modern farm technology. The analysis in this book includes a discussion of the shift in emphasis toward chemical fertilizers and the use of mechanical power that began in the 1960's. It is the belief here that the significance of this change is best understood in historical perspective.

SOURCES AND DATA PROBLEMS

Nine appendixes, and additional discussion in the individual chapters of this book, deal with the quality and internal consistency of the statistics and qualitative data used. An important feature of this study is that it makes use of a wide range of materials from many different kinds of sources. There is some point, therefore, in a brief description of the kinds of sources used and the general view of the validity of the data in them.

For the period prior to 1911, I have relied principally on three types of materials. First are the population and cultivated acreage data kept for tax purposes by the Ming and Ch'ing governments. These figures are subject to biases and for some periods are not usable at all. But for certain periods crucial to the analysis in this study, I believe these figures are an adequate approximation of reality. The reasoning behind this belief is presented in Appendixes A and B.

Second, I have made considerable use of Chinese local histories or gazetteers. Each county (*hsien*), prefecture (*fu*), and province in China kept a record of events and data that were considered significant. The majority of the local histories available in the Harvard-Yenching Library were compiled in the eighteenth and nineteenth centuries, but a number were compiled earlier. More important, the later gazetteers have often faithfully recorded data from earlier editions. Since much of the information was recorded without comment or copied without change from earlier editions, these gazetteers can, for some purposes, be treated as primary sources for data originally published centuries before. For other purposes, however, these histories must be treated as secondary sources. Their principal limitation is that they are commonly little more than records of official activities in a district. Actions in the private sector can sometimes be seen through the eyes and records of officialdom, but only imperfectly.

Finally, I have used agricultural "handbooks" published over the past several centuries by individuals with an interest in farming technique. These are particularly useful in any attempt to discern changes in farm technology over time.

A glance at the References Cited section at the end of this book will make apparent that many other sources besides those described above have been of some use in this study. Memorials from local officials to the emperor sometimes contain useful information. More important, Chinese and Japanese historians have culled large amounts of data from local histories and other sources and have published these data in a readily usable form. I have only scratched the surface of Chinese and Japanese studies completed in recent years.

Any work attempting to make use of such a vast amount of material cannot be the work of a single analyst, even one far more knowledgeable about Chinese history than I. I have had the benefit of many hours, months, and years of highly skilled labor and advice from several assistants and from numerous scholars in this country and abroad. Nor could this study have been attempted if it had not been preceded by a number of pioneering efforts by others, particularly that of Ping-ti Ho.

Materials used in the analysis of agricultural development in twentieth-century China are almost as voluminous as those for the earlier periods. The surveys of the National Agricultural Research Bureau and of John Lossing Buck provide the core data for the 1930's. Substantial use has also been made of the reports and returns of trade of the China Maritime Customs, of the provincial gazetteers compiled by the Ministry of Industries (*Shih-yeh pu*), of village surveys done under the direction of the South Manchurian Railway Company, and of village studies by Chinese and Western scholars, including those of the Joint Commission on Rural Reconstruction. I have even attempted to use some of the data of the Ministry of Agriculture and Commerce (*Nung-shang pu*) for the 1914–1918 period. The most useful single source for the study of the twentieth century has been the national income monograph of Ta-chung Liu and Kung-chia Yeh (1965).

The key data for the twentieth century, from the viewpoint of this study, however, are the State Statistical Bureau estimates for the 1950's, particularly the year 1957. The reporting of economic statistics in China has improved substantially in the twentieth century. This improvement occurred by fits and starts and there have been long periods of retrogression. The best available statistics are those for the 1930's and for 1955–1957. As I argue at greater length in Appendixes A through D, there is reason to believe that the margin of error remaining in the 1955–1957 figures is narrower than those of any other period including the 1930's.[1]

I have, in fact, frequently judged the validity of data for the decades and centuries prior to the 1950's on whether these earlier figures were consistent with those for 1957 and with historical developments in the intervening periods. I have also attempted to judge the pre-1911 and early twentieth-century data on the basis of their internal consistency, totally apart from the 1957 figures. But for many issues, the comparisons with the 1957 data are crucial.

Finally, it must be made clear from the outset that all conclusions and statements in this study are first approximations only. No statement about past history can be made with absolute certainty, and conclusions in this study are anything but certain. China is a large and diverse country, a period of six centuries is long, and the sources used are themselves great in number and variable in quality. This study is an attempt to open discussion on several important issues, not to close it.

An alternative approach would have been to carve out a narrower segment of Chinese agriculture in terms of area, time, and subject matter covered. For some purposes, this more limited approach is clearly superior. In my own opinion, however, analysis of many of the important questions dealt with in this study is best begun on as broad a base as possible.

THE ORGANIZATION OF THE BOOK

The seven core chapters of this book can be grouped under four broad headings. In the first (Chapter II), an attempt is made to demonstrate that, in order to keep up with a rising population, Chinese grain yields per unit of cultivated land had to rise substantially. The argument that grain yields more or less doubled between the fourteenth and nineteenth or twentieth centuries is the central proposition of the entire book. The discussion in Chapter Two is basically a summary of the more detailed analysis of Appendixes A, B, F, and G on this point. Also included in Chapter II is an index of agricultural growth in the twentieth century (1914–57), based on Appendixes C and D.

---

1. In discussing the reliability of statistics compiled by the State Statistical Bureau for the 1950's, there are two separate issues. The first is whether the Bureau had the ability to collect reliable data. The relevant aspects of this issue are discussed in Appendixes A through D. The second is whether the figures were deliberately falsified by the statistical authorities for propaganda or other purposes. The answer for the 1953–1957 data is, I believe, "no," but those interested in a more complete discussion of this issue should refer to *Market Control and Planning in Communist China* (Perkins, 1966), Appendix A.

The principal explanations of how this rise in grain yields was achieved are provided in Chapters III and IV. Chapter III analyzes changes in China's cropping patterns over time, including the spread of double cropping, new seeds, and new crops. Chapter IV contains a discussion of the increase in capital inputs, both traditional and modern. Particular emphasis is placed on water control construction activities and on the increase in organic and chemical fertilizers.

In other countries in the past, a rise in agricultural productivity has sometimes been brought about by a major reform in the institutional framework rather than by an increase in capital and labor inputs within an unaltered institutional framework. But in China there were few institutional changes between the fourteenth century and the land reform and cooperative campaigns of the 1950's. The institutions that did exist, however, although not ideal, did not greatly impede rising productivity. The subject of Chapter V is the distribution among individual farmers of income, land, and capital, with particular emphasis on the degree of inequality in the distribution of land and on the institutions surrounding the land tenure system. Chapters VI and VII include an analysis of the rural marketing system and the lack of great changes in it prior to the twentieth century. Also included in Chapter VII is a discussion of the relationship between urbanization, famine, and the marketing of grain in the pre-modern era.

Land tenure and marketing institutions were, of course, changed after 1949. The short-run effect of a number of these changes was to reduce productivity. The long-run effect remains to be determined. Perhaps the key institutional change of the 1950's and 1960's has been the rise of modern industry. Although this industrial base has created opportunities for increasing China's agricultural productivity (discussed in Chapter IV), it has also required a larger marketed surplus from the rural areas, a demand that placed a burden on that sector in the late 1950's and 1960's (discussed in Chapters VI and VII).

A basic theme of all six chapters (II–VII) is that China in the late 1950's and early 1960's was at the crossroads as far as agricultural policy was concerned. A spurt in population growth together with an end to many of the pre-modern sources of increased grain production necessitated a major change in the pace and direction of Chinese efforts to raise farm output.

With the analysis of Chapters II through VII as background, an attempt is made in Chapter VIII to relate the discussion of China's rural economy to the political system. Was a centralized government a natural outgrowth of such an economy or was it instead constantly undermined by decentralizing tendencies in that economy? Chapter IX attempts to summarize and synthesize the principal arguments of the entire study.

CHAPTER TWO

Six Centuries
of Rising Grain Production

Between the late fourteenth and the early nineteenth centuries, China's population increased five- or six-fold. From the early nineteenth century to the 1950's it rose another 50 per cent. These people had to be fed, and food for such an increase in population in China could be obtained only by increasing grain production.

The central proposition of this book is that Chinese farmers were able to raise grain output and that they did so in more or less equal measure by expanding the cultivated acreage and by raising the yield per acre. The expansion in cultivated acreage requires little discussion beyond presenting the basic data and evaluating their quality. Demonstrating that grain yields per acre did in fact rise is much more difficult.

The first part of this chapter, therefore, is devoted to proving or, more accurately, establishing the plausibility of the existence of a rise in grain yields between the late fourteenth and nineteenth or twentieth centuries. The arguments in support of this proposition are long and rather technical. Only a summary version is presented in this chapter. The remaining arguments appear in Appendixes A, B, F, and G. The term *grain*, as used in this chapter, includes not only rice, millet, wheat, *kaoliang*, and all other cereals, but also potatoes and other tubers.

The latter half of the chapter includes an analysis of the pace of change in grain productivity during particular periods. Special emphasis is placed on developments since the middle of the eighteenth century. For the twentieth century, I have constructed a crude index of gross agricultural output (not just

13

grain) for several years between 1914 and 1957. However, no such index has been attempted for earlier periods.

The chapter ends with a discussion of the level of Chinese output in the 1950's and 1960's. The implications of this level of output are explored by comparing Chinese yields per acre and per capita consumption with comparable data for other nations such as Japan and India.

THE RISE IN GRAIN YIELDS (1400–1957)

Two different approaches can be used to demonstrate that grain yields probably rose significantly between 1400 and the early nineteenth or twentieth centuries. The first starts with an argument to the effect that per capita grain output in China fluctuated, if at all, only within rather narrow limits. With this argument, together with estimates of the size of population and the amount of cultivated acreage, an average yield figure can be readily obtained from the following formula:

$$\frac{(\text{per capita grain output}) \times \text{population}}{\text{cultivated acreage in grain}} = \text{yield}$$

The resulting yield figure is the yield per unit of cultivated land, not per unit of sown acreage. An increase in double cropping would appear as a rise in yields in the former case but not in the latter.

The second approach involves an attempt to collect yield estimates for different periods and different regions in China. Yield figures in most countries today are obtained by sampling procedures. It is impossible to go into the countryside in China and ask a farmer what yields his ancestors were able to achieve several centuries earlier. But one can attempt to extract a sample from historical records. In this study, both the first and second approaches are used.

The three necessary ingredients of the first approach are assumptions about per capita grain output in earlier periods together with reasonably reliable population and cultivated acreage statistics. Grain imports (and exports) were too small to significantly affect these calculations and hence have been ignored. There is reason to believe that average per capita grain output in China was seldom, if ever, below 400 catties (200 kilograms) or above 700 catties (350 kilograms) of unhusked grain.

This range cannot be established for earlier periods directly. There are occasional references in historical records to per capita grain consumption levels. Even if the relationship between consumption and output could be established, however, these references are too few and scattered to be of much use. Instead it is necessary to use a more indirect approach. The full argument is presented in Appendix F.

The lower end of the range (400 catties) represents something like a minimum level of subsistence. "Minimum subsistence" is an imprecise term. To attach a precise number to such a concept, one should know the age, height, and weight distribution of the population; the nature of the climate; how hard the people work; and the minimum health standard desired. All one can say here is that in no province of China in 1957 was per capita output as low as 400 catties and in over 130 villages surveyed by John Lossing Buck in the 1930's, fewer than ten fell below this level.[1] In addition, in over thirty countries listed in Table F.3 in Appendix F, only two, Peru and Colombia, had a per capita grain supply well below the 400 catties (200 kilograms) level.[2]

The upper end of the range (700 catties or 350 kilograms) has been surpassed in a number of countries, but in each case these nations were major producers and consumers of meat. Direct consumption of grain by people fluctuates within a rather narrow range. There is a limit to the amount of grain a person can eat in a year. All the evidence suggests that China has never been a major producer and consumer of meat and that the number of draft and meat-producing animals per capita has not changed much during the past several centuries.[3] Therefore, the upper limit on per capita grain output is determined by a generous estimate of direct consumption plus seed grain and a small amount of feed grain.

Actual per capita output in China in 1957 was 572 catties (286 kilograms). Provinces with levels of output significantly higher than this generally were major grain exporters. That is, farmers could not or at least did not consume all they produced.[4] Further, the national average was itself quite high. The figure of 286 kilograms was surpassed by very few underdeveloped nations and is just matched by the per capita supply (including imports) of Japan in 1934–1938 and 1957–1959.[5]

In most of the calculations in this chapter, I have used the narrower range of 500 to 600 catties (250 to 300 kilograms). It seems more likely that China's production in Ming and Ch'ing times fell below 500 catties per capita for long periods than that it rose above 600 catties for any sustained period. It is possible that consumption levels in China rose slowly (and unevenly) perhaps by as much as 20 to 30 per cent over the six centuries with which we are concerned. It may also have risen for a time and then fallen. Declining consumption over time appears less likely. To decline to the 1957 level of 572 catties over time would imply that levels in the past were extraordinarily high.

The population and cultivated acreage data used in the calculations in this chapter are presented in Table II.1. The key figures for estimating yields are those for the early Ming period (A.D. 1400), the mid Ch'ing (A.D. 1770–1850) and either 1933 or 1957. The issue is whether these statistics are "reliable" or fall within some usable margin of error.

1. The Buck data in Appendix F were originally given in terms of per capita consumption of grain in calories. I have converted these to kilograms (or catties) in the appendix. To convert the figures from per capita consumption to per capita output, one must also add grain used for seed, feed, and alcohol.

2. The grain supply per capita in Peru and Colombia was 328 catties (164 kilograms) and 294 catties (147 kilograms) respectively. Several other countries were at levels below 400 catties (200 kilograms) but just barely.

3. See discussion in Appendix F.

4. For data on grain surplus and deficit provinces, refer to Chapter VII.

5. See Table F.3.

TABLE II.I. POPULATION AND CULTIVATED
ACREAGE ESTIMATES FOR CHINA—
NATIONAL TOTALS (1400–1957)
(Constant Boundaries)

Year	Population (millions)	Cultivated Acreage (million shih mou)
1400	65–80	370 ($\pm$70)
1600	120–200	500 ($\pm$100)
1770	270 ($\pm$25)	950 ($\pm$100)
1850	410 ($\pm$25)	n.a.
1873	350 ($\pm$25)	1,210 ($\pm$50)
1893	385 ($\pm$25)	1,240 ($\pm$50)
1913	430 ($\pm$25)	1,360 ($\pm$50)
1933	500 ($\pm$25)	1,470 ($\pm$50)
1957	647 ($\pm$15)	1,678 ($\pm$25)

Cultivated acreage: Includes all land on which crops are grown, but excludes pasture land.
15 *mou* = 1 hectare = 2.5 acres.
SOURCES: See Appendixes A and B.

There are those who dispute the validity of the early Ming census data. The subject is discussed at length in Appendix A. Ping-ti Ho's work (1959) has already presented a case for a belief in the comparative reliability of the early Ming figures based on an analysis of the institutions concerned with carrying out the census. In Appendix A, I present the case for the internal consistency and historical plausibility of these data. In particular, the Ming statistics are consistent with estimates independently arrived at during the Sung (for A.D. 1080 and 1173) and Yuan (for A.D. 1270 or 1290) dynasties and with what we know of the various Mongol military campaigns. Although some underestimation seems likely, it is here argued that population in 1400 probably fell somewhere between 65 and 80 million persons (in contrast to the official census figure of 60.5 million).

The Ming acreage figures are less reliable, but still, as indicated in Appendix B, usable, but with major revisions. The official estimates are revised downward from a total of 851 million to 425 million Ming *mou*. Following the lead of the Japanese scholar, Hiroshi Fujii, these revisions are made primarily on the basis of textual analysis rather than from an analysis of internal consistency and plausibility. That is, the most frequently used figures were compared with those appearing in other sources, checks were made for recording errors such as the Chinese equivalent of a misplaced decimal point, and the like. Hence, the revisions could be and were checked for internal consistency without the reasoning becoming circular. In addition to establishing the consistency of the estimates, with each other and with data for the Han, Sung, and Yuan periods, reasoning similar to that used in setting limits on per capita grain consumption was used to set an upper limit on the amount of cultivated acreage in 1400. The result is a range centered on 370 million *shih mou* ($\pm$ 70 million *mou*).

The institutional case (i.e., the case based on an analysis of the institutions responsible for the censuses) for the comparative reliability of the mid-Ch'ing (1770–1850) population data is also taken from Ping-ti Ho and that of the 1953 census from John S. Aird (1968). The institutional case for the usefulness of the 1957 acreage data appears in Appendixes B and C.[6] The mid-Ch'ing acreage figures are of particularly low quality. Two independent approaches are used in a crude attempt to reconstruct an approximation to the true cultivated acreage in the mid-Ch'ing period. The individual estimates are then checked for consistency with each other and with historical events in the late nineteenth and early twentieth centuries. The case for the general reliability of the 1950's population and acreage data rests primarily on a belief in the effectiveness of the 1953 census and the statistical collection procedures of the State Statistical Bureau. The institutional case for the mid-Ch'ing figures is less convincing and hence the plausibility of the data depend rather heavily on the tests for consistency.

Given the three basic sets of data (per capita output, population, and acreage), together with an assumption that 80 per cent of the cultivated acreage was planted in grain, an estimate of yield per cultivated acre (or *mou*) can be readily obtained. To illustrate, I shall assume that per capita grain output was 570 catties in 1400, 1770, 1850, and 1933 as well as 1957. The results are as follows:

$$(1400) \quad \frac{570 \times 72}{370 \times 0.8} = 139 \text{ catties per } shih \ mou$$

$$(1770) \quad \frac{570 \times 270}{950 \times 0.8} = 203 \text{ catties per } shih \ mou$$

$$(1850) \quad \frac{570 \times 410}{1,200 \times 0.8} = 243 \text{ catties per } shih \ mou$$

$$(1933) \quad \frac{570 \times 500}{1,470 \times 0.8} = 242 \text{ catties per } shih \ mou$$

$$(1957) \quad \frac{570 \times 650}{1,680 \times 0.8} = 276 \text{ catties per } shih \ mou$$

These are, of course, not the only possibilities. For 1400, for example, one could obtain an estimate as high as 250 catties per *shih mou* if one assumed the population was 100 million, per capita output 600 catties, and grain acreage only 240 million *mou*. Such a result, however, is not very plausible. As argued in Appendixes A, B, and F, the "true" total acreage figure is more likely above 370 million *mou* than below, a figure of 100 million people is well above the most likely range, and 600 catties of grain output per capita is also a rather high figure.

These examples could be readily multiplied. If one were prepared to assume

---

6. The institutional case for the 1933 acreage data is made by Liu and Yeh, 1965, pp. 279–83.

that all the acreage estimates used here for the years prior to 1957 were biased upward (were higher than the true figures) or that population estimates had a substantial downward bias, one could raise the early yield estimates to something approximating the 1957 (or 1933) level. An assumption that per capita output was substantially higher in earlier periods than in 1957 would have much the same result. The reader must judge for himself how plausible these alternative formulations are.

National totals, however, obscure much that is relevant to the argument that yields increased. For example, could a shift in population onto high yielding land explain the rise in yields after 1400? The answer to this question is clearly no. Data in Table II.2 if anything suggest the opposite. The richest lands in China are the rice fields of the Yangtze River area in the south. The proportion of this

TABLE II.2. REGIONAL DISTRIBUTION OF CULTIVATED ACREAGE (PER CENT)

	1400	1770	1873	1913	1957
Northeast	0⎤	2⎤	2⎤	9⎤	15⎤
Northwest	6 ⎬41	6 ⎬50	13 ⎬48	13 ⎬53	19 ⎬60
North	35⎦	42⎦	33⎦	31⎦	26⎦
East-Central	45⎤59	39⎤50	31⎤52	27⎤47	23⎤41
Southeast-Southwest	14⎦	11⎦	21⎦	20⎦	18⎦
Totals	100	100	100	100	100

SOURCE: Tables B.8, B.12, and B.14.
Northeast: Heilungkiang, Kirin, and Liaoning.
Northwest: Shensi, Inner Mongolia, Sinkiang, Tsinghai, and Kansu.
North: Hopei, Shantung, Shansi, and Honan.
East: Kiangsu, Anhwei, and Chekiang.
Central: Kiangsi, Hunan, and Hupei.
Southeast: Fukien, Kwangsi, and Kwangtung.
Southwest: Kweichow, Yunnan, and Szechwan.

land to total cultivated acreage in China declined significantly between 1400 and the twentieth century. There was new settlement in the rich lands of the southwest, but this was more than matched by the resettlement of the dry lands of the northwest. The average quality of land declined over time. If the yield per unit area on any given quality of land had remained unchanged, the average on land of all types would have declined. Even a constant national average yield would imply that the yields on particular kinds of land were rising.

National totals can also obscure many errors in the underlying data. Major biases in the estimates of population and acreage in a small number of provinces could conceivably dominate the national totals, changing a picture of constant yields into one where yields appeared to rise or fall. It is desirable, therefore, to apply the method used in deriving yield estimates to the acreage and population figures for the individual provinces. This is done in Table II.3 for 1400, 1776, and

1851. The 1957 figures in Table II.3 were obtained by dividing State Statistical Bureau data on total grain output for each province by the cultivated acreage in grain.

TABLE II.3. APPROXIMATIONS TO GRAIN YIELDS (ALL GRAINS)
(*shih* catties/*shih mou* of cultivated area)

		YEAR		
Province	*1400*[a]	*1776*[a]	*1851*[a]	*1957*[b]
Northwest				
Shensi	57–68	77–93	113–136	133
North				
Hopei	45–55	95–114 (–)	109–130 (–)	171
Shansi	48–57	136–163	171–205	144
Shantung	86–103	99–118	152–174	193
Honan	44–53	103–124	124–150	296
East				
Anhwei	} 105–125	209–251	285–342 (+)	327
Kiangsu		244–293	375–451 (–)	414
Chekiang	182–218	329–395 (–)	532–614 (–)	674
Central				
Hupei	} 146–175	206–247	469–563 (–)	482
Hunan		188–225 (+)	195–234 (+)	485
Kiangsi	183–220	255–306 (+)	371–446 (+)	465
SE				
Fukien	185–222	432–518	385–464	442
Kwangtung	81–97	265–315 (–)	278–334 (–)	467
Kwangsi	88–106	336–404	122–147 (?)	316
SW				
Yunnan	— —	258–291	272–326	381
Kweichow	— —	104–125	309–370	424
Szechwan	98–117	118–151	265–320	495

Underscore indicates figures more or less unchanged over time.

(+) Provinces which were major exporters of grain (hence their yield estimates should be raised slightly).

(–) Provinces which were major importers of grain (hence their estimates should be lowered slightly).

(?) Implausible approximation.

— — Indicates data were not available.

[a] The assumptions used in constructing the figures for these three periods were as follows:
(1) Per capita grain output was either 500 catties or 600 catties (250 to 300 kilograms).
(2) Population per province was as indicated in Table A.4.
(3) Cultivated acreage per province was as indicated in Tables B.8 and B.12. The year 1766 was used instead of 1776 and 1873 instead of 1851.
(4) The percentage of the cultivated area sown to grain was the same as the percentage of the sown area planted in grain in 1957. For Kiangsu, Chekiang, Hupei and Kiangsi a figure of 70 per cent was used; for Anhwei, Hunan, and the southwest a figure of 80 per cent was used; and for the remaining provinces, 90 per cent was used.

[b] These figures were derived from official grain output and cultivated acreage data in Tables B.14 and F.2 together with assumption (4) under footnote a.

If the pre-modern estimates of provincial population and acreage had been arrived at by arbitrary methods, one would expect yield data derived from such figures to rise in certain periods and fall in others with no apparent pattern. The estimates would also probably bear little relation to the 1957 figures. But most of the estimates in Table II.3 for 1850 bear a close relation to the 1957 figures. Furthermore, the changes in yields over time are almost all in one direction: rising. Only the estimates for Kwangsi (SE) and Yunnan (SW) behave in a completely implausible way. Thus the provincial yield estimates tend to support the contention that grain yields per unit of cultivated area rose between 1400 and the nineteenth or twentieth centuries.

With these provincial estimates in mind, it is useful to turn to the second approach to establish the plausibility of this increase in yields—that of use of direct yield data for different periods and different regions in China.

In local histories of Chinese *hsien* (counties) and provinces various kinds of yield and rent data occasionally appear. Rent data can be used to estimate yields because rents were generally about half of the main crop and seldom were less than 40 or more than 60 per cent of that crop.[7] In converting these yield and rent figures into common units one is faced with major problems due to lack of comparability of grain capacity and land measures over time and among regions. Perhaps even more serious is that yields within any given region and period differ greatly even when properly measured in comparable units. These difficulties are discussed at greater length in Appendix G.

The greatest supply of rent and yield data is for the rice crop in the east, central, and southern provinces. Averages derived from nearly 900 individual observations in over 100 different sources are presented in Table II.4. With the possible exception of Kwangsi (SE), the data from the local histories for all nine provinces in the table indicate some rise in yields over time. The figures for Kwangsi in the eighteenth century are difficult to interpret (see Appendix G) and there is only one Kwangsi (SE) observation for an earlier period. The Szechwan (SW) data for the nineteenth century are also of low quality. I have used only a single observation for seventeenth century Chekiang (E), but this figure is from a particularly reliable seventeenth-century agricultural handbook and is meant to be representative of a rather large area.[8]

If one averages the earliest figures available for each of the provinces, and compares this average with that for nineteenth-century data [1957 figures are used for Chekiang (E) and Yunnan (SW)], the rise is almost 70 per cent whether or not Kwangsi (SE) and Szechwan (SW) are included.[9] The figures are also broadly consistent with the estimates in Table II.3. In both tables, for example,

7. One can, of course, find a few examples of higher and lower rents, but too few to be a major source of bias. "Main crop" as used here refers to the crops harvested in the summer and fall. In the south, this crop is most generally rice (if there are two rice crops a year, both would be included in this concept), while in the north the crop is millet or *kaoliang*.

8. This figure is from the *Fu nung shu* as reported in Ch'en Heng-li, 1958, pp. 26–28. The figure is a rounded average of the yields on four different kinds of land.

9. The figure 70 per cent is derived from a simple unweighted average of the average yield of each province.

TABLE II.4. ESTIMATED RICE YIELDS (*shih* catties per *shih mou*—unhusked)

Province	PERIOD							
	Sung 960–1279	*Yuan* 1280–1367	1368–1499	*Ming* 1500–1599	1600–1699	*Ch'ing* 1700–1799	1800–1899	1957
East								
Chekiang	402 (115)	473 (28)	—	—	600	—	—	685
Kiangsu	326 (143)	347 (3)	—	450 (11)		550 (6)	501 (8)	433
Central								
Kiangsi North	—	—	—	400 (13)		423 (22)	423 (64)	400
Kiangsi Entire	—	—	—			—	—	343
Hunan	—	—	—	288 (7)		321 (16)	467 (50)	426
Hupei	255 (2)	—	—	250 (5)	249 (10)	267 (41)	555 (2)	517
SE								
Kwangtung-Swatow	—	—	—	512 (3)	484 (8)	486 (12)	1,299 (6)	900
Kwangtung-Entire	—	—	—	416 (14)	512 (11)	447 (37)	1,037 (19)	455
Kwangsi	—	—	300 (1)	—	—	438 (73)	—	400
SW								
Szechwan	178 (1)	—	—	—	—	—	263 (15)	641
Yunnan	—	—	—	—	380 (130)	—	—	447

( ) The figure in parentheses is the number of observations used in obtaining the average figure in the table.
— Indicates data not available.
SOURCE: See Appendix G. As indicated there, these figures were culled from local histories and from works by several Japanese scholars by Yeh-chien Wang in the case of Hunan and Kiangsu, and Mrs. Kuo-ying Wang Hsiao in the remainder. Many of these rice yield figures have been estimated from rent data.

there is a sharp rise in the yields of Hunan (C) and Hupei (C) in the nineteenth or twentieth centuries. The increases in Kiangsu (E), Chekiang (E), and Kiangsi (C) are much less dramatic in both tables. The figures for these three provinces in Table II.3, however, do indicate more of a rise than the estimates of Table II.4. The two tables, of course, are not precisely comparable in two respects, which may explain this difference. First Table II.4 gives figures for rice yields only, whereas the figures in Table II.3 are for all grains. Second, the data for these three provinces in Table II.4 are from the richest area in each province, areas that were heavily settled at an early date.

An additional problem with the averages in Table II.4 requires explanation— the indicated decline from the nineteenth century to 1957. This decline also results primarily from the fact that the data for the nineteenth century and earlier are biased toward high yield regions. The Kiangsu (E) figures are mostly from the rich regions of Soochow and Sung-chiang in the Yangtze delta, the Chekiang (E) data are almost all from three prefectures around the Gulf of Hangchow which were highly developed as early as the Sung; the Kwangtung (SE) statistics are from Swatow and other above average areas; and the Kiangsi (C) data are from the rich northern half of the province around Poyang Lake. Only the Hupei (C), Kwangsi (SE), Yunnan (SW), and, to a lesser degree, the Hunan (C) observations could be considered to be reasonably representative of their entire provinces. The Hunan (C) figures, however, tend to be dominated by data from the rich Ch'ang-sha and Heng-chou prefectures. The 1957 estimates, in contrast, are the average rice yield (per cultivated *mou*) on *all* the land in the province. Thus the indicated decline from the nineteenth century to 1957 is a reflection of the degree of upward bias in the earlier rent and yield data.

It would be desirable to derive a comparable table for the major grain crops of north China as well. Unfortunately, the historical records of the northern provinces are much less complete, the number of grain crops large (e.g., wheat, millet, corn, *kaoliang*, barley, oats, and potatoes), and land and capacity measures probably subject to greater differences and error than those in the south. Some data for Shantung (N), Shensi (NW), Honan (N), and Liaoning (NE) are presented in Appendix G. The Shensi (NW) figures are the most numerous (fifty observations), but too varied to admit firm conclusions, although it seems likely that yields in the seventeenth and eighteenth centuries were well under 100 catties per *mou*. The Liaoning (NE) figure is for a period (1640's) when that province was virtually unsettled, and hence not very meaningful. The Honan (N) figure for all grains of about 100 catties per *mou* in A.D. 1262 (as compared to 180 catties in the 1930's) is interesting because it is said to be the average on 96 million *mou* of land. One can surmise that the depopulation that followed immediately after this date (due to the Mongols) reduced available labor and hence yields, and that they then rose slowly again once peace was restored—but this is only surmise. In any case, it seems likely that grain yields in the north rose more or less as indicated in Table II.3, but the direct evidence is much less conclusive than that for southern rice.

The case for a rise in yields in China during the past six centuries, therefore, is not airtight. Most of the evidence available, however, tends to support the proposition that grain yields did, in fact, increase.

THE PACE OF CHANGE
(LATE FOURTEENTH–LATE EIGHTEENTH CENTURIES)

The major engine generating this rise in yields was population growth. The pace of change tended to be dominated by the rate of growth in the number of people. The methods by which this growth raised farm output and yields are discussed in Chapters III and IV. Here the task is to examine the pace of change and see how much of the increased output can be accounted for by an expansion of the cultivated acreage and how much by a rise in yields.

To state that population growth largely determined the rate of growth in farm output is to reverse the usual Malthusian direction of causality, which has the pace of agricultural development determining the level of population. Increasingly, in recent years, scholars have questioned the validity of Malthusian analysis as an explanation of the rise in population in different parts of the globe (Boserup, 1965). The case for China can suitably be made in the context of our discussion of agricultural productivity.

China's population in the late fourteenth century was not much higher than the level achieved during the Han dynasty (206 B.C.–A.D. 220).[10] But the numbers did not remain constant at this level over the intervening fourteen-century period. During the eleventh century China's population most likely surpassed the 100 million mark for a time.[11] This eleventh-century rise may have fit the Malthusian pattern to a limited degree. By this period, a significant portion of China's population[12] was living in the southern rice regions where harvest fluctuations were much less severe than on the parched northern plains. Thus, famine may not have played such a large role in keeping the number of people in check. But the principal cause of the increase was probably the relative peace and stability achieved by the early Sung government.

The subsequent two centuries, however, were anything but tranquil. Most of the turmoil was connected with the rise and fall of the Mongols in China. Initially the Mongol armies sacked almost all of north China, as well as selected regions of the south.[13] Not only were large numbers of people put to the sword, but crops and grain stores were systematically destroyed so that vast numbers starved to death. Those who escaped starvation were felled by the increase in

10. Han population data are presented in Table B.7 and range from 48 million persons (in A.D. 146) to 60 million (in A.D. 2).

11. The number of families registered in the Sung censuses surpassed 20 million in the eleventh century, but there were, according to Sung records, fewer than three persons per family. If one assumes that most women and children were not registered and hence that the average family size was over five persons, then eleventh-century population surpassed 100 million. See Appendix A for a further discussion of Sung population statistics.

12. If Sung census data can be believed, over 60 per cent of China's population in A.D. 1080 lived in rice-growing areas (see Table A.1).

13. The Mongol campaigns and their relationship to population decline are discussed in detail in Appendix A.

disease that usually accompanies so much disruption.[14] Hence lack of food helped bring about a decline in population, but the lack of food resulted from political-military action—not from inadequate capacity of the economy to produce food under stable conditions.

The formal inauguration date for the Ming dynasty is A.D. 1368. From that year until the middle of the nineteenth century, the people of China lived in what for them was comparative peace and security. As a result, between 1400 and 1800 China's population rose six-fold from over 65 million persons to about 400 million. These increases, however, were not spread evenly over the entire period. The most rapid rise in population probably took place during the almost unprecedented peace and prosperity of the eighteenth century. The fifteen century may also have been a period of above average growth.[15]

Population growth in this period, it must be stressed, was rapid only by pre-modern standards. The average rate of increase over the four centuries was 0.4–0.5 per cent per annum and it is unlikely that even in the eighteenth century the rate rose as high as 1 per cent for any sustained period.[16] This compares with a rate of more than 2 per cent in China in the 1950's,[17] and rates of 3 per cent and more in many areas of the globe since World War II. Disease and famine took a heavy toll of lives in China between 1400 and 1800, but not so heavy as to offset completely the effects of a high birth rate.

Only during a decade or two of the seventeenth century was there apparently any sharp decline in the total number of people. In the first half of that century, battles between the Ming and the Manchu took a toll. Most important, Chang Hsien-chung with his army set out to murder virtually everyone in Szechwan and neighboring areas and may have come close to success.[18] Again, therefore, the cause of the decline in population was political-military in origin.

As in many other countries, the people of China did not spread themselves evenly across the available cultivable land. Prior to the T'ang period, they concentrated on the North China Plain. In the early Ming, they gathered in five east-central provinces mainly along the lower Yangtze River. There was almost

14. See, for example, the discussion of disease in the city of K'aifeng at this time in Hartwell (1967).

15. There is every reason to believe that population rose slowly during the Ming period, and some reasons for believing that the rise may have been more rapid in the fifteenth than the sixteenth century. There is, for example, some inconclusive evidence that floods and drought were more severe in the latter century (see Appendix A, nn. 27–29).

16. This conclusion is based on the data in Table II.1, on other official Ch'ing population data some of which are in tables in Appendix A, and on what we know of the performance of Chinese population under varying circumstances in the twentieth century prior to 1949.

17. Official Chinese estimates place the rate of growth of China's population in the 1950's at a little over 2 per cent. Some analysts in China and elsewhere, such as Ma Yin-ch'u, believe that the rate may have been a bit higher than that indicated by the official estimates.

18. James Parsons (1956, p. 92) quotes Li Wen-chih to the effect that about one million people were killed in the terror unleashed by Chang Hsien-chung, but any estimate has to be arbitrary because of the lack of meaningful population data for China in the sixteenth and early seventeenth centuries. The actual number of people put to the sword may have been well under one million, but disease, lowered birth rates, etc. may have reduced Szechwan's population by several times one million.

continuous migration out of these highly populated areas, but not at such a rate during these four centuries that the remaining total failed to rise.[19]

The migrations themselves were largely to a few areas in any single period. Parts of southwest China (Yunnan and Kweichow) were probably not heavily settled until the nineteenth century, and Manchuria was virtually empty until the late nineteenth and twentieth centuries. The resettlement of most of north China during either Ming or early Ch'ing times proceeded very rapidly, and then slowed markedly in the late eighteenth and nineteenth centuries with rapid rise renewed only with the advent of industrialization in the twentieth century.[20] The pace of settlement in southeast China was probably similar to that of the north.[21] Szechwan (SW) was resettled in Ming, laid waste by Chang Hsien-chung, and resettled again in the eighteenth century.

This uneven pace of settlement was not simply the result of peasant conservatism and reluctance to leave the home of their ancestors—although such influences undoubtedly played some role. In many instances, these areas were frontier regions in every sense, populated, however sparsely by hostile and warlike non-Han peoples.[22] Perhaps equally important, during the early development of several of these regions, crop fluctuations due to weather could be particularly severe, because of lack of adequate water control facilities. Furthermore, with the underdeveloped state of the commercial network, discussed in more detail in Chapter VII, a crop failure of a given magnitude undoubtedly took a heavier toll of human life in the outlying than in the more developed areas. Over the long run a farm family might be more prosperous in Yunnan (SW), but in the short run half its members might die.

Whatever the constraints on migration, there is little reason to believe that prior to 1800 people in China were so concentrated into a few areas that they were pressing at the upper limit of the potential food supply in those areas. Many died of starvation, but in particularly bad years and not because long-run

19. For a discussion of several of the major migrations in this period see P. T. Ho, 1959, pp. 136–68.

20. These conclusions are based on population data in Appendix A, but most can be verified by qualitative evidence as well. The hardest to verify is the resettlement of the north China plain, probably because of the poor quality of the records for the area. One can, however, find evidence that Hopei (N) was resettled by people from Shansi (N) and northern Kiangsu (E) during Ming times (e.g., in Gamble [1963], Village C was founded by migrants from Shansi in the late fifteenth century and Village A by a Ming eunuch in 1440). The principal basis for believing that there must have been northward migration is the fact that the population of the four northern provinces rose from something over 13 million in 1393 to 75 million in 1776, an increase of 480 per cent as compared to a rise of 300 per cent for the country as a whole.

21. Memorials written in the fifteenth century indicate that there was large-scale migration into Hu-kwang (C), the southeast, and southwest at that time. In the fifteenth century there may still have been some migration out of the north, but this latter trend must have been reversed later. See memorials of Sun Yuan-chen (1454), Ma Wen-sheng (1426–1510) and others in Ch'en Tzu-lung, Hsü Fu-yuan, and Sung Hui-pi (1964), 3/715–16 and 5/429–30.

22. Anyone who doubts this statement should read the accounts of European travellers to Manchuria in the late nineteenth century and Yunnan somewhat earlier (e.g., James, 1888, and Margary, 1876).

average grain output was inadequate. Only in periods of civil war does the death rate appear to have exceeded the birth rate for any sustained period.

From the data in Table II.3 and A.4, and from national average yield calculations, it would appear that yields began to rise soon after an area was settled. People did not first spread evenly over the land in any given province. Instead, extending the cultivated acreage and raising yields proceeded together.

Because population data of sufficient quality are not available for the period between 1400 and the 1770's, it is not possible to differentiate the periods in which the principal cause of increased grain output was a rise in yields from those in which it was an extension of the cultivated acreage. One can, however, estimate the share of each in rising output over the entire period. One way of doing this is to ask what grain output in the 1770's would have been if yields had remained at the 1400 level and only the cultivated acreage had been expanded. Using the acreage data in Table II.1 and a yield figure of 139 catties per *mou* for 1400 and for 1770, grain output would have risen from about 20 million tons to about 50 million tons. If yields were to have risen enough to maintain per capita grain output at the 1400 level, output in 1770 would be approximately 75 million tons. Hence of a total increase in output of 55 million tons, 30 million tons (55 per cent) was accounted for by increased acreage, and 25 million tons (45 per cent) by a rise in yields.[23] Alternate assumptions would give rise to slightly different figures, but the result of most such calculations is that rising yields and expanded acreage share more or less equal credit for the increase in total grain output in this period.

A Declining Growth Rate, 1800–1900

From the calculations of an estimated national average yield earlier in this chapter, and assuming constant per capita consumption, one would have to infer that yields rose about 46 per cent between 1400 and 1770 and another 17 per cent in the short span of the next eighty years. This would be an acceleration in growth in yields, even allowing for the fact that these eighty years were the one period when the increase in acreage in the south was greater than in the north. It would appear more reasonable to assume that per capita output was declining slightly in this latter period as a result of increased population pressure on the land (and perhaps that it was rising prior to 1770).[24] If per capita output did not decline between 1770 and 1850, then the credit for the rise in total grain output was shared more or less equally by increased yields and expanded acreage. If per capita output was declining, the share of yield increases would correspondingly be reduced.[25]

---

23. See calculations and discussion of alternative methods of arriving at the share of yields and acreage in rising output in the notes to Table II.10.

24. All statements about trends in per capita output and consumption refer to long-run trends. Within any long-term movement, of course, there will be considerable short-run fluctuation.

25. See Table II.10.

By the nineteenth century, China had begun to run out of readily cultivable land. To be sure, the amount of cultivated land increased about 40 per cent in the hundred years prior to 1957, but about 80 per cent of this increase was onto low quality land in Manchuria, Inner Mongolia, and elsewhere in the northwest.

This pressure on available land was accompanied by the decline in power and vitality of the Ch'ing dynasty. An argument frequently made is that dynastic decline was generally accompanied by a failure to tend the dikes and irrigation works, which in turn led to crop failures and general economic decline. Whatever the explanation, it would appear that economic conditions in the nineteenth century, particularly the latter half, had worsened. There are numerous observations by individuals living in China to this effect, but such statements are notoriously unreliable indicators of real economic performance. Tables II.5 and II.6 contain information culled by mainland Chinese historians from official

TABLE II.5. IMPLIED INDEX OF FARM YIELDS (1821–1911)

| Year | Summer Harvest | Fall Harvest | Average | Implied Index |
		(per cent of standard yield)		
1821–1830	71.0	74.0	72.5	100
1831–1840	66.8	66.6	66.7	92
1841–1850	66.7	66.0	66.4	92
1851–1860	63.0	63.5	63.3	87
1861–1870	58.5	60.0	59.3	82
1871–1880	57.5	58.8	58.2	80
1881–1890	58.8	57.0	57.9	80
1891–1900	57.5	55.0	56.8	78
1901–1911	57.5	55.0	56.8	78

SOURCE: *CKNY*, Vol. I, pp. 755–760. These figures are simple arithmetic averages of the percentage yields of nine provinces in the case of the summer harvest and ten provinces for the fall harvest. The original figures were expressed in terms of tenths and not carried to any further decimal place. The trends in each province were similar enough so that an average weighted by some other means would not have changed the results significantly. The provinces included in these indexes are: Hopei (N), Honan (N), Shansi (N), Shensi (NW), Anhwei (E), Kiangsi (C), Hunan (C), Hupei (C), and Fukien (SE). Chekiang (E) is included in the fall harvest index, but not that for the summer harvest.

reports of the period. Needless to say, estimates by officials of the quality of the harvest in their region expressed as a percentage of some ill-defined ideal level are not reliable. The figures used to construct Table II.5, however, all point in the same direction. If the percentages are not precise, at least the official reporters were in near unanimous agreement that the harvests were poorer than previously. There is, however, a certain lack of consistency between the yield estimates and the figures for the number of *hsien* effected by natural disasters (Table II.6). The latter indicate considerable improvement during the T'ung Chih restoration period (1862–1874), as one might expect given the political stability of that period, but the former data indicate steady decline. Both sets of figures indicate very poor conditions during the last three decades of Ch'ing rule (1881–1911).

TABLE II.6. AREA AFFECTED BY NATURAL AND MANMADE
DISASTERS (1846–1910)
(No. of *hsien* and *chou*; annual averages)

Year	Yangtze Area	Yellow River Area	Total
1846–1850	129	116	245
1851–1860	116+	54	170
1861–1870	59	66	125
1871–1880	73	145	218
1881–1890	183	256	439
1891–1900	186	217	403
1901–1910	167	200	367

SOURCE: *CKNY*, Vol. I, pp. 720–22, 733–35. The 1851–60 figures for the Yangtze area are incomplete because of the Taiping rebellion.

a The original source lumps *hsien* (counties) and *chou* (districts) together. There is thus no way of separating one from the other.

The most important effect of political decline on the economy in this period operated not so much through the failure to maintain irrigation and flood control works, however. In the 1850's China was again visited by that most effective of checks on population growth, civil war. The largest rebellion, that of the Taipings, was probably directly responsible for the deaths of over 20 million people.[26] The Moslem rebellions in the northwest in the 1860's and 1870's also wreaked their share of havoc on the population, making up by viciousness for their failure to be located in the most densely populated regions. Altogether these midcentury conditions probably accounted for a decline in population of over 50 million, due partly to war casualties and famine and partly to lowered birth rates and higher death rates indirectly attributable to the fighting. For those who find such a large decline difficult to accept, the issue is argued at greater length in Appendix A.

TABLE II.7. STAGNATION IN THE TAIPING PROVINCES

	POPULATION (millions)		CULTIVATED ACREAGE (million mou)	
	1861	1953	1873	1957
East				
Kiangsu	44.3	47.5	84	93
Anhwei	37.6	30.3	82	88
Chekiang	30.1	22.9	42	33
Central				
Kiangsi	24.5	16.8	47	42
Hupei	33.8	27.8	51	65
Total	170.3	145.3	306	321
All China	405.1	581.3	1,210	1,678

SOURCES: See Appendixes A and B.

26. See discussion in Appendix A.

It is interesting to speculate on the extent to which the Taiping rebellion was the result as well as the cause of economic decline. In four of the five provinces most affected by the rebellion, population by 1957 had not recovered to the reported levels of 1851 and the same would be true of the fifth if it weren't for the rise of Shanghai (Table II.7). This lack of full recovery may simply reflect the impact of the rebellion, but it is more likely to indicate that these provinces were badly overpopulated in the early nineteenth century.

In one sense, therefore, it may be argued that the Taiping rebellion, by alleviating population pressure, helped delay a Malthusian day of reckoning for Chinese agriculture, but this is getting ahead of the story. What is relevant here is that by the nineteenth century the share of increase in output that could come from extending cultivated acreage had declined sharply. Were it not for the Taiping rebellion, rising population in the late nineteenth and early twentieth centuries might have outstripped the ability of Chinese agriculture to provide adequate food supplies.

AGRICULTURAL GROWTH IN THE TWENTIETH CENTURY

If the declining availability of rich uncultivated land began to put pressure on consumption standards in the nineteenth and twentieth centuries, China's traditional agriculture had not completely run out of growth potential. From 1911 through 1957, farm output was probably able to nearly keep pace with a population that rose 50 to 60 per cent or a little less than an average of 1 per cent per year.[27] It was not until population growth accelerated to over two per cent per year in the 1950's and 1960's that, as is argued in subsequent chapters, an approach was required that did not rely on traditional methods of raising productivity.

If output kept up with population growth in the first half of the twentieth century, it did so with little margin to spare. In Tables II.8 and II.9, the results of an attempt to measure agricultural output during the period 1914–1957 are presented. The 1957 data are generally viewed as the most reliable of those published by the State Statistical Bureau, the 1931–1937 figures are full of problems, and many would argue that the 1914–1918 statistics cannot be used at all. Unlike the estimates for the period prior to 1914, data cover crops other than grain for the post 1914 period at least well enough to warrant an attempt to calculate the gross value of all agricultural output, not just of grain.

In constructing these estimates I have started from the insight of Ta-chung Liu and Kung-chia Yeh that the Nationalist estimates for 1931–1937 (or 1933) for the acreage sown to rice result from the application of an essentially correct percentage (for a given province) to an incorrect total acreage figure (for that province) (Liu and Yeh, 1965, p. 284). The same assumption was applied to all other crops not only for 1931–1937 but for those provinces that were effectively

27. The case for believing that population growth in the first half of the twentieth century must have approached 1 per cent a year is made in Appendix A. There is direct as well as indirect evidence suggesting that such a rate must have prevailed.

TABLE II.8. GROSS VALUE OF FARM OUTPUT (1914–1957)
(billions of 1933 *yuan*)

	1914–1918[a]	1931–1937		1957	
		This study[a]	*Liu-Yeh*[b]	*This Study*[a]	*Liu-Yeh*[b]
Grain	9.15[c]–10.17	10.31[c]–10.96	12.64	12.32	13.58
Soybeans	0.43	0.66	0.92	0.78	0.78
Oil-bearing crops	0.51	1.13	0.75	0.77	0.42
Cotton and other fibers	0.78	0.86	0.74	1.28	1.32
Tobacco, tea, and silk	0.49	0.52	0.59	0.32	0.34
Sugar cane and beets	0.11	0.11	0.05	0.14	0.14
Animals	1.14	1.40	1.34	2.74	1.70
Subtotal	13.63	15.65	17.03	19.36	18.19
Other Products	[3.40][d]	[4.14][e]	4.14	[4.91][e]	4.91
Total Gross Value	16.01–17.03	19.14–19.79	21.17	24.27	23.10
Per capita[f] (*yuan*)	36.1 –38.4	38.1 –39.4	42.2	37.5	35.7

Exchange Rate: one 1933 *yuan* = 1933 U.S. $0.26 = 1957 U.S. $0.655.

[a] For the methods used in arriving at these estimates, refer to Appendixes C and D.

[b] Liu and Yeh, 1965, pp. 397–400. The Liu-Yeh estimates are for 1933, not 1931–1937.

[c] The lower ends of these ranges were arrived at by assuming that the value of grain output in 1914–1918 was 10 per cent below the higher figure for 1914–1918 and in 1931–1937 was 5 per cent below the higher figure for 1931–1937. The lower figures, in effect involve the assumption that yields rose by slightly more than 5 per cent between 1914–1918 and 1931–1937 and between 1931–1937 and 1957 over and above any increase in yields due to changing the mix of grain crops or an increase in double cropping.

[d] This figure was obtained by taking 25 per cent of the subtotal (approximately the same percentage (24.7) as in 1931–1937).

[e] I have used the Liu-Yeh estimates to fill the gap in my data. These figures have almost no effect on the percentage increase in my estimates.

[f] Population data used in this calculation were taken from Table II.1.

TABLE II.9. INDEXES OF PER CAPITA FARM OUTPUT

	1914–1918	*1931–1937*	*1957*
Grain	100	89–106[a]	90–100[a]
Other Crops	100	163	97
Animals	100	109	165
Total	100	99–109[a]	98–104[a]

SOURCES: Table II.1 and II.8.

[a] These ranges are the highest and lowest figures that can be derived from the ranges in Table II.8.

controlled by the Peking government in 1914–1918 as well. For provinces not controlled by the Peking government, or where other factors make the data clearly unreliable, I have projected the 1931–1937 figures backward. In effect, in order to obtain the acreage sown to each crop, the percentage sown to each crop in each province in every year has been calculated and then applied to provincial sown acreage figures independently arrived at (see Appendix C).

Output figures were arrived at first by applying 1957 yields to the other two periods, with a few exceptions where there is clear evidence of change. A second calculation was then made, using the assumption that individual grain crop yields rose 5 per cent between 1914–1918 and 1931–1937 and another 5 per cent from 1931–1937 to 1957. This procedure differs from that of Liu and Yeh, who for their 1933 estimates averaged the yield estimates of John Lossing Buck and the National Agricultural Research Bureau. Their procedure leaves one with the problem of explaining a sharp drop in yields for several grain crops from 1933 to the 1950's—an event not likely to have occurred. The Buck grain yield figures, in particular, are in several important instances as high as the admittedly falsified Communist estimates of 1958, while those of the NARB are only a little below or roughly the same, as far as national averages are concerned, as those of the Communists.[28] The prices used are those of Liu and Yeh for 1933, the year for which the most complete price data are available.

Some may argue that the use of the 1914–1918 figures, even only to calculate the percentage share of each crop in the total acreage, is unwise. A survey of the tables in Appendix C, in my opinion, shows a high degree of consistency among the data for the various periods including 1914–1918. The trends shown also are roughly consistent with independent estimates of Buck, although the trends in my figures are considerably more pronounced.

The principal trends involved are major increases in acreage sown to corn and potatoes and more modest increases in the acreage sown to wheat and rice. At the same time, the importance of barley and *kaoliang* declined. Accompanying these trends was a net increase in total acreage sown to grain of almost 400 million *mou*, over half of which was in corn and potatoes.[29]

The performance of cash crops will be analyzed in more detail in the chapters on marketing. Here it should simply be pointed out that several of these crops grew substantially in the decades prior to 1937, particularly soybeans and other oil-bearing seeds, and then fell off markedly by the 1950's. These trends are quite clear and readily documented. The high figure for animals in 1957 is less easily supported. Liu and Yeh reject the figure and substitute a lower estimate of their own. On the other hand, this high figure, due primarily to hogs, may simply reflect distortions resulting from collectivized agriculture. Hogs were privately raised and could be sold on a free market in 1957, but this was not the case for grain. The 1914 to 1931 rise in oxen, water buffaloes, sheep, and donkeys may also be a statistical illusion.

Whatever assumptions one makes about hogs, it is reasonably clear from data in Tables II.8 and II.9 that agricultural output in the first six decades of the twentieth century could not, over the whole period, have done much more than

28. See Appendix D.
29. See Tables C.5–C.12. Acreage of expanding grain crops increased by just under 500 million *mou* and that of *kaoliang* declined by about 80 million *mou*.

keep up with population growth. Unless one is prepared to argue that yields rose much more rapidly than suggested by these estimates or that population growth was significantly lower, it is difficult to see how per capita consumption of grain or of total farm produce could rise. This conclusion seems inescapable, however one stands on the rate of growth in agriculture between 1952 and 1957[30] or the magnitude of the difficulties since 1957.[31]

If a rate of growth of one per cent a year or less represents the long-term potential of Chinese agriculture within the context of a traditional technology, then the implications of the sharp decline in death rates in the 1950's are dramatic. In effect, the Chinese Communists must at least triple the long-run average rate of growth in Chinese agriculture if they are to break out of poverty into sustained increases in their standard of living. Such increases will have to be achieved without much expansion in cultivated acreage. Easily usable land has mostly been exploited and new land can be made suitable for crops only with large expenditures on irrigation works and the like. In 1958, the government even experimented with a reduction in total acreage in order to try to raise output by concentrating non-land inputs.

If China had run out of easily cultivated new land by 1957, however, this was not the case during the first half of the twentieth century. The opening up of Manchuria was the principal source of new land, but there was also an extension of cultivation in the northwest. In fact, the expansion of cultivated acreage in the twentieth century may have accounted for a greater share of the rise in grain output (*vis-à-vis* a rise in yields) than in previous periods. The likely range of possibilities for the twentieth century together with the estimates for the earlier periods are presented in Table II.10. The numbers in the table are, of course, subject to a wide margin of error.

CHINESE AGRICULTURE IN THE MID-TWENTIETH CENTURY

For six centuries China's population grew and somehow Chinese agriculture managed to keep pace. This growth was anything but even. Population stagnated or fell at times as a result of civil war and accompanying disasters, and agricultural output probably stagnated or fell along with it. Nor did the productive capacity of the farm always keep up with the increased number of people during periods of comparative stability. The early nineteenth century, for example, may have been a time when the rate of population growth began to creep ahead of the rise in grain production. The first half of the twentieth century, on the other hand, may have witnessed a more or less equal match between a rising population and increased output.

30. The official rate of growth in agricultural output for the 1952–1957 period is over 4 per cent per year, but many Western analysts feel this figure is too high.

31. Probably the best guess for the 1957–1966 period would be a sharp drop in grain output in 1959–1961 of about 15 to 20 per cent in *absolute* terms and a recovery by 1964 or 1965 to something approaching the *per capita* levels of 1957. The average rate of increase in total grain output over the 1957–1966 period, therefore, would be perhaps one per cent per year or slightly less. See discussion in Perkins, 1967, pp. 35–39.

TABLE II.10. SHARE OF YIELDS AND ACREAGE IN INCREASED GRAIN OUTPUT
(Percentage shares)

	1400–1770	1770–1850	1914–1957
Increases in yield	42[a]	47[b]	24–45[c]
Extensions of cultivated acreage	58	53	76–55
Total	100	100	100

EXPLANATION OF TABLE: The figures in this table are suggestive only. By changing the numbers around one can get percentages different from those in this table. It should also be pointed out that to say that 50 per cent of the increase in output was accounted for by a rise in acreage, in this context, does not mean that land alone was responsible. This increase in output would not have been possible without a commensurate increase in capital and labor inputs sufficient to maintain yields at a constant level. Some idea of the share of the factor land alone can be obtained from the calculations in the mathematical supplement to Chapter IV.

[a] The percentage shares for the 1400–1770 period were calculated according to the formula:

$$\frac{(1770 \text{ population} \times 570 \text{ catties} - 1770 \text{ grain acreage} \times 1400 \text{ yield})}{(1770 \text{ population} \times 570 \text{ catties} - 1400 \text{ population} \times 570 \text{ catties})}$$
$$= \text{the share of yields in the rise in output.}$$

The actual numbers used are

$$\frac{270 \times 570 - 950 \times 0.8 \times 139}{570 \,(270 - 72)} = 0.42$$

The 1400 yield figure is that derived in the text at the beginning of this chapter. Clearly the use of a different level of per capita output, a different 1400 yield figure, etc., would lead to somewhat different results.

[b] The formula used in deriving this percentage was,

$$\frac{410 \times 570 - 1210 \times 0.8 \times 203}{570 \,(410 - 270)} = 0.47$$

The yield figure of 203 catties is that derived by assuming per capita output in 1770 was 570 catties and using the acreage and population data in Table II.1.

[c] Using the grain output data in Table D.14 and the acreage data in Table II.1, one can derive a 1914–1918 yield figure of 208 catties per *mou*. If the yield in 1957 had only been 208 catties, output would have risen from 142 million tons to 174.5 million tons instead of 185 million tons. Under these conditions, 24 per cent of the rise in output would be accounted for by a rise in yields. These yields are sown acreage yields whereas those in footnotes a and b are cultivated acreage yields.

If instead one assumed that the per capita consumption of grain in 1914–1918 was 570 catties and derived a yield figure from that (180 catties), the share of yields would be 54 per cent. But this would imply an improbably high increase in yields (over 20 per cent). I rather arbitrarily lowered the maximum possible share of yields to 45 per cent.

Whatever the precise pace of development in per capita grain output in any given century, the level of per capita grain output in 1957 was quite high by world standards. Some comparisons with other nations are presented in Table II.11. From these it is apparent that China in the 1950's was further removed from a level of "minimum subsistence" than is commonly supposed. "Minimum subsistence" is, of course, a vague term, and there may have been a number of reasons why Chinese required higher ratios for survival than either Indians or Japanese. But the differences among these three countries are, in any case, quite striking. Only in recent years has the per capita availability of grain in Japan matched or surpassed the level of China in 1957 and per capita supplies in India in the late 1950's were only two-thirds of those in China. Japan in the early Meiji period at the beginning of her century of growth was able to feed itself only at a level comparable to that in India today.

TABLE II.11. PER CAPITA GRAIN OUTPUT AND SUPPLY

Country	Year	Per Capita Output	Per Capita Supply
		(kilograms of unhusked grain)	
China	1953	269[a]	267[a]
China	1957	286	285
Japan	1878–1882	—	230[b]
Japan	1934–1938	246	286
Japan	1947–1948	213	230
Japan	1957–1959	246	289
India-Pakistan	1934–1938	202	208
India	1957–1959	183	191
Pakistan	1957–1959	215	230

SOURCE: Except where otherwise noted, these data are from Table F.3.

[a] These figures were all derived from official Chinese estimates. The population figure is that obtained in the 1953 census, the production figure is from *Ten Great Years* (*TGY*) p. 119, and the grain export figure is from *T'ung-chi kung-tso* data office, "The Basic Situation With Respect to Our Country's Unified Purchase and Sale of Grain," *Hsin-hua pan-yueh-k'an*, Nov. 25, 1957, pp. 171–172. The export figure excludes soybeans.

[b] According to Y. Hayami and S. Yamada, between 1878–1882 and 1918–1922, Japanese per capita calorie intake (from grains and potatoes) rose 24 per cent from 1,664 to 2,059 calories per day (Rosovsky, 1968). Per capita consumption changed little in the 1920's and 1930's so I applied this percentage to the FAO figure for 1934–1938 to obtain the figure in the table.

The low levels of output in India in the 1950's or Japan in the late nineteenth century were not compensated by greater production of other farm products. Even in 1952, the gross value of all farm output (per capita) in China was 25 to 29 per cent higher than in India at roughly the same time (14 to 22 per cent if livestock are included).[32] If 1957 gross value figures for China are used, the difference in per capita farm output is about 40 per cent.[33] In Japan in 1878–1882, some 72 per cent of the nation's gross agricultural product came from grain, as contrasted to 55 per cent in China in 1957.[34] Therefore, differences between

32. Eckstein, 1961, p. 67. The lower figure is that obtained by using Chinese prices, the higher figure by using Indian prices. I have stressed the figure exclusive of livestock because India's livestock population is hardly an unqualified asset.

33. Official Communist figures show a rise of 11 per cent in per capita gross agricultural output between 1952 and 1957. The Eckstein estimates are in essence based on disaggregated official data so application of this 11 per cent figure to his estimates is proper as long as not too much precision is claimed.

34. The Japanese percentage was derived from data in Ohkawa, 1957, pp. 57–58. The Chinese figure was derived from data in Table II.8.

Chinese and Japanese per capita levels of total farm output would be even greater than for grain alone.

Chinese agriculture thus managed not only to keep the people of China alive, it even was able to produce a small "surplus" above survival. This surplus allowed China to raise the rate of investment in industry in the 1950's to a level comparable to that in a number of industrial nations[35] and to survive a sharp drop in farm output in 1959–1961—a decline of perhaps 20 per cent—apparently without widespread starvation (Perkins, 1967).

Perhaps half of the increase in grain output over this six-century period was accounted for by the expansion of the cultivated acreage. But if expanding acreage had been the only way of raising output, China's population would long ago have begun to feel the pressure of inadequate food supplies. As it was, yields rose rapidly enough to assure not only survival but, as already mentioned, a small surplus.

By 1957, Chinese yields were equal to or slightly above those of early Meiji Japan and double or triple those of India and Thailand (see Table II.12). In the case of India, different weather and soil conditions account for part of the gap, but Thai rice is grown on a rich semitropical river delta. Interestingly, present

TABLE II.12. RICE YIELDS
(catties/*mou*)

		YIELD (UNHUSKED RICE)	
		per sown mou	per cultivated mou
Country	*Year*		
China	1957	359	457
Chekiang	,,	489	685
Szechwan	,,	440	641
Hunan	,,	341	426
Japan	1878–1882	337	—
Japan	1953–1962	631	—
Taiwan	1953–1962	391	—
India	1953–1962	181	—
Thailand	1953–1962	184	—
Indonesia	1953–1962	232	—
Korea	1953–1967	367	—

SOURCES: The Chinese sown acreage yields are from Chen, 1967, pp. 318–35. The cultivated acreage yields are from Table II.4. The other sown acreage yields are from Rosovsky (1958), whose data in turn are based on the estimates of Y. Hayami and S. Yamada. For a different view of the level of rice yields in Japan in 1878–1882, see Nakamura (1966).

35. The Chinese rate of investment (GDI/GDP) was about 20 per cent in the late 1950's.

day yields in India and Thailand are only slightly higher than the estimated yields in the comparatively empty and semitropical provinces of southeast and southwest China in 1400.

The question to be asked in the next two chapters is how was this increase in yields achieved. Was the rate of rise determined by population growth or was it independent of the number of people per unit of cultivated land? Was the pace of yield increases more rapid when an area was first settled or at some later date? Evidence suggesting a correlation between population growth, the rise in output and yields, and the stage of development of a particular province has been presented in this chapter. In the next two chapters, I shall attempt to explain more fully the relationship between these and other elements and hence must turn to an analysis of the inputs other than land.

CHAPTER THREE

Improved Seeds, Changing Cropping Patterns, and New Crops

"Traditional agriculture" can be defined as a system possessing certain cultural values, patterns of personal relationships, or any number of other characteristics. For the economist, the most useful definitions involve differentiating between a "modern" technology and a "traditional" technology. A traditional technology may stagnate and remain unchanged for centuries, or there may be gradual improvements introduced into it. If there are improvements, however, they are generally discovered by the farmer himself or adopted from other farmers. Sometimes the spread of new techniques is aided by government officials and merchants, but the original source is usually an individual peasant's tinkering with the methods available to him. Modern technology, in contrast, involves the application of the scientific method to the problems of agriculture and is generally done by trained specialists, not the farmers themselves. When new equipment or other materials are involved, they often, but not always, are produced outside of the agricultural sector in modern industrial enterprises.

In some rural societies the traditional methods have been known for so long that production has gradually approached an equilibrium where further increases in output are not possible (see, e.g., Schultz, 1964). But in China population and presumably output rose about six times between the fourteenth and nineteenth centuries and then by another 50 per cent by the middle of the twentieth century. As indicated in the previous chapter, only about half of this rise can be accounted for by an extension of cultivated acreage. The remainder was brought about by a doubling of the yields of the major grain crops.

If there was something like a doubling of grain yields, how did it happen? The central theme of this chapter and the next is that improvements in the "traditional" technique, including the spread of "best technique" from "advanced" to "backward" regions, explain only a small part of the rise in yields. Most of the increase, in fact, seems to have resulted from greater capital and labor inputs in conditions of a stagnant technology.

The focus in this chapter is on changing cropping patterns. The discussion begins with an analysis of the gradual improvement in grain seeds over the past several centuries and is followed by a description of changes over time in the extent of wheat and rice double cropping. A key question in the latter discussion is what were the principal factors inhibiting an increase in the amount of double cropping. In the final section, the effects of the introduction of new crops from the Americas are analyzed. The roles of such capital inputs as tools, fertilizers, and water control works in the rise in grain yields are discussed in Chapter IV.

IMPROVED SEEDS

Chinese farmers, like those in many other countries, have always been on the lookout for better seeds. Over the past several millenia, thousands of varieties of grain and other crop seeds have appeared and disappeared. What differentiates "modern" from "traditional" seed selection is the way in which the improved varieties are discovered. Today such seeds are scientifically developed on experimental farms designed for just that purpose. In China prior to the twentieth century, farmers discovered new varieties when they migrated into previously lightly settled areas, officials and traders brought back special seeds from abroad, and accidents of nature created useful mutations.

An example of the latter case is described by T. H. Shen. A particular variety of rice was found growing on top of a hill where no rice had previously been grown. The farmer who made the discovery planted the seed, found it gave a good yield, and gradually expanded its use, naming it *T'ien-lo-chun* ("seed dropped from heaven") to show his gratitude to heaven. In the 1930's this seed was being planted on many thousands of *mou* in the area (Shen, 1951, pp. 198–99). An example of a seed brought from abroad is an early ripening variety of rice from Champa (present-day Viet Nam) described in detail by Ping-ti Ho. This seed was introduced by the Sung Emperor Chen-tsung (A.D. 998–1022) into Fukien province whence it apparently spread to other provinces.[1] It is impossible to prove, yet quite likely that the number and significance of varieties discovered within China and then spread dwarfs those brought in from abroad by officials or traders. Officials, in particular, were rather faithful in recording for posterity their own good deeds, and the lack of written evidence of the dissemination of improved seeds by officials thus suggests that varieties discovered and spread by farmers themselves were the dominant source of new seeds.

1. Ho, 1959, pp. 169–76. Professor Ho appears to argue that all early ripening rice seeds were descendants of this Champa variety. This may be true, but I doubt it and there is no evidence to that effect.

A similar argument can be made concerning the spread of given varieties within China. Officials played some, but only a minor role in this process. A prefect in Kwangsi (SE), for example, is given credit for introducing a variety of early ripening rice from a neighboring province in the second quarter of the nineteenth century.[2] In 1835, Lin Tse-hsü, then governor of Kiangsu (E), brought in a thirty-day ripening seed from Hupei (C).[3] But there were at least one thousand and perhaps several thousand varieties of grain seeds. In Kiangsu (E) Province alone there were in 1933 several hundred kinds of rice seeds and about one hundred wheat seeds in use.[4] Undoubtedly many varieties are given different names in different areas, but even when such duplication is eliminated the number remaining would be large.

There were no artificial barriers to the spread of improved seeds around the country. Particularly important varieties such as *Hu-pi no* ("tiger skin glutinous") could be found in the early eighteenth century in the northwest (Shensi), the southwest (Yunnan), and southeast (Fukien) (Hung Chou, 1956, pp. 437–75). The normal pattern of movement of new seeds, if there was a "normal pattern," is unclear. Some evidence, however, can be obtained from seeds named for place of origin.[5] One source originally published in 1742 lists some one hundred rice varieties named after localities. The most common origin of improved seeds, if this source is a guide, was a nearby prefecture within the same province (over one-third of the examples listed). Almost as many came from a province bordering on the one where the seed was listed as being used. Perhaps most interestingly, there does not seem to have been any general progression from highly developed provinces to the less developed and more recently settled areas. Yunnan (SW) varieties, for example, were found in Hunan (C) and Kiangsi (C), whereas Chekiang (E) varieties were found only in Kiangsu (E) and Anhwei (E).[6]

An important consideration in estimating the impact of improved seeds on the rate of growth in productivity is the pace at which new varieties were discovered and adopted. Some relevant but hardly definitive data are presented in Table III.1. Because of the difficulty of finding more than one gazetteer for a particular *hsien*, only a few areas are represented. These figures indicate that the pace of adoption of new rice seeds was not reduced over time within any given area.

However, although it cannot be proved or even supported with direct evidence, I suspect that over time the impact on productivity of a new seed did tend to decline. When an area was first settled, the seeds used were probably brought from outside and often unsuited to the conditions in the new region. Initially, therefore, a hunt for more suitable varieties might achieve substantial results. Later improvements would more likely be marginal.

2. Li Yen-chang, *Jun ching t'ang tzu-chih kuan shu*, 3.110b and 114b.
3. *Kao-yu chou chih* (1843 preface) 2.1a.
4. *Chung-kuo shih-yeh chih* (*Kiangsu Sheng*), pp. 3–9, 43–45.
5. A seed named after a place might have been discovered in that place, but in some cases it may have originated elsewhere and acquired different names as it passed from place to place.
6. Derived from data in Hung Chou, 1956.

TABLE III.1. NEW VARIETIES OF RICE

Location	before A.D. 1500	1500 to 1740[a]	1740 to 1850–1920
		NET INCREASE IN VARIETIES	
Kiangsu			
Ch'ang-shou[b]	29	6	—
Chiang-yin[c]	—	35–56	55
Chekiang			
Yin hsien[d]	59	18	15
Kwangtung			
P'an-yu[e]	—	15	40
Shih-ch'eng[f]	—	29	8
Tung-kuan[g]	—	13	6
Tseng-ch'eng[h]	—	10	6
Kwangsi			
Hsin-ning[i]	—	12	20
Huai-chi[j]	—	25	0
Fukien			
Chien-ning[k]	—	36	17
Cheng-ho[l]	—	6	24
Szechwan			
Kuan hsien[m]	—	10	21
Total	—	215–236	212
Average	—	18–20	19

— Indicates data not available.

[a] The 1500 to 1740 period does not fit each *hsien*'s data precisely. The period for Ch'ang-shou *hsien*, for example, should be 1539 to 1687 and that for Yin *hsien* 1560 to 1850, but for most *hsien* 1740 is the best dividing line. For Kwangtung's *hsien* and from there on down, I have assumed all rice seeds listed in the 1740's gazetteers were discovered between 1500 and 1740, an assumption that slightly exaggerates the number of varieties discovered in this period.

[b] *Ch'ang-shou hsien chih* (1539 ed.), 4.16–18 and *Ch'ang-shou hsien chih* (1687 ed.), 9.37–38.

[c] *Chiang-yin hsien chih* (1640 ed.), 2.71; (1683 ed.) in *Shou shih t'ung k'ao*, pp. 448–49; *Chiang-yin hsien chih* (1744 ed.), 3.1–2; *Chiang-yin hsien chih* (1840 ed.), 10.1; and *Chiang-yin hsien hsü chih* (1920 ed.), 11.1–2. The lower end of the range for 1500 to 1740 assumes all 21 varieties known in 1640 were discovered before 1500, the upper end assumes they were discovered after 1500.

[d] *Ning-po fu chih* (1560 ed.), 12.1–2; *Yin hsien chih* (1877 ed.), 71.1; and *Yin hsien t'ung chih* (1935 ed.), natural science section, 4b–5.

[e] Hung Chou, 1956, p. 469; *P'an-yu hsien chih* (1871 ed.), 7.1; and *P'an-yu hsien hsü chih* (1931 preface), 12.5–6.

[f] *Shou shih t'ung k'ao*, p. 471; *Shih-ch'eng hsien chih* (1819 preface), 1.22; *Shih-ch'eng hsien chih* (1888 ed.), 2.36b.

[g] *Tung-kuan hsien chih* (1798 ed.), 40.1; *Tung-kuan hsien chih* (1911 ed.), 13.2.

[h] *Shou shih t'ung k'ao*, p. 469; *Tseng-ch'eng hsien chih* (1921 ed.), 9.2.

[i] *Shou shih t'ung k'ao*, p. 473; *Hsin-ning chou chih* (1879 ed.), 2.22.

[j] *Shou shih t'ung k'ao*, p. 473; *Huai-chi hsien chih* (1916 ed.), 10.34.

[k] *Shou shih t'ung k'ao*, p. 468; *Chien-ning hsien chih* (1916 ed.), 27.8.

[l] *Shou shih t'ung k'ao*, p. 468; *Cheng-ho hsien chih* (1919 ed.), 10.1b–2.

[m] *Kuan hsien chih* (1786 preface), 10.32b; *Tseng-hsiu Kuan hsien chih* (1886 ed.), 12.1a; *Kuan hsien chih* (1932 ed.), 7.1.

But what is meant by the "impact of new seeds"? Some seeds, of course, raised per acre yields without changing anything else. Other varieties increased resistance to drought, a feature which reduced harvest fluctuations and only secondarily raised the average yield. Still others were used because they ripened quickly and hence could be planted in the short growing season remaining after the end of a severe flood or drought. The popular *Chiu-kung-chi* ("rescue from famine") variety which ripened in fifty to sixty days was probably used this way.[7]

Early ripening was most important, however, because it made possible double cropping. Early ripening, in fact, is one of the principal features of Chinese seeds, not just of rice but of most other grains as well (Shen, 1951, pp. 40–41). But seeds are only one of several prerequisites for double cropping and not necessarily the most important. It is, therefore, desirable to turn to the nature of the cropping pattern in China and the elements causing it to change over time.

China's Cropping Pattern

The principal changes in the cropping pattern relevant here are the possible extension of rice northward, increased double cropping of rice, and greater double cropping of rice or millet with wheat or barley.

One crop rice yields are double or more the yields of competing summer crops such as millet or *kaoliang*. Thus, substitution of rice on acreage formerly sown to other grain is one means of raising overall grain yields. It is quite clear, however, that Chinese efforts in this direction have been quite modest. Most of the regions where rice is an important crop today were major rice producers a thousand years ago.

For example, rice was a major product of northern Anhwei (E) in the Sung period,[8] and the principal product of Szechwan (SW) in the seventeenth century and probably in the Sung dynasty as well.[9] For the eighteenth century more detailed comparisons are possible. The results of an investigation of a number of *hsien* histories published in the eighteenth century are presented in Map III.1. In a number of *hsien* in both Honan (N) and Shensi (NW), the major grain crop in the eighteenth century was rice, while in a much larger number of *hsien* in these two provinces, rice either is not listed or was clearly not a major crop. In all cases, *hsien* that were not rice producers in the eighteenth century also did not grow rice in any quantity in the twentieth century and vice versa.[10]

If there was any extension of rice cultivation northward, therefore, it involved the spread of paddy acreage in transitional regions where rice was already planted, but was perhaps not the principal grain crop. For example, there may

---

7. *Ibid.*

8. *Sung hui yao chi kao*, Vol. 5, p. 4,843 and Vol. 7, p. 6,013.

9. Sung Ying-hsing, 1966, p. 13. Rice was exported from Szechwan to Hupei in the Sung period (Han-sheng Ch'uan, 19, 222–33).

10. In the notes to Map III.1, only eighteenth-century *hsien* histories that state that rice was a major crop are listed.

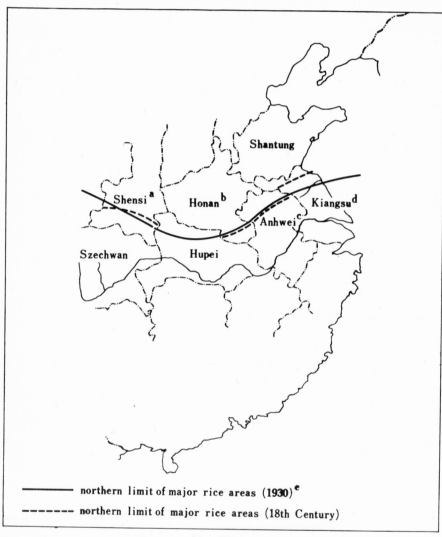

northern limit of major rice areas (1930)[e]

------- northern limit of major rice areas (18th Century)

Map III. 1
Northward Extension of Rice Cultivation

NOTES

[a] The *Cheng-ku hsien chih* (1717), 4.9a, indicates that at that time irrigated rice was already a major product of this *hsien* in the southwest corner of Shensi. Two other *hsien* gazetteers either list rice as a product of the area or state that school land rent was paid in rice (*Chou-chih hsien chih* [1785], 9.2b, and *Lan-t'ien hsien chih* [1796] 6.2a). Both *hsien* are south of the Wei river, but not far enough south to be in the main rice-producing area of Shensi. I have found no eighteenth-century reference to a *hsien* in what is today the major rice-producing area that states that no rice was grown there in the eighteenth century. The only such references I have are for *hsien* north of the Wei river.

ᵇ Both the *Kuang chou chih* (1770), 27.3b, and the *Ku-shih hsien chih* (1786), 14.14b, state that rice was the main crop in their area. In 1953 this area, the southeast corner of Honan, was still the only major rice-producing area in Honan (Sun Ching-chih, 1957, p. 158).

ᶜ Rice was the major product of Huai-hsi (modern northern Anhwei), at least as early as the Sung dynasty (*Sung hui yao chi kao*, Vol. 5, p. 4,843, and Vol. 7, p. 6,013).

ᵈ The embassy of the Earl of Macartney to China (1793) first mentions rice observed as the major crop of the area as they were passing down the grand canal. The exact spot where it first becomes a major crop is difficult to pinpoint, but it seems to be near the Shantung-Kiangsu border (Staunton, 1799, Vol. II, pp. 155–56).

ᵉ J. L. Buck, 1937, p. 25.

have been minor extension of rice cultivation north of the Hwai River in Kiangsu (E) Province in the seventeenth or eighteenth centuries.[11] There may also have been some expansion of rice north of the Yangtze River in Hupei (C) Province, but no direct evidence that this happened is at hand.

The immovability northward of rice cultivation was and is primarily the result of inadequate rainfall. One-season rice requires about 130 days during which the water supply must be substantial. On the North China plain, 60 to 70 per cent of what rainfall there is is concentrated in three months, June through August, or only ninety days; and even that amount is subject to wide fluctuations.[12] In a country such as Thailand, the months when rice growing is possible, are those when rainfall is over 150 millimeters per month (Ogura, 1963, p. 596). In Hopei (N) and Shansi (N) Provinces peak period rainfall is under 100 millimeters per month and even in Honan (N) Province June to August rainfall averages only just over 150 millimeters a month.

The frost-free period in North China is shorter than in the south, but it is still over 225 days or much longer than necessary for single-season rice. In fact, when water is adequate, rice can be grown almost anywhere in China, as it is in southern Shensi (NW) and even Manchuria (NE) for example.[13] If the rice area is ever to be extended further, therefore, it will only be done by means of irrigation. Irrigation, however, is the subject of the next chapter.

The technique of growing two crops of rice in one year has been known in China for many centuries. It is clear from data in Table III.2, however, that even by the 1930's the practice was largely confined to the provinces of Kwangtung, Fukien, and Kwangsi in southeast China. Nearly 80 per cent of the double-cropped rice acreage was in these three provinces. If the yield data in Table II.3 are a reliable guide, even these provinces were not heavily double cropped until

11. According to the *Chiang-nan t'ung chih* (1736 preface) 86.14b, rice had only recently (at that time) been planted around, and become a major product of, Hsü-chou (in Kiangsu). A Korean traveler in the late fifteenth century was fed wheat noodles, bean curd, but no rice for the first time on his trip north from Chekiang when he approached Hsü-chou (Meskill, 1965, p. 102).

12. See Sun Ching-chih, 1958, pp. 2–3.

13. Rainfall in southern Shensi is 200 to 500 millimeters per year above that in Honan (which is in the same latitude). Paddy rice in Liaoning Province in Manchuria is concentrated in areas that can be irrigated by mountain springs or by canals and rivers (Sun Ching-chih, 1959a, p. 90).

TABLE III.2. RICE DOUBLE-CROPPING
(1,000 *mou*)

Province	1930's	1957
SE		
Kwangtung[a]	28,000	28,000
Kwangsi[a]	9,600	9,600
Fukien[a]	8,500	8,500
SW		
Szechwan[b]	0	19,500
Yunnan[b]	0	0
Kweichow[b]	0	*
Central		
Kiangsi[c]	3,600	8,600
Hunan[c]	2,000	11,340
Hupei[c]	700	3,300
East		
Chekiang[d]	6,000	8,000
Anhwei[d]	0	5,000
Kiangsu[d]	0	1,600
Total	58,400	103,440

* Some but very little double cropping of rice.

[a] The 1957 data are derived from materials in Sun Ching-chih, 1959b, pp. 66, 247, 252, and 380. This source gives a figure of 38 million *mou* for the double-cropped rice acreage, but this is inconsistent with other data in the same source, all of which indicate the "3" should be a "2." The Kwangsi figure is derived by subtracting the paddy field acreage from the total area sown in rice. The data in Buck, 1937, pp. 192–99, indicate that these three provinces were heavily double cropped in the early 1930's. There was some expansion in double cropping in Kwangsi in the 1950's, but it could not have been very great except perhaps where recovery from wartime lows was involved. The assumption that double cropping in the 1930's was the same as in 1957, therefore, appears to be a reasonable one. The Fukien 1950's figure is for the year 1955. The Kwangsi figure was derived by subtracting the paddy field acreage from the total sown acreage in rice.

[b] The data for the Southwestern provinces are from Buck, 1937; Sun Ching-chih, 1960, pp. 362, 365, 520; and Y. A. Afanas'yeskiy, *Szechwan*, translated in JPRS No. 15308. All sources indicate that there was no double cropping of rice in these provinces in the early 1930's. Experimentation with double cropping began in Kweichow in 1954–1956. In Szechwan, experimentation with double cropping began in the late 1930's, and was taken up on a large scale in the 1950's.

[c] Sun Ching-chih, 1958, pp. 82, 269, 409, 413. The 1930's figures are those given in this source as being the "pre-liberation" estimates. The 1930's figures are consistent with Buck's estimates for these provinces.

[d] Sun Ching-chih, 1959a, pp. 57, 59, 142, 217. For Chekiang, this source states that double cropping rose from about 25 to 33 per cent of the paddy acreage between 1953 and 1957. I have assumed the 1953 figure is equal to that for the 1930's, an assumption that is roughly consistent with Buck's data. Neither Anhwei nor Kiangsu had any rice double cropping in the 1930's, and only a small beginning had been made in Kiangsu in the 1950's. In Anhwei in 1957, there were 6 million *mou* planted in early rice, but some of this was still only single cropped. The 5 million figure is only a rough guess.

the nineteenth century.[14] If one assumes that the area of double-cropped rice in 1400 was very small, the extension of this technique by the 1930's may have accounted for a 6 million ton rise in grain output.[15]

In the 1950's the government in Peking put considerable effort into pushing the development of two-crop rice. By 1957 they succeeded in raising the acreage by nearly 42 million *mou*, or enough to raise output by perhaps 4 million tons. The principal barriers to increasing the double-cropping acreage result from a combination of weather, inadequate labor and animal power, and inadequate fertilizer. As Professor Kenneth Walker has shown (1968), the labor requirements at the time of harvest and transplanting are substantial. The shorter the growing season, the shorter the period of time available to harvest the first crop and plant the second and hence the heavier the requirements for labor. Walker's figures indicate that in such provinces as Hunan (C), Kiangsi (C), Kiangsu (E), and several others, the available labor supply is on the average less than half that necessary for ideal double-cropping conditions (Walker, 1968, Table III). For this reason, if no other, there is no year-round underemployed labor in south China in the sense of labor whose marginal product is zero. It is also evident that machinery that could replace labor during this period would have a marked effect on output. For example, after 1932 power threshers in Japan increased the efficiency of the annual switchover from wheat to rice (Ogura, 1963, p. 415). Mechanized transplanting of rice, however, is yet to be done efficiently.

In some cases the growing season for rice could be extended by improvements in the supply of water. Two-crop rice requires from 160 to 180 days of water as compared to 130 days for a single crop.[16] The longer the period for which adequate water supplies are available, the longer the time available for harvesting one crop and planting the next and hence the lower the peak period labor requirements. More fertilizer would eliminate situations where a second crop is not planted because it is more efficient to concentrate limited supplies of water on a single crop.

It is an interesting question whether expansion of rice double cropping in the 1950's reflected an increased man–land ratio in those areas. Table III.2 indicates that the principal provinces involved were Szechwan (SW) and Hunan (C), and to a lesser degree Chekiang (E), Kiangsi (C), and Anhwei (E). Although the man–land ratio in Szechwan (SW) did rise, the rate of increase was less than the average for the country as a whole. In Hunan (C), Chekiang (E), and Kiangsi (C) population did not rise at all from 1933 to 1953. Thus an increased supply

14. Average yields in Kwangtung (SE) in the eighteenth century and before, if the data in Table II.3 are a reliable guide, appear more in line with a one crop rice culture. By the nineteenth century, the average more than doubled which would suggest much more double cropping, among other things. The technique of double-cropping rice was known in Kwangtung and Fukien, but it doesn't appear to have been used on a great scale. According to one source, these two provinces were famous for their rice double cropping as early as the Ming period, but it does not follow from this that the double-cropped area was large in comparison to the present day situation.

15. The second crop of rice in Kwangtung typically yields about 200 catties of rice. Applying this figure to 60 million *mou*, one arrives at 6 million tons.

16. Sun Ching-chih, 1958, p. 271.

of labor would not appear to explain the expansion of double cropping. The more likely explanation is that these were areas well suited to double cropping, where innate conservatism or the lack of demand from outside for surplus rice[17] had inhibited its development in the past. Szechwan (SW) and Hunan (C), in particular, are provinces where the man–land ratio is almost identical with that in Kwangtung (SE), Kwangsi (SE), and Fukien (SE), where water is abundant, and where the growing season is almost as long or longer than that in the southeast.[18] Thus, the Chinese in the 1950's in part, at least, were exploiting underutilized capacity. By the late 1950's there may have been little unused capacity left, and further large increases could only be achieved in conjunction with more capital and labor inputs.

More important than two-crop rice is the rotation involving winter wheat or barley followed in the summer by millet or rice. A rough picture of the magnitude of double cropping of this type is presented in Table III.3. In the 1950's there has been little increase in double cropping of this type. The principal change has been a decline in the planting of barley in favor of wheat. Prior to the twentieth century, however, increased planting of wheat as a second crop made a significant

TABLE III.3. DISTRIBUTION OF DOUBLE-CROPPED
AREA BY TYPE OF CROP
(1,000 *mou*)

	1931–1937	1957
Rice[a]	58,400	103,440
Winter Wheat[b]	274,000	307,000
Barley[c]	84,570	47,990
Rapeseed[d]	78,200	34,619
Field Peas,		
Broad Beans, etc.[e]	68,000	103,000
Subtotal	[563,170]	[596,049]
Total	610,000[f]	681,200[g]

[a] See Table III.2.

[b] In 1957, winter wheat accounted for 86.7 per cent of the wheat area. In the far north (12.5 per cent of the total wheat area), winter wheat was not double cropped. Much of the winter wheat on the North China Plain was grown on a two-year, three-crop rotation, but I have not taken this into account in my calculation. See Chin Shan-pao, 1961, pp. 25 and 29. These percentages were then applied to the data in Table C.6.

[c] These figures are the total acreage figures for barley in all central and southern provinces (Kiangsu on down) in Table C.11.

[d] Taken from data in Table C.15.

[e] This figure is 60 per cent of the miscellaneous grain acreage estimates for Shansi Province on down in Table C.12.

[f] The double-cropping index in Buck (1937, p. 216) of 149 was supplied to all the cultivated acreage of China except Manchuria and Sinkiang and Tsinghai.

[g] *TGY*, p. 128.

17. In Szechwan, in particular, almost no grain was shipped out of the province in the nineteenth and twentieth centuries until it was opened up by the extension of railroad lines into the province (see discussion in Chapter VII on the grain market).

18. See the rainfall and frost-free period maps in T. H. Shen, 1951, pp. 14 and 16.

contribution to rising yields per *mou*. The principal evidence in support appears in the *T'ien-kung k'ai-wu* published in the early seventeenth century. That source states that in all of the rice-growing provinces, only one-twentieth of the people sow wheat and one-fiftieth sow barley and buckwheat (Sung Ying-hsing, 1966, pp. 13–14). This statement is consistent with another in the same text (p. 4) to the effect that 70 per cent of the people's grain consumption was rice and only 30 per cent, wheat, millet, and the like. Data for two villages in the thirteenth century in southern Kiangsu (E) Province indicate that the wheat and barley crop at that time was less than half that of rice and other summer-fall crops in one village and less than one-quarter in the other. In the 1930's, the wheat and barley crop in this *hsien* had risen to a position of equality with the rice and soybean (fall) crops.[19] In Hunan (C) in the seventeenth century only one crop, rice, was grown, but in the late seventeenth and eighteenth centuries great effort was made by officials to promote the planting of second crops [20] It seems likely that the expansion of wheat or barley double cropping raised grain output by about 14 million tons[21] or about twice the impact of double cropping and extension northward of rice cultivation combined.[22]

New Crops

By the sixteenth century, the European discovery of the Americas had caused knowledge of such crops as corn and potatoes to reach China. The main advantage of corn was that it could be grown in rather barren mountainous regions. Corn's adaptability to adverse conditions has also made it a popular crop in

TABLE III.4. CORN AND POTATO ACREAGE
STATISTICS (1914–1957)
(in million *mou*)

Year	All Grain[a]	Corn	Potatoes
1914–1918	1,427	78	25
1931–1937	1,575	104	55
1957	1,813	196	157

* Includes corn and potatoes.
SOURCE: Tables C.5 through C.12.

19. The Sung data appear in Sudo, 1962, pp. 276–77. The 1930 data appear in *Chung-kuo shih-yeh chih (Kiangsu sheng)*, pp. 11 and 49.

20. This information appears in *Liu-yang hsien chih* (1818 ed.) 15.1a, 36.100a and (1873 ed.), 14.20b–24a; *Ch'ang-sha hsien chih* (1810 ed.), 17.69–70a and (1867 ed.) 6.2b–7a; *Li-ling hsien chih* (1870 ed.) 1.24a; and *Ning-hsiang hsien chih* (1867 ed.) 24.8a.

21. This is the figure one obtains when one multiplies the wheat and barley acreage in all provinces from Kiangsu on down in Tables C.6 and C.11 by 150 catties. Such a calculation slightly exaggerates the impact of wheat and barley double cropping in south China, but this bias is offset by the existence of considerable double cropping of wheat and barley in north China (or at least three crops in two years).

22. I have made no estimate of the impact of the extension northward of rice cultivation, but it is unlikely to have raised output by more than one or two million tons.

northern Manchuria.[23] In addition corn yields are somewhat higher (5 to 15 per cent) than those of such competing crops as millet and *kaoliang*. Prior to 1914–1918 (or 1931–1937), however, the acreage sown to corn was quite small— only about 5 or 6 per cent of the total area sown to grains of all kinds (see Table III.4). If all the land on which corn was raised would otherwise have been unusable, the introduction of corn would have made possible a rise in grain output of 7 to 8 million tons.[24] If, alternatively, the rise in corn acreage between the sixteenth century and 1914–1918 were simply a substitution for millet and *kaoliang*, the net rise in output would be only about one million tons.[25] Between 1914–1918 and 1957, the share of corn in the rise of grain output would range between 1 or 2 and 11 million tons.[26]

Potatoes, principally sweet potatoes, have made an important contribution to grain output because of their high yields and ability to grow on poor dry land. In terms of calories per *mou*, potatoes are roughly twice as productive as other dry-land crops. Their principal shortcoming, in Chinese eyes, is their taste: eating potatoes is considered to be an act of desperation preferable only to starvation. The rapid expansion in the twentieth century of acreage sown to potatoes, therefore, was probably mainly to hedge against possible disaster, and potatoes were often grown only after the regular crop had failed. To the degree to which potatoes replaced other dry-land crops on a more permanent basis, their total impact on grain output between 1918 and 1957 was, using generous assumptions, to raise it by about 9 million tons.[27] Their impact prior to 1918 was more marginal—perhaps 4 million tons.[28]

The new crops from the Americas and elsewhere are more interesting for the way in which they illustrate the response of Chinese farmers to innovations. In the span of 1,500 years prior to the sixteenth century, only three new major crops, tea, Asian cotton, and *kaoliang*, entered China (see Tables III.5 and III.6). Their arrival apparently pretty well exhausted the possibilities available to China from her border regions. Their acceptance by Chinese peasants, however, was slow. Cotton, for example, did not become the main fiber for manufacturing cloth until well into the Ming period, several centuries or more after the crop was first grown in China.

In the sixteenth century, four major new crops were brought in. The timing of their introduction was determined by the European discoveries of the Americas and the Pacific islands. More than one of these crops, for example, apparently

23. In Manchuria it is also a crop that can be usefully interplanted with soybeans.
24. I have applied a yield of 193 catties per *mou* (the 1931–1937 average yield as given in Table D.6) to the 1914–1918 acreage figure for corn to arrive at this figure. Corn acreage in the early sixteenth century, of course, did not exist.
25. If corn yields on the average are 15 per cent higher than those of competing crops, the rise in output would be 0.15 times 7 or 8 million tons.
26. This range was derived in the same way as that for the pre 1914–1918 period. This increase in output is net of the increase prior to 1914–1918.
27. This figure was derived by assuming that potatoes had yields double those of competing crops. Potato yields in 1957 were 278 catties per *mou* (in grain equivalent which is one quarter the actual gross weight of potatoes).
28. This figure was derived in the same way as the 1914–1957 estimate.

TABLE III.5. CHINA'S CROPS AND ANIMALS
(Han dynasty: 206 B.C.–A.D. 220)

Grains: Rice
Wheat
Barley
Millet (3 varieties)
Sesame

Beans: Soybeans
Small beans

Vegetables and Fruits: "a thousand varieties," dates and chestnuts

Melons: Squashes
Pumpkins
Cucumbers
Gourds of several varieties

Fibers: Silk (and mulberry trees)
Ramie[a]
Hemp[a]
Flax[a]
Jute[a]

Bamboo

Meats: Pigs
Chickens
Fish
Edible dogs

Ginger

Domestic Animals: Horses
Oxen
Sheep
Pigs
Dogs
Fowl

[a] Most sources simply refer to fibers (*ma*), but a study of those fibers (Liu Hung-chu, 1956, p. 7) gives specific references to ramie and hemp and states that flax and jute have been grown in China for a "very long time."

SOURCES: Swann, 1950, pp. 54–55, 109, 123–25, 414, and 435–38, and Hwang Nai-lung, 1963, p. 114. The list in this table is not exhaustive, but it does cover the major crops and animals (draft and meat-producing only).

TABLE III.6. INTRODUCTION OF NEW CROPS INTO CHINA

Crop	Century in which Introduced	Province in which First Planted	Origin
Tea[a]	3rd–5th	?	Southeast Asia
Cotton (Asian)[b]	6th–8th	?	Northern and Southern Border Regions
Early Ripening Rice[c]	11th	Fukien	Champa, Indo China
Kaoliang (Sorghum)[d]	12th–13th	Szechwan	Central Asia
Sweet Potato[e]	16th	Fukien-Yunnan	America
Tobacco[f]	16th	Fukien	America
Corn[g]	16th	Fukien-Chekiang	America
Peanuts[h]	16th	Kwangtung-Fukien	America
Irish Potatoes[i]	17th	Fukien	America
Cotton (American)[j]	late 19th	Yellow River Area	America

[a] Reischauer-Fairbank, 1958, p. 178.

[b] Cotton Research Office of the China Agricultural Sciences Yuan, 1959, Chapter 1, p. 2. There was weaving of cotton cloth in Kwangtung, Kwangsi, and Yunnan in the first to fourth centuries (A.D.), but these areas were only nominally a part of China at this time and were populated principally by non-Han peoples. In the sixth century, cotton was grown in Sinkiang, and from the sixth century on, cotton is mentioned in T'ang poetry and other sources, hence the date in the table.

[c] Ho, 1959, p. 170. This is not strictly speaking a new crop.

[d] *Ibid.*, p. 181. Argument on subsequent pages convincingly rejects proposition that *kaoliang* (sorghum) was introduced first by the Mongols.

[e] *Ibid.*, p. 186.

[f] International Trade Office of the Ministry of Industries, 1940, p. 1. Tobacco came to China from America via the Philippine Islands.

[g] P. T. Ho, 1959, p. 183. For a discussion of possible alternative routes into China taken by corn, see Sung Ying-hsing, 1966, p. 32, n. 12.

[h] *Ibid.*, p. 184.

[i] *Ibid.*, p. 188.

[j] Cotton Research Office, Chapter 5, p. 1.

reached the Fukien coast via the Philippine Islands. All of these crops were known in China within a century of Columbus' arrival in the West Indies in 1492.

As Ping-ti Ho has shown (1959, pp. 184–90), knowledge of these crops also spread rapidly across China. As already indicated, however, knowledge of and widespread use were not synonymous. Why this was the case is not clear. With corn, the answer may simply be that the areas where the crop is most suited were developed only recently. Over half of the corn acreage in China in 1957 was in Manchuria, Inner Mongolia, Sinkiang, and the southwestern provinces of Yunnan, Kweichow, and Szechwan.[29] In the case of potatoes, taste may have proved a major barrier that could be overcome only by deliberate government policy or other severe pressures. Between 1931–37 and 1957, the acreage sown to potatoes tripled (see Table III.4). About half of this increase took place after 1950, with the other half probably the result of wartime conditions.

The cases of corn and potatoes give some support to the notion that the pace of adoption of new crops accelerated in the twentieth century. An even better example is the response to the introduction of American cotton. Where it took Asian cotton many centuries to replace hemp, it took only a few decades for American cotton to make major inroads on Asian cotton.[30] The introduction of Virginia-type tobacco is a less dramatic case in point. Before 1917 there was virtually no Virginia-type tobacco produced in China, but by 1920 the amount had grown to 27,000 tons although it was still only 3–4 per cent of total tobacco output (Wiens, 1966, p. 13). Improved communications may have played some role in accelerating the introduction of these two new varieties, but the principal explanation appears to be the rise of modern industry which had both the interest in and capacity to push improved quality.

One thing appears clear. By the 1950's there were few if any new crops which China could usefully import and grow at home. Further increases in output would have to come from improvements of existing crops. Unless great strides are made outside China in the development of improved seeds which prove usable in China, further increases in yields will have to be achieved by China's own efforts.

CONCLUSION

Improved seeds, changing cropping patterns, and new crops have all contributed to rising agricultural productivity in China. By the beginning of the twentieth century the latter two improvements had perhaps raised output by 25 to 33 million tons. Between 1914–1918 and 1957 these same improvements may have raised grain production another 14 to 24 million tons for a total rise over the

29. These areas were only sparsely settled until the eighteenth or nineteenth and in some cases even the twentieth century. Although they include half the corn acreage, these areas represent only about one-quarter of total grain acreage as of 1957 (see Appendix C).

30. See, for example, data in Chinese Cotton Statistics Association, 1935, and *TGY*, p. 131.

six-century period of perhaps 39 to 57 million tons.[31] The largest single component in this rise prior to 1914–1918 was the increased double cropping of wheat and barley. After 1914, corn and potatoes played the major role. If total grain output rose between 1400 and 1957 by over 160 million tons, the changes discussed in this chapter, except improved seeds, made up from one-quarter to one-third of this increase and about half of the rise attributable to yields.[32] It is, unfortunately, impossible to separate the effects of improved seeds from other changes.

Increased productivity due to new crops and changing cropping patterns also cannot really be separated from rising capital and labor inputs and other changes. The figures presented in this chapter indicate how much less output today would be if these measures had not been introduced. But double-cropped rice would not have been possible without a rising man–land ratio. This same rising man–land ratio together with the increased availability of fertilizer presumably also raised the per-acre yields of all crops including corn, potatoes, and particularly both crops of rice.

There is no reason to believe that these traditional means of raising grain output had ceased to function by the 1950's. Improved seed selection, to be sure, had lost its traditional character as early as the 1920's and 1930's with the introduction of modern experimental farms and scientific seed development. In a mere decade in the 1950's, grain seeds in use at the beginning had been almost completely replaced by its end. In the years 1955 to 1957, the acreage sown to improved grain seeds rose from 20.6 per cent of the total to 55.2 per cent.[33] The speed with which these new seeds were introduced may often have led to inefficiency,[34] but, whatever the case, Chinese farmers were no longer dependent on the whims of nature for the provision of improved varieties. What effect this change will have on future grain yields will depend on what new kinds of seeds are developed and the care with which they are adopted.

Expansion of double-cropped rice and of the acreage sown to new crops is still possible even within the context of traditional technology. However, without devices that will reduce labor requirements during the time of harvest of the first crop and transplanting of the second, or improved water control that will allow the extension of the switch-over period, increases in productivity from this source are certain to be small. The rapid extension of rice double cropping in the 1950's was probably only a temporary spurt made possible by the full use of existing potential, a potential that was quickly exhausted.

31. These figures were obtained by adding up the effects of individual measures as estimated in this chapter. The upper and lower end of the ranges represent various assumptions as to whether corn and potatoes were grown on otherwise unusable land, were substitutes for other crops, etc.

32. If corn was sown on otherwise unusable acreage, then the increase in output from this source should perhaps be included under rises in grain output due to the extension of the cultivated acreage. As indicated in the previous chapter, however, the division between output increases due to rising yields and those due to an extension of acreage is imprecise at best.

33. *TGY*, p. 131. It is not really clear, however, what the Chinese Communists mean by improved seeds.

34. See my discussion in *Market Control and Planning in Communist China* (1966), pp. 78–81.

A changing cropping pattern that emphasized the replacement of fallow land with winter crops was not a development unique to China. Population pressure has brought about similar changes in other countries as well (see Boserup, 1965). By the twentieth century, however, China was in a rather different position from that reached by Japan in the early Meiji period.

Because of a variety of artificial political and social barriers within Japan in the Tokugawa Period, there appears to have been a considerable backlog of improved technique that had built up in certain advanced areas, but had not spread to more backward regions. When these barriers were removed, the spread of the better techniques led to several decades of slow but significant increases in productivity.[35] In China there were no such artificial barriers. New seeds, new crops, and better cropping patterns, when useful, spread steadily if not rapidly across the entire country. By the 1950's there was no great back-log of advanced but essentially "traditional" technique of this type that could be exploited readily.

New seeds and changing cropping patterns over time were not the only "traditional" ways of raising farm output and yields in China (or Japan), however. The other techniques are the subject of the next chapter.

35. I am principally indebted to Professor Henry Rosovsky for this analysis.

CHAPTER FOUR

Farm Implements,
Water Control,
and Fertilizer

About half of the rise in yields between 1400 and the 1950's cannot readily be explained by new seeds, new crops, or changing cropping patterns—more than half if it is further recognized that many of the new cropping patterns could not themselves have been introduced except in conjunction with other complementary factors.[1] What then were the other factors involved in the six-century rise in Chinese yields? Were the techniques connected with the use of these factors changing over time, and were improved methods gradually spreading from "advanced" to "backward" regions of China?

The factors analyzed in this chapter are distinguished from those in the previous chapter by the fact that they each involve significant levels of capital investment. Seeds, to be sure, also involve some capital, but only a rather small amount. The factors discussed here are farm implements and draft animals, water control construction, and natural and chemical fertilizers. Underlying this discussion of capital inputs is an analysis of the dependence of these inputs on population growth and an increasing agricultural labor force.

The principal argument in this chapter is that rural capital formation in China was substantial, but that, prior to the 1960's, the technology connected with these forms of capital was, with a few exceptions, stagnant. As long as population was increasing and there were new territories to open up, however, this capital did not run into diminishing returns. But by the nineteenth and twentieth

1. In fact the yields on new land would have been well below the existing average on old land if complementary factors had not been introduced at the time the land was brought into cultivation.

centuries China's new lands had filled up and water-control investment, at least, began to run into diminishing returns. This decline was reversible, but only if combined with a revolution in agricultural technique.

FARM IMPLEMENTS, DRAFT ANIMALS, AND HUMAN LABOR

As population grew between 1400 and the twentieth century, the number and value of farm implements presumably rose with more or less equal speed. It is quite clear, however, that the increase in the number of tools was not accompanied by any great change in their quality or variety. Farm implement technology was generally stagnant.

On the north China plain, most tools used in the twentieth century were well known as early as the Northern Wei Dynasty (fifth century A.D.) and perhaps the Han.[2] What is perhaps somewhat more surprising is that there is little evidence of change in the implements used anywhere in China, at least after the fourteenth century.

Agricultural handbooks have been published in China for many centuries and a number of these are still available today. These books all contain long lists of agricultural implements complete with descriptions and often pictures. The problem of comparing listings in each of the books, therefore, is straightforward. The three handbooks compared and their approximate dates of publication are:

1. Wang Cheng, *Nung shu* (A.D. 1313)
2. Hsü Kuang-ch'i, *Nung-cheng ch'uan-shu* (A.D. 1628)
3. Hung chou, compiler, *Shou-shih t'ung-k'ao* (A.D. 1742)

Seventy-seven different kinds of farm implements are listed in the *Nung shu* even when irrigation devices are excluded. Of these seventy-seven, all but one, and that an insignificant exception, are listed in the later works. These later works in turn do not contain any tools not listed in the *Nung shu*. It is possible the similarity among the lists indicates that the later works were simply copied from the earlier. However, if this were true and in fact many new tools had been discovered in the interim, it is difficult to understand why the individuals bothered to write the later handbooks at all. Further, the implements appearing in these works can still be seen in use all over China today.

It may be, of course, that these implements were unknown in more backward regions of China in the fourteenth century and that their gradual spread contributed to rising yields. There is almost no evidence that such a spread did occur, however.[3] Furthermore, since settlement of new areas was largely accomplished by migration from old areas, it is probable that migrants brought their tools

2. This statement is based on a soon to be published work of Ramon Myers (*The Chinese Peasant Economy: A Study of Agricultural Development in Hopei and Shantung Between 1890 and 1949*). His work in turn draws heavily on that of Amano Gennosuke.

3. The only case turned up by any of my researchers was the introduction of a new type of water wheel in the second quarter of the nineteenth century into Kwangsi (SE) province. Li Yen-chang, 3.110b and 114b.

with them or, at the least, brought the knowledge of how to make these tools. Since most of the implements used were well known long before the fourteenth century, even farmers in remote areas could hardly have remained ignorant of their existence. The rapid dissemination of knowledge of new seeds and new crops across China is evidence that significant improvements in technology were not confined for long to the farms of an enlightened few.

The only changes in implements of any kind that I have been able to discover for the post-1400 period are those mentioned by Amano Gennosuke (1962, pp. 719, 729–30, 784). But the changes Amano discusses seem to have involved little more than such things as the thickening of a plow frame or an improved method of using an already known implement.

Given little change in tool technology, there was not much increase in productivity per man that could be achieved by simply producing more implements. A man can only use one hoe at a time. Poor farmers may have lacked a full set of all possible useful implements, and some that they had may have been in poor repair, but it is difficult to see how these shortcomings could have significantly reduced grain output.

The one area where increased investment without a change in technique could have contributed significantly to rising yields would have been an increase in the number of draft animals per capita or even per unit of cultivated area, if draft animals can be treated here as a farm implement.[4] It is quite clear that in neither the Ming nor Ch'ing periods did all farmers own or rent draft animals.[5] The poor commonly harnessed themselves to plows or to devices to pump water. Draft animals represented a large outlay in terms of both fixed and working capital, an outlay that could be lost quickly to disease or roving armies.

Assuming the marginal product of labor was higher than the capital outlay on draft animals,[6] an increase in the average number of animals per capita would presumably have raised per capita grain output. Whether such an increase actually occurred can only be surmised. Some relevant data are presented in Appendix F,[7] but those figures are too scattered to allow a conclusion to be reached concerning the average number of draft animals per capita.

It is interesting to note that in Japan as well as China there were few changes in mechanical farm implements during the Tokugawa Period (1603–1867). The only new device introduced was the *semba koki*, a threshing tool that greatly reduced the amount of labor required at harvest time (Smith, 1959, p. 102).

One possible explanation for the stagnation in China's farm-tool technology in the centuries prior to 1900 is that peasants were either too conservative or too lacking in imagination to try new methods. Such a conclusion, however, does not

4. Draft animals are treated as farm implements for convenience only. They can, for example, be thought of as a substitute for tractors.

5. A seventeenth-century agricultural handbook, for example, gives a number of reasons why it considers draft animals an inappropriate investment for the poor (Sung Ying-hsing, 1966, p. 8).

6. See the discussion below of the marginal product of labor in China.

7. These data are presented in Appendix F in connection with the argument that the amount of grain used as fodder did not increase over time (in per capita terms).

jibe with what we know of their response to new seeds or the fact that they were able to develop so many different kinds of implements so long ago.

A more plausible explanation is that there weren't many further advances that could be made without a major technological breakthrough, a breakthrough that could be achieved only by means of the techniques of modern science. Perhaps the most important need was for implements that could conserve labor used during the harvest and transplanting seasons (see discussion in Chapter III) or in the pumping of water. The most significant changes in this area, however, have involved the use of implements whose power was derived from diesel or electric engines rather than men and animals. Diesel and electric engines were obviously devices that could not be developed by the peasants.

It has only been since 1958 and really since the 1959–61 agricultural crisis that the Chinese Communists have demonstrated clear awareness that power machinery of this type could make a major contribution to raising farm productivity. In the years 1952 through 1958, total output of power machinery supplied to rural areas was only 1.6 million horsepower, even if once accepts the 1958 figure without adjustment (*TGY*, p. 171). By the middle of 1964, this total had reached 6 million horsepower.[8] The principal purpose of such equipment has been to power irrigation and drainage pumps, but motors can be and apparently are easily detached and used to run other machinery, for example threshers at harvest time. As a result, the number of power threshers supplied to farms in 1958–1962 was ten times the 1953–1957 level (Kuo Tung-ts'ai, 1964, p. 16), a figure that is as indicative as anything else of the low level of production of such items in 1953–1957. As pointed out in the previous chapter, power threshers played a significant role in raising productivity in Japan because of the amount of labor saved during the peak harvest period.

Along with the increase in power machinery has come rural electrification. An exact figure for the rate of increase in the use of electricity in agriculture is difficult to come by because of the vagueness of official Chinese statements,[9] but these statements together with eyewitness accounts do indicate rural electrification has progressed from a negligible level in the 1952–1956 period[10] to a point where most of the villages of China have at least a little electric power.[11]

Another area where improved tools might have made a significant difference is local transport. A source (Ts'ao and Liang, 1965) states that one-third of all agricultural labor is used in taking manure to the fields and bringing grain from those fields. Since much of this labor must be expended at the time of harvest

8. Kuo Tung-ts'ai, 1964, p. 17. This figure is stated to be the amount of powered drainage and irrigation equipment, but such a figure must be close to or the same as the total amount of power equipment supplied to agriculture.

9. One source states that by 1963, rural electric power consumption had increased by 1,600 per cent over 1957 (Hu Chi, 1964, p. 25). The problem is that the 1957 figure does not appear to be available.

10. *Wo-kuo kang-t'ieh, tien-li, mei-tan, chi-chieh, fang-chih tsao-chih kung-yeh-te chin-hsi*, 1958, p. 72 gives data for 1952–1956 which indicate that farm consumption was less than one per cent of the nation's total electric power consumption.

11. See, for example, Guillain, 1966, pp. 120–21. I have also heard similar statements from recent visitors to and former residents in China.

and transplanting, improvements in transport would undoubtedly have aided productivity. There may also be some benefits accruing from improved plows and the like. However, in the mid-1950's the Chinese Communists placed more emphasis on the double-wheeled, double-bladed plow than on any other single modern farm improvement—only to discover that the plow was unsuited to most of south China (Perkins, 1966, p. 80).

There is an implicit assumption in much of the above discussion that labor-saving devices, at least during periods of peak labor demand, would not only free labor for nonfarm occupations but would also have a significant impact on per acre yields. The principal basis for such an assumption, which runs counter to some of the simpler assumptions regarding the existence of underemployment, is the analysis of labor requirements of double cropping in the previous chapter and in the work of Kenneth Walker. Given its importance in the economic literature, however, a few additional remarks are in order

If underemployed labor exists anywhere in the world, China, India, Pakistan, Java, and Egypt are the most likely candidate countries. Theodore Schultz used evidence from the Indian influenza epidemic of 1918–1919 to argue that no significant underemployment existed at that time on the Indian subcontinent.[12] There are no data that allow one to do for China what Schultz did for India. In addition to the analysis of double cropping, however, there are a number of ways of obtaining some evidence on this point.

First, there are Buck's figures from 260 localities, 81 per cent of which reported that they had a shortage of labor for either harvesting, cultivating, planting, irrigating or a combination of these and other activities. Only 19 per cent reported no labor shortage, let alone a surplus (Buck, 1937, p. 301). It is, of course, possible that in areas reporting an overall shortage, some farms had a surplus while other farms in that area were undermanned. Usually, however, farmers without enough to do hired themselves out to those with a labor deficit. Buck's figures presumably refer to a shortage *after* the possibilities for hiring local labor had been exhausted.

Various anthropological studies also shed some light. Two village studies, one in Yunnan (SW) and the other in Shantung (N), give evidence that wartime conscription and banditry syphoned off enough able-bodied men so that labor demand exceeded the supply and hence real rural wages rose significantly (Fei Hsiao-tung and Chang Chih-i, 1948, pp. 67, 215; M. C. Yang, 1945, pp. 30–31). In an area of Kwangtung (SE), during the peak seasons, all members of the family were mobilized, the village school was let out so the children could help, and many migratory laborers came into the village (C. K. Yang, 1959, p. 37). It is also worth noting that the size of the average farm in the Yunnan (SW) and Kwangtung (SE) villages studied was in each case well below the average for all

12. Schultz, 1964, pp. 63–70. For several qualifications that must be made to the Schultz arguments, see S. A. Marglin, "Industrial Development in the Labor Surplus Economy: An Essay in the Theory of Optimal Growth," pp. 2–4.

of south China.[13] One would have expected these villages to have a larger labor surplus than most. Instead they had none at all during peak periods.

There is evidence that large amounts of potentially cultivable land, particularly in hilly areas, were not utilized because the return per labor day invested was too small. If there were a surplus of labor, one would expect that all such land would be cultivated rather than left idle. Finally, one of the most potent arguments for inducing reluctant peasants to join the cooperatives in 1955–56 was that they would no longer be able to obtain hired labor because it would all be used by the cooperatives (Myrdal, 1965; Chou Li-po, 1961). Generally the peasants to whom references were made were "middle peasants" with only a little larger than average holdings.

Thus there does not appear to have been a labor surplus in China during peak seasons. What the situation was in non-peak periods cannot really be answered without first undertaking a study of rural handicrafts—a subject that goes well beyond the scope of this book. Nevertheless it is clear that labor-saving machinery should raise agricultural output. What would happen if population growth continued without any introduction of machinery is difficult to predict. Certainly output would rise in areas where more water could be pumped by hand or where double cropping could be extended. Given the situation in China in the 1950's, however, the resulting rise in output was unlikely to have been sufficient to provide adequate food for the increased population. Once the new lands were filled up, the marginal product of labor must have begun to decline. By the middle of the twentieth century it had almost certainly fallen well below the minimum subsistence level, but not to zero.

WATER CONTROL

The existence, or lack of it, of underemployed labor in China has as many implications for the usefulness of water-control projects as for labor-saving farm implements. Throughout Chinese history irrigation, flood control, and drainage works have been constructed using large numbers of laborers and little machinery. Dirt removal equipment, for example, even today involves little more than two baskets, a bamboo pole, and a strong back. If the productivity of this labor in farm occupations were negligible, then almost any useful water control scheme would be justified. But if productivity was not negligible, then irrigation projects could be undertaken rationally only when the return on the labor invested was higher than in competing occupations. The remainder of this section deals primarily with historical trends in water-control construction and their probable effects on farm output.

Elaborate water-control schemes were carried out in China many centuries prior to the unification of the empire in 221 B.C. Such water-control activities have been used to explain not only agricultural productivity, but the rise and fall

13. The average for all of south China in the 1950's was about 12 *mou*. The average in the Kwangtung village studied and one of the Yunnan villages was 6 *mou* per family. In two other of the Yunnan villages the average was under 9 *mou* and only in the fourth did it reach 12 *mou*.

of dynasties and numerous other political and social phenomena as well. These political questions, however, will not concern us in this chapter. Nor will those water-control schemes—the largest and most famous of which was the grand canal—which were related primarily to the problem of how to transport grain to the capital.

Because water-control schemes were a major concern of government officials, local histories are replete with information about them. In many provinces, the name of every project in use at the time the gazetteer was written is listed. Unfortunately, for many projects the name is all that is recorded. We are concerned in this study, however, not with the total number of projects, but with the pace of their development over time. To estimate the rate of growth in capital inputs of this type, information is required on the size of the various projects and their date of construction. Although there are more than 50,000 projects listed in the various gazetteers, for only about 5,000 are dates of construction given.[14] For many others, dates are given when major repairs were undertaken, but these are of little use in determining net capital formation. For about 10,000 works, information is included on the length of dikes constructed or the area newly irrigated. Of the 5,000 dated projects, however, information on the length of dikes or area irrigated is available for about 60 per cent of the total.

The first scholar to attempt to exploit these materials was Chi Ch'ao-ting.[15] But he only recorded projects according to the dynasty during which they were built, and, as a result, many interesting fluctuations within dynasties are obscured, particularly between the fourteenth and nineteenth centuries. Chi also does not come to grips with very serious problems of potential biases in the data.

The number of projects built in each century in the various regions of China and their percentage breakdown by period are presented in Tables IV.1 and IV.2. In Appendix H, I have attempted to look at possible sources of bias. The

TABLE IV.1. WATER-CONTROL PROJECTS (NUMBER)

| Region | CENTURY | | | | | | | | |
	Before 10th	10th–12th	13th	14th	15th	16th	17th	18th	19th
Northwest	6	12	1	2	9	28	6	78	92
North	43	40	30	53	65	200	84	186	32
East	168	315	93	448	157	314	291	128[a]	9
Central	50	62	21	52	91	361	85	116	131
Southeast	27	353	43	106	101	88	53	115	34
Southwest	19	10	6	5	31	83	61	195	96
Total	313	792	194	666	454	1,074	580	818	394

SOURCE: Table H.1.
[a] The number of projects in the eighteenth and nineteenth centuries is probably under-reported because the gazetteers for two of the three provinces were published in 1736.

14. See Appendix H for further discussion on each of these points.
15. *Key Economic Areas in Chinese History* (London, 1936).

TABLE IV.2. WATER-CONTROL CONSTRUCTION
(PERCENTAGE BREAKDOWN BY PERIOD)

Region	PERCENTAGE OF WATER CONTROL PROJECTS COMPLETED BY		
	A.D. *1400*	A.D. *1700*	A.D. *1900*
East	53	40	7[a]
Southeast (except Kwangsi)	58	26	16
Central	19	56	25
North (except Honan)	23	48	30
Southwest (except Kweichow)	8	35	58
Northwest (Shensi only)	9	18	73

SOURCE: These percentages are all derived from data in Table H.1.

[a] Projects in the eighteenth and nineteenth centuries in East China were probably a greater share of the total than indicated by this percentage. The Chekiang gazetteer was published in 1736 as was the Kiangsu gazetteer, although Kiangsu prefectural gazetteers for the nineteenth century were also searched.

conclusion reached there is that although errors and distortions undoubtedly exist, they do not appear to be so serious as to render the figures in the two tables meaningless. Two of the more important sources of bias, however, should be mentioned here. First, for several provinces, projects recorded as being built in the twelfth century or earlier appear to be significantly larger on the average than those built from the thirteenth through nineteenth centuries. Thus the data in Table IV.1 understate the amount of construction in Sung and earlier periods. Second, data for some provinces are much more detailed than for others. These differences between provinces do not present problems so long as the data are used to explain the timing of water-control construction efforts within a particular province. They do make it necessary to exercise caution in comparing the level of activity in one province with that in another or in adding projects in several provinces together. The groupings by region in Tables IV.1 and IV.2, however, do not introduce distortions of this type. Where several provinces have been grouped, the pattern of development of each province within the group was similar to that of the total for the group as a whole.

Even if the data for the periods prior to the thirteenth century were adjusted to offset their downward bias, the bulk of all water-control construction occurs after the tenth century. From the tenth through the thirteenth centuries, most of this construction was confined to five provinces of east and southeast China. This concentration is not surprising, since these provinces contained nearly half of China's population in the Sung period and most other rice-growing areas, except possibly Szechwan (SW), were only sparsely settled at that time.[16]

With the restoration of unity and political stability under the Ming in the fourteenth century, the rice-producing provinces of central China became heavily settled—resulting in a spurt in water-control construction. There also

16. See Table A.1.

appears to have been an increase in the pace of activity on the North China Plain that was presumably connected with the settlement of that area. In both central and north China, the projects undertaken may in part have simply replaced works destroyed or left to deteriorate during the Chin and Yuan periods. The pre-Ming records available to compilers of gazetteers for these provinces were probably very incomplete and hence the small number of projects recorded for T'ang and Sung may be misleading. Whatever the case, there appears to have been a major increase in the pace of construction in these areas, particularly in the sixteenth century, followed by some decline in activity thereafter.

Only in the southwest and in Shensi (NW) province did water-control construction accelerate in the Ch'ing period. The eighteenth century, when China's population rose from under 200 million to about 400 million, was, to be sure, an active one for water-control activities everywhere, but not so active in most provinces as was the sixteenth century.

Thus several forces have influenced the pace of construction of irrigation and flood-control works. The settlement of new areas opened up many new possibilities. Population growth made the extension of water control activities both necessary and by increasing the available supply of labor, possible. Severe droughts or floods also spurred local officials and farmers to greater efforts in order to prevent a repetition.[17] Finally, because these construction activities were in part the responsibility of the government, the pace of construction was also related to the political vigor of the reigning emperor and his bureaucracy. The sharp decline in activity in the seventeenth century was partially at least a result of the political disruption that accompanied the fall of Ming and the rise of Ch'ing. The declining vigor of the Ch'ing may account for the sharp drop in construction in the nineteenth century, although it was also true that there were few new lands being opened up.

Of these alternative explanations for the pace and pattern of water-control construction, population growth and migration appear to be the most important. Particularly in the rice-growing provinces, population and construction activities followed similar paths. By early Ming, the eastern provinces together with Fukien (SE) were heavily settled and water-control activity had been carried on on a large scale for centuries. The next major rice-growing areas to become heavily settled were Hunan and Hupei in central China while the southwest did not become the destination of large numbers of migrants until the eighteenth and nineteenth centuries. Similarly, water-control activities accelerated in Hupei and Hunan in late Ming and in the southwest during Ch'ing. The two major exceptions to this pattern are Kwangtung (SE), whose population growth was most like that of central China, but whose water-control activities followed the pattern of Fukien (SE) and east China, and Kiangsi (C), where the situation was reversed.

Two further questions regarding water control should be raised here. First,

17. For example, some of the increased activity in the sixteenth century may have resulted from such considerations. The number of droughts recorded in the sixteenth century in these five provinces was 63 as against 34 in the fifteenth century (Yao Shan-yu, 1943, pp. 375–78).

what was the probable effect of water control activities on yields? Second, what further possibilities were there for increased productivity through extension of traditional irrigation and flood control construction?

Figures showing the irrigated acreage in China in the twentieth century are presented in Table IV.3. There is no way of obtaining a reliable figure for

TABLE IV.3. IRRIGATED
ACREAGE (ALL CHINA)
(1,000,000 *mou*)

Year	Acreage
1904–1909	351[a]
1914–1919	352[a]
1924–1929	395[a]
early 1930's	398[a]
1950	250[b]
1952	320[b]
1953	330[b]
1954	350[b]
1955	370[b]
1956	480[b]
1957	520[b]
1963	560[c]

[a] These figures were derived from percentages given in Buck, 1937 (Statistical Volume), p. 52 and the acreage data for 1913 and 1933 in Table B.14.

[b] *TGY*, p. 130.

[c] According to one source, the irrigated acreage was one-third of the total arable acreage (*Jen-min jih-pao* editorial, November 30, 1965, quoted in "Water Conservancy," *China News Analysis*, No. 579, September 3, 1965, p. 1). I have multiplied the 1957 cultivated acreage figure by one-third to obtain the figure in the table. Chinese data on increases in irrigated acreage after 1957 are confusing, and, as a result, the figure in this table may be biased in either direction. In 1958, the government reported that irrigated acreage had climbed to one billion *mou* (*TGY*, p. 130), but no such claim has been made since 1960.

A.D. 1400, but a rough estimate can be made. If one assumes that the percentage of irrigated land in the five central east provinces was roughly the same in 1400 as in the 1930's and that virtually all cultivated land in the other southern provinces was irrigated, one gets a figure of 160 million *mou*. This figure can be considered an upper limit on the amount of irrigated acreage. A second method begins by assuming that the percentage of projects listed as being built before 1400 is a good indication of the amount of irrigation that had been developed by that time. By this method one arrives at an estimate of 65 million *mou*, but this figure is almost certainly too low. If the number of pre-1400 projects is doubled to take account of probable downward bias in the original data, the result is 130 million *mou*. Thus irrigated acreage in 1400 was in the neighborhood of 130 million *mou* (± 30 million *mou*).

Therefore, it would appear that the amount of fixed capital represented by water-control works tripled or quadrupled between the fourteenth century and

1900. This figure is not changed significantly by the inclusion of flood-control construction activity in north China.[18]

Unfortunately, there is no real way of estimating the impact of this construction on yields. Much of the double cropping in China would not have been feasible without tight control over the timing of the water supply, but as indicated in this and the previous chapter, labor supply conditions were even more important. Certainly sharp declines in output due to drought or flood were reduced by water-control projects, and hence the average yield was raised, but by how much it is impossible to tell. In many cases, irrigation made it feasible to switch from dry land crops to rice, thus doubling yield, but again there is no way of estimating how much acreage was effected in this way. Whatever the exact figure, the amount of attention given to water-control construction over the centuries would suggest that its impact on yields was significant.

The question of the additional potential left in traditional water-control activities by the mid-twentieth century also cannot be answered with precision. Part of the answer depends on whether any improvement in irrigation and flood-control technology was possible within the traditional context. The other part of the answer depends primarily on the amount of additional acreage which could be irrigated by traditional means.

If there was any improvement in irrigation and flood-control technique, it cannot be discerned. The agricultural handbooks used to analyze tools also include pictures of many kinds of water wheels. There is no change in these, as there was none in the case of farm implements. There were, to be sure, improvements in the quality of construction. In certain areas there was a substitution of stone for earth or bamboo as in the dikes along the Chekiang (E) coast in the seventeenth century and in embankments built in Anhwei (E) in the sixteenth century,[19] but stone was hardly a new construction material. Such improvements fit more properly under the rubric of capital formation than of technological change. To the degree that such improvements could not be taken into account when counting the projects, the above statistics understate the amount of capital formation.[20]

Perhaps there was some spread of improved technique from advanced to backward regions, but if there was, one suspects that its full impact was felt long ago when the areas were first opened up. There were undoubtedly technological improvements devised within the newly opened areas (rather than brought in from outside) to take into account local conditions, but the practice common in much of south China of building large ponds in elevated positions and then running ditches down to the fields was not very complicated, and the room for improvement in technique was consequently not very great.

18. If one doubles the number of pre-fourteenth–century projects in the four north China provinces in Table IV.1, then the total number of projects by the end of the nineteenth century was nearly 1,100 as against 260, or roughly a quadrupling.

19. *Chung hsiu Anhwei t'ung chih* (1877 edition) 65.17a and 68.8b and *Liang-che hai t'ang t'ung chih* (1736–1795) 4.9b–11.

20. In counting projects, whenever it was stated that there was an improvement of this type, I counted it as a separate project. There were, however, comparatively few such references.

The more important question is whether China's irrigated acreage as it existed in the mid-twentieth century could be expanded by traditional means. In effect, were the returns on future investment in traditional water control schemes high enough to be worthwhile? Mao Tse-tung and others have certainly thought so. One of the principal economic reasons for setting up first the cooperatives in 1955–56 and then the communes in 1958 was to enable cadres to mobilize rural labor for local water control construction (see Perkins, 1966, chap. IV). There was a belief that individual interests connected with the ownership of private property were in conflict with each other to a degree that made such labor mobilization impossible unless these property interests were first abolished. Pre-Communist village studies in China give some support to this position (e.g., C. K. Yang, 1959, p. 26).

Another indicator of Communist intentions in the field of water control are the proposals put forward in the draft 12-year plan for agriculture (1956–1967). By 1967, the regime intended to expand irrigated acreage to 900 million *mou*, and 90 per cent of this expansion was to be accomplished by small-scale, that is, "traditional," projects.[21] What few large-scale projects were undertaken in the 1950's were principally concerned with hydroelectric power and flood control, not irrigation (Lindsay, 1958).

Two kinds of arguments can be presented to support the view that the Chinese Communists overestimated the expected returns from further investment in "traditional" water control construction. First, the data in Tables IV.1 and IV.2 indicate that the pace of such construction in east, central, and southeast China slowed markedly by the Ch'ing dynasty. A reasonable explanation of this phenomena is that the possibilities for further gain in these regions, which were heavily settled in Ming times, had been substantially exhausted. Only in areas nearly empty at the beginning of Ch'ing, particularly the southwest, did the pace of construction accelerate.

Further support for this line of reasoning can be obtained from an investigation of the percentage of irrigated land in each province. The figures are presented in Table IV.4. The data for 1949 and 1952 are misleading if not inaccurate and are included only for the sake of completeness. A glance at the data for either the 1930's or the late 1950's suggests immediately that in at least eight provinces [Kiangsu (E) through Kwangtung (SE)] there could not have been much land left that could suitably be irrigated by traditional means. Undoubtedly the quality of existing irrigation works in these provinces could be improved, but the returns on this kind of investment are normally much lower than on irrigating the land in the first place. What unirrigated land there is in these southern provinces is probably mainly in hilly or mountainous regions. To irrigate such land—where it is feasible at all—power pumps and similar modern equipment are more important than ponds and ditches.

Only in Kwangsi (SE), the three southwestern provinces, and in the north and northeast have the Communists been able to achieve a major expansion in the

21. Ho Chi-li, 1958, pp. 60–65. It is not clear whether the 90 per cent figure refers to the number of projects or the amount of investment, but I have assumed the latter.

TABLE IV.4. IRRIGATED ACREAGE BY PROVINCE
(PER CENT OF THE CULTIVATED ACREAGE)

Province	1904–1909[a]	1914–1919[a]	1924–1929[a]	Early 1930's	1949[b]	1952[b]	1957[b]	1958[b]–1959
Sinkiang	—	—	—	—	—	—	89	—
Kansu	(30)	(30)	(28)	(26)	—	—	—	—
Tsinghai	49	49	49	50	—	—	—	—
I.M.A.R.	—	—	—	—	3	5	9	15
Heilungkiang	—	—	—	—	2	2	5	14
Kirin	—	—	—	—	2	3	6	—
Liaoning	—	—	—	0[b]	—	—	2	17
Shensi[d]	(6)	(7)	(9)	(4)	—	—	—	23
Shansi	8	8	7	7	6	11	19	54
Hopei[e]	1	5	13	14	—	13	—	55
Shantung	3	3	5	6	3	5	23	70
Honan	14	20	23	25	—	10	—	—
Kiangsu	—	—	—	—	—	—	—	—
Anhwei	41	41	43	45	27	—	39	63
Hupei	64	65	64	63	12	29	46	58
Hunan	68	67	65	65	23	—	72	—
Chekiang	64	64	65	65	60	—	75 +	85
Fukien	57	57	57	57	34	—	66	82
Kiangsi	75	75	75	75	37	—	—	74
Kwangtung	72	70	69	68	52	—	62	84
Kwangsi[f]	—	—	—	—	18	—	53	—
Kweichow[f]	—	—	—	—	11	—	—	64
Yunnan	32	32	33	34	11	—	26	47
Szechwan	35	25	36	37	10	—	31	60

— Indicates data not available.

[a] Except where otherwise stated, all 1904–1930's data are from Buck, 1937 (Statistical Volume), p. 52.

[b] These figures were taken or derived either from one of the economic geographies edited by Sun Ching-chih (agricultural section) or from CIA, "Agricultural Statistics," *Weekly Reports on Communist China*, and N. R. Chen, 1967, p. 298.

[c] The Kansu figures for 1904–1930's appear to be too high. I have replaced them with the government estimate for 1918 (*NSTCP*), but have used the Buck data as representative of the change over time.

[d] The Buck figures for Shensi do not include estimates from the one major area of irrigation in that province. I have arbitrarily decided to multiply the Buck figures by 10, which brings them into line with the government 1918 figure.

[e] One high observation for Hopei (in Buck) was eliminated on grounds that it made the sample unrepresentative.

[f] Buck's figures indicate that no land at all was irrigated in the *hsien* he surveyed in Kwangsi and Kweichow, but given the large paddy acreage in these two provinces, it is unlikely that the Buck samples are representative of these two provinces.

irrigated acreage. As already pointed out, in the southwest the pace of water control construction did not accelerate until the Ch'ing period and it is probable that there were many areas suited to traditional irrigation where no construction had taken place. In these areas, the Communists with the cooperatives and communes were probably able to achieve substantial, if one-shot, gains.

Water-control developments in north China in the 1950's, both traditional and modern, were not so clearly beneficial. Traditionally, irrigation water on the North China Plain has mainly been obtained from wells.[22] Shallow wells have been of limited use, however, because of the instability of the deposits of shallow water and the fine texture of the soil. Over 5 million wells, mainly shallow wells, were sunk in campaigns in 1952 and 1956, but only 40 per cent of those were later reported to be of good quality and efforts to dig more shallow wells were halted or greatly slowed in the 1960's.[23]

One of the great advantages of shallow wells was that they could easily be dug without much or any well-digging equipment. This was not so for deep artesian wells. In the pre-1949 period, most of the irrigation water on the North China Plain came from artesian wells (Erisman, 1967, p. 31). Although the digging of artesian wells has continued into the 1960's, there are apparently limits on how much can be accomplished in this manner as well, due to the inadequacy of artesian water supplies in many areas and the great depth (in the eastern part of the North China Plain) at which these supplies are often found.

Governments of China also have long hoped to use the rivers of North China to irrigate that parched land. But in the words of A. L. Erisman,

Frequent flooding and waterlogging made it impractical to construct permanent irrigation projects in . . . [most of the] areas of the North China Plain. With the exception of an area of high land in the north-central part of the Southern Plain, virtually the entire North China Plain has been subject to frequent or occasional flooding. The flooding washed away or clogged irrigation facilities with sediment, often almost as quickly as the facilities were completed. In the areas most prone to water logging, the land was in danger of becoming alkaline or saline if irrigated (1967, p. 32).

Thus the use of rivers for irrigation purposes made it necessary to eliminate water-logging, and water-logging could only be ended if flooding were brought under control. One of the major problems in both cases was and is the enormous quantities of silt carried by North China's rivers, particularly the Yellow River. Because of silting, the life expectancy of China's celebrated *San-men* gorge dam is only 50 to 70 years and even this may be optimistic. In 1963 the spillways of that dam were already so clogged with silt that they were no longer operative (Erisman, 1967, pp. 147, 152; the dam was only completed in 1961). Centuries of silting have caused the Yellow River to flow at a level above the surrounding plain, further compounding the flood-control problem.

Because of these various problems, the rivers of North China can only be

22. This discussion of water-control activities in north China is based on Erisman, 1967. See also R. Myers, *op. cit.*

23. A. L. Erisman, 1967, pp. 98–99. These figures were taken from official Chinese sources.

controlled and made useful for irrigation by means of a large-scale, coordinated, and more or less simultaneous development program for the whole of the North China area. Labor corvees can play a part in such a program, but there must also be heavy "modern" investment, including the use of large quantities of cement and steel.

Some idea of the cost of controlling North China rivers can be obtained from several plans drawn up in the 1950's. Plans to control the Hwai and Hai Rivers estimated costs at 12.6 billion *yuan* and these were only two of the rivers in the area. The initial phase of a program to control the Yellow River was to cost 5.3 billion *yuan* in state investment and that was only the beginning (Erisman, 1967, p. 108; these are the official Chinese source figures). As it was, during the first five year plan period (1953–1957) the state invested 2.5 billion *yuan* in water conservancy, two-thirds of which went directly or indirectly towards the control of water resources on the North China Plain.[24]

Given these high costs, it is not difficult to understand why the state after 1963 shifted its investment in agriculture away from expensive attempts to control the rivers of North China and toward raising productivity in the rice areas of the south.[25] A continuation of the rate of investment of the 1950's held out little hope for significant return on that investment, and upping the rate to an effective level would have cut deeply into all other economic programs. Total investment in the first five year plan averaged 11 billion *yuan* a year (*TGY*, pp. 57–58), and putting several billion of that amount into water control efforts for some one-third of the population or less could hardly have appeared very sensible to the government.

Thus an analysis of both north and south China suggests that returns on investment in water control were not very high by the twentieth century except in a few more recently settled provinces. The opportunities for investment in traditional water-control activities in the north were particularly limited unless carried out in conjunction with modern large-scale projects.[26] And these modern large-scale projects themselves were very expensive in relation to the returns that could be expected from them and in relation to the overall investment capacity of the state. In the regions south of the Yangtze, except for the southwest, most easily constructed irrigation facilities had long since been built.

If the return on investment in "traditional" and many "modern" water-control activities was low and, as previously pointed out, the productivity of labor in alternative farm occupations was higher in the 1950's than was often believed to be the case, then the opportunity cost of using labor for water-control construction may often have been higher than the returns from that

24. The total state investment figure for water control activities can be found in *TGY*, pp. 57–58. The two-thirds to north China is an estimate by Erisman, 1967, pp. 66–67.

25. Erisman, 1967, pp. 54 and 67. The specific policy was stated in terms of shifting emphasis toward stabilization of yields on high yield fields.

26. Erisman's own estimate (1967, p. 206) is that diversion of river flow for irrigation purposes by the exclusive use of labor and land inputs could raise the irrigated area by 15 million *mou*. For a larger area, more grain would be used in construction and maintenance than would be produced by the expansion in irrigated acreage.

construction. It would seem, therefore, that the underlying economic logic of the cooperatives and communes set up after 1955 was based in part on a miscalculation of the costs and returns associated with the mobilization of labor for small-scale "traditional" projects.

Thus it is not surprising that the government in Peking in the 1960's shifted emphasis toward rural electrification and power pumps, particularly in areas that already had adequate supplies of water readily available. Unlike major dam construction and similar activities, power pumps are cheap to produce and probably have considerable impact on the ability of farmers to regulate their water supply properly.

TRADITIONAL AND CHEMICAL FERTILIZERS

The worldwide revolution in the production and use of chemical fertilizers has greatly altered the possibilities for raising farm productivity in China as elsewhere. World production in 1906 (in terms of nutrients) was 2 million tons. By 1947 output had only risen to 10 million tons, but in the ensuing 18 years the level reached 40 million tons and, according to one forecast, may reach 113 million tons by 1980 ("The Quiet Revolution," 1965, pp. 18–21).

The implications of this revolution for Chinese agriculture will be discussed below. The use of fertilizers in East Asia, however, did not begin in the twentieth century. In Japan one can distinguish three separate stages in the development and use of fertilizer. The first involved the use of grasses cut by the farmers themselves. Second, in the Tokugawa period (1603–1867) Japanese peasants began to shift over to the use of various commercial fertilizers—principally dried fish, oil cakes, and night soil (Smith, 1959, p. 92). Finally, in the early decades of the twentieth century industrially produced chemical fertilizers came into extensive use.

In China, farming practice did not really begin to enter the third stage until the 1960's and the changeover from the first to the second stage may in part have occurred long before the period of six centuries with which we are concerned. Night soil, lime, mud from ponds, sewers, and rivers, and even feathers of birds and poultry were used at least as early as the Yuan dynasty (thirteenth-fourteenth centuries) and in most or all cases much earlier.[27]

The changeover to the second stage, however, was probably less than complete by the fourteenth century. The *Nung shu* (1313) also lists a variety of grasses, beans, straw, and roots which could be used as fertilizers. By the 1920's and 1930's these items were no longer a significant source of fertilizer (Buck, 1937, p. 263). The disadvantage of such fertilizers was that their soil nutritive value was low and their collection required large amounts of labor, often during peak periods. If their extensive use was continued in the Ming and perhaps even the early Ch'ing period, it was probably because of inadequate alternative sources of fertilizer.

27. These fertilizers are listed in Wang Cheng, *Nung shu* (1313 ed.) 3.4–6.

Part of the explanation for the inadequacy of alternative sources was that at least one such source had not yet been discovered. Beancake may not have appeared until around 1500, although the evidence is hardly conclusive.[28] The discovery of the fertilizer potential of beancake is a significant exception to the more general picture of a stagnant technology.

A more important reason for changes in the availability of alternatives to grass and straw had to do with the rising man–land ratio. Nightsoil per *mou* increased because population grew about twice as rapidly as did the cultivated acreage.

The rising ratio of hogs and draft animals to cultivated acreage probably had eight times the impact of the increasing supply of nightsoil.[29] In an earlier section of this chapter, it was argued that draft animals probably increased at least as rapidly as population. Hogs, however, present a more difficult problem.

The role of hogs in China's rural economy does not appear to have changed much over the past several centuries. During the period with which we are concerned, pork has always been the principal meat consumed by the common man in China. No precise figures are available on the amount of pork consumed per capita in various periods in China, but we do know that in the capital of the Southern Sung in the thirteenth century (Hangchow) several hundred hogs were slaughtered every day or perhaps in the neighborhood of 100,000 hogs a year for a population of over one million, or a ratio of one hog per year for ten persons (Gernet, 1962, p. 46). This compares with ratios of one to nine in the 1930's and one to six in 1957. Given that a capital is likely to have a higher rate of pork consumption than outlying areas, these figures suggest that the number of hogs per capita probably did not decrease over time and may have increased.

A somewhat more solid basis for an assumption that the number of hogs was correlated with the size of population can be derived from an analysis of the way in which hogs were raised in China. Hogs have generally been scavengers feeding off garbage in the streets, or have received the husks of rice, pulverized stalks, beans and the like. When they are fed grain, it is only the cheaper varieties such as barley.[30] Even when the fodder is made up of such low-priced items, cost data in a number of sources indicate that the price of pork in China has apparently never been high enough to make raising hogs for pork alone profitable. This was the case in the latter part of the Ming dynasty and it is still

28. Beancake is not mentioned in the *Nung shu* (1313 ed.). The first reference of which I am aware is referred to in Ch'en Tsu-kuei (1958, p. 99). It is also mentioned in Hsu Kuang-ch'i, 1628, and in the *T'ien-kung k'ai-wu*, both seventeenth-century publications. I am indebted to Professor Ch'uan-sheng for the latter citations.

29. According to Buck (1937, p. 258), an animal unit produced sixteen times as much manure as a human did nightsoil. If the nutrient value of each is the same (?), then the fact that there were twice as many humans as animals in 1957 would reduce the ratio indicating their relative impact to 8 to 1.

30. See, for example, C. K. Yang, 1959, pp. 66–67: Fei Hsiao-tung and Chang Chih-i, 1948, pp. 49–50, 166, and the discussions of hog raising in the 1950's in the various economic geographies edited by Sun Ching-chih.

Supply and Demand for Hogs

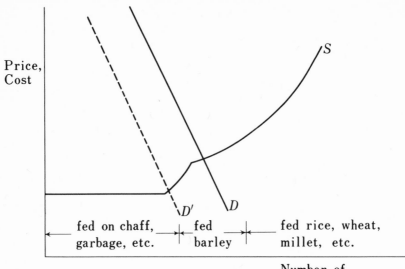

S — Supply schedule for hogs — the cost of raising
hogs rises steeply when farmers switch from
feeding hogs chaff to feeding them grain. The
cost of grain rises more and more rapidly as
farmers cut increasingly into their own (or the
nation's) grain consumption.

D'— Demand schedule for hogs where hogs are only used as
the source of pork.

D — Demand schedule for hogs where hogs supply both pork
and fertilizer.

Chart IV. 1

true today.[31] What makes hogs profitable is that they are not only a source of
pork, but of fertilizer as well. The amount of fertilizer they produce is just
enough to make them profitable.

A roughly drawn supply-and-demand schedule for hogs is presented in Chart
IV.1. If this chart is accurate, then the number of hogs raised depends on the
amount of chaff, other waste, and perhaps barley produced. These materials, in
turn, will be closely correlated with grain output and hence population. There is,
of course, no one-to-one relationship that can be clearly established from such

31. For the late Ming, see Ch'en Heng-li, 1958, pp. 100–101. This book is an analysis of a
book on agriculture in northern Chekiang published in the late Ming or early Ch'ing. For the
1930's see, among other sources, Fei and Chang, 1948, pp. 49–50.

evidence, but the argument does indicate that such an assumption is reasonable. In this light it is interesting to note that the amount of manure and night soil applied on land in Chia-hsing Prefecture in northern Chekiang (E) in the late Ming period was exactly the same as in south China in the 1930's.[32] The man–land ratio in this prefecture at that time was about the same as in all of south China in the 1930's.[33] Presumably in less populated areas the amount applied was much smaller.

By 1957 hogs supplied about 3 kilograms of ammonium sulphate equivalent per *mou* (less than 1 kilogram of plant nutrients).[34] If one adds nightsoil and manure from draft animals, the amount converted into ammonium sulphate equivalent might come to 10 kilograms per *mou* (about 2 kilograms in terms of plant nutrients). If in the early Ming period, the number of hogs per capita was the same as in 1957, then the number of hogs and hence the amount of fertilizer per *mou* from this source in the Ming period would have been half the 1957 level. Although our knowledge of yield responses to fertilizer in China is extremely limited even for chemical fertilizers, for purposes of illustration it can be assumed that one kilogram of fertilizer (in terms of nutrient) can raise grain output by from 15 to 20 kilograms.[35] The increase in nightsoil and manure between early Ming and 1957, under these assumptions, would have caused yields per *mou* to rise by from 15 to 20 kilograms[36] and this rise would in turn have increased total grain output by from 20 to 25 million tons.[37] Not all of this increase can be attributed to fertilizer alone, however, because successful fertilizer application usually requires adequate supplies of water.

32. The late Ming data are in Ch'en Heng-li, 1958, p. 158. For the 1930's I have used the data in J. L. Buck, 1937, Table 12, p. 259.

33. Acreage data for Chia-hsing Prefecture for 1553 (Table B.9) together with figures for the number of families for the early Ming (*Chekiang t'ung chih* [1899 edition] p. 1370) times five indicates that per capita acreage was 2.2 *mou*. In the 1930's the average for south China was about 2.2 *mou* per capita (see Tables A.5 and B.14).

34. This statement is based on data in Walker, 1965, pp. 54–56. I used the official figure for the number of hogs in 1957 and 40 kilograms of ammonium sulphate equivalent per hog (rather than Walker's intentionally conservative estimate of 30 kilograms).

35. The yield response for such small amounts of fertilizer is difficult to calculate. According to data in Jung-chao Liu (1965, pp. 929–30) and Walker (1965, p. 49) yield responses eventually level off at 3 kilograms of grain for every one kilogram of nitrogenous fertilizer, but the marginal yield for lesser amounts of fertilizer per *mou* is quite a bit higher. It takes about 5 kilograms of nitrogenous fertilizer to be equivalent to one kilogram of nutrient. Therefore, the yield response per kilogram of nutrient would be about 15 kilograms (3 × 5) for large amounts of fertilizer and more than 15 kilograms for smaller amounts.

36. If the nutrient equivalent of nightsoil and manure rose from one kilogram per *mou* in the fourteenth century to two kilograms in 1957, then the net increase was one kilogram. This yield increase figure is thus arrived at by multiplying one kilogram of nutrient times a yield response of 15 or 20.

37. The total increase in fertilizer would amount to one kilogram (nutrient) for every cultivated *mou* in China (1.68 billion *mou*) plus one additional kilogram for every *mou* of increased acreage since 1400 ([1.68 billion − .37 billion] × 1). Under these assumptions, fertilizer output (nutrient) would be 3 million tons and the yield response 45 to 60 million tons. But 1.3 million tons would have been necessary to maintain yields at their 1400 levels and some of this fertilizer would be used on cash crops such as cotton. If no fertilizer were used on cash crops, the increase in grain output would be 25 to 30 million tons. I have reduced these figures by 5 million tons to allow for fertilizer used on cash crops.

Few things point up the significance of Communist China's expansion of chemical fertilizer output more clearly than to compare the amount of fertilizer from this new source with the quantities available from "traditional" sources. By 1965, chemical fertilizer output in China together with imports amounted to 5 kilograms per *mou* (gross weight). The data for the 1950's and 1960's are presented in Table IV.5. Because of chemical fertilizers, China was able in 11 years from 1955 to 1966 to nearly match an increase in "traditional supplies" (per *mou*) which it had taken 600 years to obtain.[38]

TABLE IV.5. CHEMICAL FERTILIZER OUTPUT, IMPORTS AND CONSUMPTION
(1,000 Metric Tons Gross Weight)

	OUTPUT		IMPORTS[a]	CONSUMPTION	
	Reconstructed Official[b]	*Current Scene (Hong Kong)*[c]		*Reconstructed Official*[d]	*Current Scene (Hong Kong-derived*[e]*)*
	(1)	(2)	(3)	(4)	(5)
1949	27	—	—	—	—
1950	70	—	—	—	—
1951	134	—	—	—	—
1952	188	—	137	318	—
1953	249	—	366	592	—
1954	326	—	504	802	—
1955	353	—	923	1,255	—
1956	601	—	1,083	1,608	—
1957	871	—	1,313	1,944	—
1958	1,462	—	1,797	2,708	—
1959	1,777[f]	—	1,500	[3,300]	—
1960	2,000[f]	2,480	1,134	[3,100]	—
1961	1,431[g]	—	1,172	[2,600]	—
1962	2,150[h]	2,120	1,318	[3,500]	—
1963	3,000[i]	3,000	2,050	5,054	—
1964	4,000[j]	3,600	1,200 +	[5,500–6,000]	[5,000]
1965	5–6,000[j]	4,500	2,500	[7,500–8,500]	[7,000]
1966	6–7,000[k]	5,000	3,500	[9,500–10,500]	[8,500]

[   ] figures enclosed in brackets were obtained by adding (1) + (3) or (2) + (3). They are not independently arrived at.
— Indicates data not available.

   [a] The 1952–1962 figures are taken from Jung-chao Liu, 1965, p. 924. The 1963 figure is the difference between (1) and (4). The 1964 figure is that of Owen L. Dawson, 1965, p. 13. Dawson's figures seem to be less complete and hence lower than those appearing in other sources (e.g., his estimates for 1961, 1962, and 1963 are 0.88, 1.00, and 1.70 million tons respectively). The 1965 figure and 1966 preliminary estimate appear in The Editor, *Current Scene*, vol. IV, no. 20, p. 6.
   [b] The 1949–1959 output data are taken from Kang Chao, 1965, pp. 123 and 129. The totals include ammonium nitrate and phosphorous fertilizer as well as ammonium sulphate.

   38. The 1400–1955 increase was 3 million tons in terms of nutrient. The 10-million ton increase since 1955 is equivalent to about 2 million tons of nutrient.

ᶜ These figures appear in The Editor, *Current Scene*, vol. III, no. 17, p. 10 (which also includes a lower estimate for 1963 and 1964 of 2.8 and 3.4 million tons) and, The Editor, *Current Scene*, vol. IV, no. 20, p. 4.

ᵈ The 1952–1958 data appear in *TGY*, p. 171. The 1959–1962 and 1964–1966 figures were obtained by adding columns (1) and (3). The 1963 figure was obtained from the percentage increase (160%) over 1957 given in Hu Chi, 1964, p. 25.

ᵉ These figures were obtained by adding columns (2) and (3).

ᶠ These figures appear in Jung-chao Liu, 1965, p. 918. The 1959 figure is an official one. The status of the 1960 figure is unclear.

ᵍ This figure appears in Yuan-li Wu, *et al.*, 1963, vol. III, p. 34, and was originally taken from the Peking *Ta kung pao*.

ʰ The 1962 figure was obtained by applying the percentage increase over 1961 (50%) appearing in, "Nationwide Industrial and Communications Work Conference," *Jen-min shou-ts'e, 1963*, p. 365.

ⁱ The 1963 figure was obtained by applying the percentage increase over 1961 (40%) appearing in Kao Kuang-chien, "Great Stride Forward in Fertilizers," 1965, p. 39.

ʲ The data for 1964 and 1965 refer to the first half of the year (or the first 8 or 9 months) only. One source states that output in the first half of 1964 was 53 per cent above the first half of 1963 and that the first half of 1965 was 1.6 million tons above the first half of 1964. (Kao Kuang-chien, 1964, p. 25 and Fang Chung, 1965, p. 17). Output in the first half of 1963 was presumably not below that of 1962 (in terms of annual rate) or above that for the entire year 1963. This range (slightly reduced) provides the basis upon which estimates for 1964 and 1965 are constructed. The total output for the year was assumed to be somewhat higher than the rate during the first half of the year.

ᵏ According to official reports, 1.1 million tons of new chemical-fertilizer capacity was added in 1966. Capacity and output are not, of course, synonymous, but in estimating the figure in this table, I have assumed that if these new plants were operating below capacity, other, older plants were producing closer to capacity than previously (for the 1.1 million-ton estimate, see Chu-yuan Cheng, 1967, p. 150).

A more important comparison for the future, however, is between the rate of increase from 1955 to 1966 and the rate that will be required if China is to feed her population and raise its standard of living. Population is no longer creeping upward at well under one per cent per year. Barring the introduction of an effective birth control program, China will probably have to provide for a rise in the number of people of over 2 per cent per year. If standards of living are to rise, then grain output must be increased by at least 3 per cent per year. How much fertilizer this growth will require cannot be estimated precisely, but a rough figure can be obtained. A ton of fertilizer (nutrient) will increase grain output by perhaps fifteen tons.[39] To raise output of grain by 3 per cent (or 6 million tons as of 1965), fertilizer output must, therefore, rise by 400 thousand tons (nutrient—2 million gross tons) a year in the 1960's, more if any substantial portion is allocated to non-grain crops.[40] The expense of such a fertilizer development program is more difficult to estimate. If all fertilizer plants were imported, the cost would probably be about U.S. $300 million in the initial years and would rise by 3 per cent a year thereafter.[41] Whether domestically designed and equipped plants would be more or less expensive is difficult to say, although they would probably use up less foreign exchange. Increased fertilizer

39. See discussion in the previous footnote.

40. For an estimate of the amount of fertilizer used on cotton, see Dawson, 1966.

41. Individual fertilizer plants of about 50,000 tons capacity (probably in terms of gross weight) cost China U.S. $7–10 million in 1964 (MacDougall, 1964, p. 156).

production alone, of course, would not by itself raise farm output indefinitely. Other inputs, particularly improved irrigation facilities, would become increasingly necessary. How much additional annual investment these facilities would require is also difficult to say. Under fairly extreme assumptions, total investment in agriculture might reach 30 per cent of gross investment in the nation's economy as a whole, more if the overall rate of investment fell below first-five-year-plan levels. A more likely range would be from 20 to 25 per cent. Of this amount, fertilizer investment would constitute less than 5 per cent of gross domestic investment or about 20 to 25 per cent of total investment in agriculture.[42] Thus China's fertilizer requirements are costly, but not prohibitively so.

A final question concerning fertilizer is how much further can its use be increased, even if all necessary complementary inputs are provided. Will fertilizer investment run into sharply diminishing returns as has been the case with traditional inputs such as water-control construction? In this context it is useful to note that chemical fertilizer application in China (per *mou*) in 1965 was only about half Japan's level of 1919–1927 of 4.8 kilograms of plant nutrient per *mou* (Ogura, 1963, pp. 26 and 33). By 1959, the Japanese were using nearly 20 kilograms of plant nutrient per *mou* (United Nations, 1963, pp. 340–42) and achieving rice yields nearly double those of China (see Table II.12). There is every reason to believe, therefore, that for the next few decades at least, an investment program focused on chemical fertilizer can provide China with the necessary increases in farm output without running into significantly diminishing returns.

CONCLUSION

From the discussion in this and the previous chapter, it is apparent that there is no single explanation for the rise in grain output in China over the past six centuries. The extension of cultivated acreage to the west and to the northeast played a large role, but it did not play it alone. If the "new" lands had not been combined with "new" capital inputs and labor, the yields on these lands would have been well below even those of the early Ming period and the national average yield would have declined instead of rising. The opening of new rice lands in the south, for example, would not have been possible in many areas except in combination with water-control construction investment, and a new

---

42. Gross domestic investment in China during the years 1953–1957 (excluding nonstate investment in agriculture) was 113.9 billion *yuan* (Liu and Yeh, 1965, p. 74). During the same period, nonstate investment in agriculture was about 14 billion *yuan* (S. Ishikawa, 1965, p. 187) making for a total of 128 billion *yuan*. Over a five year period, an annual investment of U.S. $300 million would, at the official exchange rate, be about 4 billion *yuan* or 3 per cent of gross domestic investment. The 4 billion *yuan* figure, however, may not include many local construction costs, working capital, etc. If total agricultural investment were to reach 30 per cent of all investment, China would have to invest in all the rural projects she was investing in in 1953–1957 (20.95 billion *yuan*) plus another 17–18 billion *yuan* of new investment (of which 5–7 billion *yuan* would be in chemical fertilizers). If data for the 1960's were used, and the 1953–1957 investment rate were maintained, these figures for agricultural investment would have to be raised.

crop such as corn was often grown on land that otherwise would have been unusable.

The other inputs, however, not only grew along with land, but often at a significantly faster pace. The rural labor force, in particular, increased at a rate half again that of land.[43] As a result, more and more areas could practice double cropping of rice or of rice and wheat. A rising population also meant more nightsoil, and, indirectly, more organic fertilizers of all types so that by the nineteenth or twentieth centuries the amount of fertilizer per unit of land was double the level of the early Ming period. The number of farm implements and draft animals probably increased along with population. Only water-control construction proceeded at a much slower pace. Population growth and migration into new areas initially made possible large investments in irrigation and drainage works, but after several centuries the opportunities for further increases in productivity from this source declined and construction activity slackened while population continued to grow.

A major theme of these two chapters has been that increases in inputs accounted for most of the six-century rise in grain output, including the portion attributable to a rise in per acre yields. Only a small share of the rise in yields can be explained by improvements in the "traditional" technology. The belief that rural technology in China was nearly stagnant after 1400 can be supported with two separate lines of argument. First, given that output was rising very slowly (at less than half of 1 per cent per year) and that capital and labor inputs per unit of cultivated land increased substantially, there isn't much of an increase in yields left over to be explained by changes in technique. This argument is made in a more systematic form in the mathematical supplement to this chapter.

Second, a search of relevant historical materials did not turn up much in the way of direct evidence of improvements in technology. There were some changes of course. New seeds were continually appearing and spreading to neighboring provinces. New crops from the Americas also made possible a rise in output (aggregate and per unit area), particularly in the twentieth century. Beancake made its appearance for the first time in the Ming period and there may have been a number of minor improvements in farm implements.

It is relatively easy to establish that most techniques used in the early twentieth century were known somewhere in China in the fourteenth century. It is not so easy to establish that these techniques were known nearly everywhere in China (where they could be used). The most that can be said is that there is little direct evidence of any transfer of "best technique" from "advanced" to "backward" regions, nor were there barriers to mobility such as those in Tokugawa Japan that would have inhibited such a transfer. Further, the few new techniques that did appear in the Ming and Ch'ing period (principally new seeds and new crops) appear to have spread rapidly across China soon after first becoming known. Perhaps studies of such aspects of the rural economy as seeding dates will turn up additional evidence of improvements in China's "traditional"

---

43. Population grew on the average at a rate of 0.39 per cent per year between 1400 and 1957 while land rose at 0.26 per cent per year.

technology, but it does not seem likely that these additions could overturn the principal conclusions of the analysis made here.

It should also be pointed out that the evidence in these chapters is much fuller for rice than for many other grain crops such as millet or wheat. As a result, it is easier to explain the nature of the rise in yields and output in the south than in the north. Still, northern yields also increased and it is reasonable to assume that increased labor and fertilizer together with improved drainage and flood control must have played a major role in that increase.

If the reasoning in these chapters is generally correct, then China's "traditional" agriculture was able to meet the food requirements of a slowly rising population without much stimulus from improvements in technology. But in the twentieth century and particularly in the 1950's and 1960's changes occurred that made it impossible for the "traditional" system to feed China without outside help. First, China's population began to grow at a rate of over 2 per cent a year in the 1950's, instead of under 1 per cent as in even the highest years prior to the twentieth century. Second, two major sources of increased output in the traditional context were unable to provide much further assistance. With the filling up of Manchuria, there was little new land that could be readily brought under cultivation. In addition, opportunities for further extensions of the irrigated acreage using essentially "traditional" forms of water-control construction were quite limited.

Although the Chinese government was able to promote several "one-shot" increases in grain output in the 1950's by essentially "traditional" means (e.g., water-control construction in the southwest and the expansion of the double-cropped area of rice), opportunities of this type were quickly exhausted. In the 1960's, following the poor harvests of 1959 through 1961, the government shifted emphasis to the promotion of a "modern" revolution in agricultural investment and technology, the key to which was the rise of a large chemical fertilizer industry.

Mathematical Supplement
to Chapters III and IV

A major thesis of the previous chapters is that most of the rise in Chinese agricultural output prior to 1957 can be accounted for by increasing inputs of land, labor, and capital. Technological change, whether from improved equipment, better methods of cultivation, or new crops and new seeds, was of much less significance and accounted for only a small share of the growth of output. In Chapters III and IV, various kinds of direct evidence were brought forth in support of this proposition. The object of this supplement is to attempt a less direct but more systematic test of the essential plausibility of this argument.

The key to this test is the assumption that production of grain in China can be described by a fairly simple production function of the following form:[1]

$$Q = A(t)f(K, L, Ld)$$

Q = grain output

K = capital inputs in physical units

L = labor inputs in physical units

Ld = land inputs in physical units

t = time (put in to allow for technical change)

This particular form of the production function assumes that technological progress (a shift in the production function) is "neutral" in that it does not affect the marginal rates of substitution between the factors of production. If one further assumes that the

1. The idea of applying the kind of analysis used in this supplement to the arguments made in Chapters III and IV was suggested to me by Professor Subramanian Swamy. The basic methodology used here is that first developed by Solow (1957) for the United States economy.

production function is homogeneous to degree one and that factors are paid their marginal products, then this function can be converted into the following form:

$$\frac{\dot{Q}}{Q} = \frac{\dot{A}}{A} + W_k \cdot \frac{\dot{K}}{K} + W_l \cdot \frac{\dot{L}}{L} + W_{ld} \cdot \frac{\dot{Ld}}{Ld}$$

where

$\dot{Q}/Q$ = the rate of growth of grain output

$\dot{K}/K$ = the rate of growth of capital

$\dot{L}/L$ = the rate of growth of labor

$\dot{Ld}/Ld$ = the rate of growth of land

$\dot{A}/A$ = the rate of technological progress

W_k = the share of returns to capital (interest) in grain output

W_l = the share of returns to labor in grain output

W_{ld} = the share of returns to land in grain output

Thus to estimate the contribution of technological progress to the rise in grain output, we need to know the annual rates of increase of output; of land, labor, and capital inputs; and the share of the returns to each input in total product.

The rate of change in output can be obtained from population data together with an assumption about the likely limits on changes in per capita grain consumption. The labor force can be assumed to have grown at the same pace as population, and land data can be taken from Table B.17.[2] Capital is more difficult to deal with. Certain kinds of capital, as indicated in Chapter IV, are presumably highly correlated with population such as tools, housing for men and animals, and seed, to take several examples. Water-control construction, however, was not necessarily so correlated. If one uses the expansion in irrigated acreage as being indicative of the pace of development in this area, then the rate of growth of this kind of capital was significantly slower than that of population. Thus it is possible to think of population growth as an upper limit on the pace of capital formation and of the pace of water-control construction as a lower limit. The average annual rates of growth over different periods are presented in Table S.1.

The shares of the various factors in total product are more difficult to obtain. I decided to attempt to calculate the shares of the various factors in gross agricultural output rather than grain output because of an inability to find a plausible basis for determining what amount of capital, land, and labor should be attributed to grain. It is my guess that this procedure exaggerates the contribution of labor to grain output.[3] Because of this belief I have made what I consider to be rather generous assumptions about the contributions of land and capital to gross agricultural output in order to at least partially offset this bias. The economic implications of alternative biases will be discussed below.

2. I have made no allowance for the changing average quality of land over time. Because the share of land in the north rose over time (see Table II.2), it is likely that average land quality for the country as a whole declined slightly. The quality of land, however, cannot be measured simply by looking at differential yields between the north and the south, since higher southern yields reflected greater labor and capital intensity as well as higher quality land. Thus failure to take differing quality of land into account should not bias the results against technological change to any substantial degree.

3. It is at least plausible to argue that the share of labor in many subsidiary occupations was very large, particularly as compared to the share of land (in the weaving of straw or the making of cheap pottery, for example).

TABLE S.I. RATES OF GROWTH OF OUTPUT AND INPUTS
(Percentage Increase Per Year)*

	Population and Labor Force[a]	Output (20% rise per capita)[b]	Output (20% fall per capita)[c]	Land[d]	CAPITAL[e] (1)	(2)	(3)
1400–1957	0.39	0.58	0.35	0.26	0.25	0.34	0.39
1400–1850	0.37	0.41	0.32	0.25	0.22	0.33	0.37
1400–1770	0.32	0.38	0.27	0.23	0.21	0.34	0.32
1850–1957	0.45	0.62	0.24	0.31	0.37	0.37	0.45
1770–1957	0.51	0.61	0.39	0.30	0.32	0.32	0.51
1770–1850	0.59	0.82	0.31	0.30	0.26	0.26	0.59

* 0.26 indicates that the annual rate of growth was $\frac{26}{100}$ of 1 per cent, not 26 per cent.

[a] See Table A.7.

[b] Calculated by multiplying the population of the late year (e.g., 1957) by 1.2 and then dividing by the population of the early year (e.g., 1400) and then converting into annual rates.

[c] Calculated by subtracting 0.2 × late year population from the late-year population total and dividing by the early-year population.

[d] See Table B.17.

[e] Columns (1) and (2) were calculated from data on irrigation given in Chapter IV using the alternative estimates of irrigated acreage in 1400 of 80 and 130 million *mou*. The figure for 1850 was assumed to be identical to 1904–1909. The 1770 figure was derived assuming the increase in irrigated acreage between 1770 and 1850 was the same share of the increase from 1400 to 1850 as obtained by simply counting the number of projects. Column (3) assumes capital and population grew at the same rate.

The share of land was calculated by taking half of the output of the main grain crops, which in turn were rather arbitrarily assumed to be 80 per cent (in terms of value) of all grain output. In making this calculation, there are also implicit assumptions to the effect that actual land rents in China did in fact reflect the marginal product of land and that imputed rent on cultivator-owned land could be calculated in the same way as for landlord-owned land.

The share attributed to capital must be obtained in an even more arbitrary fashion. I have assumed that the average capital output ratio in China was 2/1 and that the rate of return on capital was 10 per cent. An assumption of a 3/1 capital output ratio and a 6 or 7 per cent rate of return gives essentially the same figure for the total return on capital in the agricultural sector.[4]

If one applies these assumptions to the 1931–37 grain and gross agricultural output data, they yield shares for capital and land of about 4 billion *yuan* each or about 20 per cent each of gross agricultural output. The share of labor can then be obtained as a residual, which in this case is 60 per cent. I have used this 60–20–20 breakdown in all subsequent calculations.

A brief glance at the original equation and the data in Table S.1 readily brings out the implications of alternative percentage shares for land, labor, and capital. Given an assumption of constant per capita output, then the higher the share of labor in

4. Although there is every reason to believe that the rate of return on capital in modern enterprises in developing countries is quite high, the rate of return on traditional capital inputs is often quite low (see, e.g., Schultz, 1964, chap. 6). Thus the assumption of a 7 to 10 per cent rate of interest should yield a rather generous estimate of the share of capital in farm output.

total product, the smaller will be the contribution of technological change ($\dot{A}/A$). The greater the share of land, the larger is the contribution of improvements in technique.[5]

Given the different possible assumptions about the rate of growth in output and capital, there are a large number of alternative estimates of the contribution of technological change to the increase in grain output. Some of these are presented in Table S.2. Both the highest and lowest estimates are presented together with one set of figures obtained when per capita output was held constant.

TABLE S.2. THE SHARE OF TECHNICAL PROGRESS

Period	$\dot{Q}/Q$	$= \dot{A}/A$	$+ 0.6\dot{L}/L$	$+ 0.2\dot{L}d/Ld$	$+ 0.2\dot{K}/K$	Share of technical progress (%)
		(HIGHEST ESTIMATES OF SHARE OF TECH. PROGRESS)				
1400–1957	0.58	0.24	0.23	0.05	0.05	42
1400–1850	0.41	0.09	0.22	0.05	0.04	23
1400–1770	0.38	0.10	0.19	0.05	0.04	26
1850–1957	0.62	0.21	0.27	0.06	0.07	35
1770–1850	0.82	0.35	0.35	0.06	0.05	43
		(ESTIMATES ASSUMING CONSTANT PER CAPITA OUTPUT)				
1400–1957	0.39	0.04	0.23	0.05	0.06	9
1400–1850	0.37	0.03	0.22	0.05	0.07	8
1400–1770	0.32	0.01	0.19	0.05	0.06	4
1850–1957	0.45	0.04	0.27	0.06	0.07	10
1770–1850	0.59	0.12	0.35	0.06	0.05	21
		(LOWEST ESTIMATES OF SHARE OF TECH. PROGRESS)*				
1400–1957	0.35	− 0.01	0.23	0.05	0.08	− 4
1400–1850	0.32	− 0.03	0.22	0.05	0.07	− 8
1400–1770	0.27	− 0.04	0.19	0.05	0.07	− 13
1850–1957	0.24	− 0.18	0.27	0.06	0.09	− 75
1770–1850	0.31	− 0.22	0.35	0.06	0.12	− 72

* Negative numbers indicate a retrogression in technique. In the case of negative technical progress, the precise meaning of the percentage contribution of technical progress to the rise in output is less clear than where technical progress is positive.

5. A number of econometric studies of cross-section data for Taiwan, Japan, and India have yielded estimates of the share of land ranging from 0.14 (for certain farms in Andhra Pradesh) to 0.85 (out of 1.14 for sweet potatoes in Honshu) and several estimates of 0.4 or 0.5 (see Heady and Dillon, 1961, pp. 620–29). It should be pointed out, however, that 2 of the 3 countries (Japan and Taiwan) had experienced rather substantial investment in modern capital the productivity from which may have in part been incorrectly attributed to land. Further, all three countries were quite crowded (had little new land that could be cultivated) and hence the marginal product of labor may have been well below that of China prior to say 1800. The one attempt to estimate Chinese shares for the 1952–1957 period of which I am aware is that by Anthony M. Tang (1968). He gives labor a weight of 0.55, land 0.25, and capital and current inputs together 0.20. His shares, therefore, are almost the same as the ones used in this study.

From Table S.2 it is apparent that only if per capita grain output rose significantly over the period concerned could technical progress have made a large contribution to output. If output per person declined by 20 per cent, then there was an actual worsening of technique, an unlikely situation.

This conclusion, of course, depends on the validity of the assumption that the production function was homogeneous to degree one. If there were economies of scale in Chinese grain production, then technique (other than scale) could have improved but been offset by the reduced scale of Chinese agriculture, if scale could be said to have been reduced.[6] Diseconomies from a reduced scale of output would imply that the marginal product of labor declined sharply if land grew more slowly than labor or not at all. Some decline in the marginal product of labor is plausible, but I doubt if it was as marked as would be necessary if there were economies of scale.[7] The subject of scale is discussed further in the next chapter.

The figures in Table S.2 assume that per capita output either fell, rose, or stayed constant over the whole period for which the estimate was made. It is quite possible that output per person rose at times and then fell only to rise again. Any number of assumptions about fluctuations in per capita output can be tested, but it is useful to look at some of the more likely possibilities.

There is a widely held belief, for example, that per capita incomes in China rose or were stable prior to 1800 and then fell steadily in the nineteenth and early twentieth centuries. But if such were the case, then technological progress was positive up to, say, 1770 or 1850 after which, for some reason, there was a retrogression.[8] I have already suggested that negative technical change is not likely to have occurred over long periods in China. It is even less likely that there was a sharp reversal from positive to negative change at the beginning of the nineteenth century. Thus, if our assumptions about the nature of the production function and the rate of growth of factor inputs are generally correct, it is unlikely that per capita grain output (or income) rose or was constant prior to 1770 or 1850 and fell thereafter.

Another possibility is that grain output per person rose by 20 per cent by 1770 or 1850 and then was constant from the 1850's to the 1950's. If this were the case, then technological progress made a more substantial contribution to the rise in output prior to 1770 or 1850, but continued to have some positive impact afterwards as well.[9] This

6. The term scale as used here implies that the "W" coefficients in the aggregate production function add up to more than "1" (economies of scale) or less than "1" (dis-economies of scale).

7. Studies of the aggregate production function for agriculture in the United States indicate that significant economies of scale do exist (e.g., Grilliches, 1964, pp. 961–74), but these production functions include such items as "research," "education," and "modern capital inputs," none of which existed in traditional Chinese agriculture to any significant degree. Estimated production functions for Japan, Taiwan, and Uttar Pradesh in India (Heady and Dillon, 1961) from cross-section data indicate there were no significant economies of scale in these countries. In Andhra Pradesh in India there were instead, significant diseconomies of scale, if the estimates can be believed.

8. If the turning point in per capita income were 1770, then the share of technical change in rising output was 26 per cent prior to 1770, and a negative 20 per cent thereafter. If the turning point were 1850, the contribution of technical change in the earlier period would be 20 per cent and in the later period a negative 45 per cent.

9. If per capita output rose only through 1770, then from 1400 to 1770, technical change accounted for 26 per cent of the increase in output up to 1770, and 16 per cent thereafter. If per capital output rose by 20 per cent through 1850, then technical change accounted for 23 per cent of the rise in output prior to 1850 and 10 per cent thereafter.

situation would be consistent with independently arrived at arguments to the effect that technical change may have slowed down after the new areas in the west and southwest had been filled up (i.e., heavily populated) for a period of time.

No one of these alternative formulations can be said with a high degree of confidence to represent what actually happened in China in the six centuries prior to 1957. This method of analysis, however, does seem to provide further support for several of the basic propositions in the text. First, a sustained decline in per capita grain consumption of 20 per cent implies negative technical change. Hence it is likely that if there was some decline in per capita output of grain, it was a decline significantly less than 20 per cent.

Second, a substantial and sustained rise in per capita grain output over time does not appear to be particularly plausible either. If such an increase did occur, then technical progress would account for a large portion of the increase in output, in some cases an even larger contribution than that of labor. This does not appear very plausible. Technical progress may have been more rapid than I have suggested in previous chapters, but not so significant as a 20 per cent rise in per capita output would imply.

Finally, the argument in Chapter I (and Appendix F) that per capita grain output did not change much over time is clearly consistent with the arguments in Chapters III and IV to the effect that technical progress was slow and made only modest contributions to the total rise in grain output. Internal consistency, of course, does not constitute proof, but, given that much of the information upon which these conclusions were based was independently arrived at, there is at least a good case for the plausibility of the key arguments in Chapters II–IV.

CHAPTER FIVE

The Distribution
of Land and
the Effects of Tenancy

Up to this point in the discussion, Chinese agriculture has been treated as if it were a machine into which one put inputs and out of which one obtained grain. Human beings were just another input called labor and a rather homogeneous input at that. Rich or poor, intelligent or dull, it mattered little. As far as grain output was concerned, it was only the average or typical performance that counted.

But there were few "typical" or "average" farmers in China. Some of the men who walked from their homes to their small plots of land every morning were hard working and always on the lookout for ways to improve their lot. Others were not. There is no effective way of measuring the intelligence or inner drive of Chinese farmers who lived six centuries ago, but at least part of that drive was related to the opportunities for advancement open to them. The extent of those opportunities in turn depended in part on the distribution of income and other factors of production and the institutions that determined that distribution.

Ideally this chapter should be concerned with the distribution of all factors of production and of income and the effects of that distribution on the productivity of agriculture per man and per unit of land. There is some discussion of the effect of inequalities in the allocation of a number of factors in the latter part of this chapter, but the bulk of the chapter is taken up with an analysis of the distribution of land. A lack of data makes it difficult to say much about the distribution of capital or income in the Ming or early Ch'ing period. In fact we do not even know much about inequalities in income in rural China today, and even less about the effect of those inequalities on agricultural output.

The principal evidence available concerning the distribution of land has to do with the relationship between landlords and their tenants, that is between men who owned considerable amounts of land but did not farm it themselves and men who owned little or no land but did farm. The institution of tenancy, in the broadest sense, made it possible to have unequal land ownership without necessarily having similar inequalities in the size of the farm managed by the individual farmer.

The question that concerns us here is whether tenancy in China created institutions that significantly impeded or enhanced the rise in grain yields and overall agricultural output between the early Ming period and the twentieth century. The answer to this question depends on the number of farmers and the amount of land subject to tenant contracts, on changes in these numbers and amounts over time, and on the nature of the contracts themselves. For example, were there incentives built into these contracts so that investment by tenants was encouraged? Did landlords play any direct role in promoting improvements?

In the latter part of this chapter, the analysis turns from a discussion of the effects of inequalities in land ownership to inequalities in the amount of land managed by a single farmer or farm family. Finally, the issue of inequalities in land ownership and management are related to land reform, the cooperatives, and the communes of the post-1949 period.

LAND TENANCY BEFORE 1400

Economic historians credit land tenure reforms for much of the increased agricultural productivity in eighteenth- and nineteenth-century Europe and England. The particular reforms varied from country to country. In England, the abolition of the open-field system of communal farming made it possible for individuals with initiative to more readily make improvements. In most areas, the commutation of feudal labor requirements into money rents also had a positive effect on farm productivity.

In China, however, major institutional reforms of this type occurred long before the fourteenth century, the period with which this study begins. In the early T'ang dynasty, for example, all land was supposed to be the property of the state and was only parcelled out to those who farmed it during their productive lifetime (age 18 to 60). Actually much of the land even then was privately owned and could be bought and sold (see Twitchett, 1963, chap. I). During this period and earlier there had been a constant struggle between the government and a semi-feudal aristocracy which attempted to build up large estates.

By the Southern Sung dynasty (1127–1279) this struggle had been lost by the feudal aristocrats. Landowners were well on their way to becoming landlords similar to those existing in the twentieth century. In the Sung, their principal claim on their tenants was a share of the annual harvest and little else. Special feudal dues of one sort or another did exist, and in a few areas still existed in the twentieth century, but they ceased to be an important feature of the rural scene. In the Sung, the government even occasionally attempted to protect the "rights" of tenants against the landlords (see Sudo Yoshiyuki, 1965).

The only major change in land tenure relationships during the early Ming involved the confiscation of large gentry landholdings. This step involved little more than the transfer of ownership from these gentry to the state. The tenant continued to pay rents as before, although failure to pay brought down the wrath of the government instead of that of the landlord.[1]

There will be more detail on the nature of the landlord-tenant contract later in this chapter. The key point here is that such major inhibitions to innovation and hard work as serfdom and communal farming did not exist to a significant degree in fourteenth-century China or anytime thereafter.

In the discussion that follows, therefore, the concern is with lesser bars to improvements in the productivity of land and labor. In turning to these questions, it is helpful to begin with a picture of the extent and regional distribution of land tenancy in China and the reasons why that pattern existed. With a knowledge of why tenancy was high in some areas and low in others, it is then possible to make some general remarks about whether tenancy increased or decreased over time and what effect these changes, if any, had on agricultural production.

LAND TENANCY: ITS CAUSES AND EXTENT

The relevant figures on the extent of land tenancy in China during the first half of the twentieth century are presented in Maps V.1 and V.2 together with Table V.1. The three sets of data are each based on different sources. I have presented all three sets of figures because so many of the data are of such low quality that little confidence can be placed in them. The fact that all the data tell roughly the same story, however, is encouraging.

In Map V.1 and Table V.1, the figures presented represent families who rented all their land expressed as a percentage of all non-urban families in the region. Statistics are also sometimes available on the amount of land cultivated by the owner or rented out. Generally, the rented land percentages are consistent with but slightly higher than the tenant family figures. In Map V.2, it was necessary to use some statistics based on land (the underlined figures) because of the lack of any alternative. The advantage of the figures in Map V.2 is that although they cover a limited area and only a few villages in any given area, we know that the surveys on which these figures are based were thorough and reliable.

Two major points emerge immediately from these data. First, in the decades of the twentieth century about 30 per cent of all farm families owned no land at all. Put differently, 70 per cent of these families did own at least part of the land that they cultivated. According to the Communists, during the land reform of the late 1940's and early 1950's, they distributed 700 million *mou* or about 43 per

---

1. One author argues that this transfer effectively raised the tenant's rent; it did not, however, change the basic nature of that rent (Nishiyama, 1950, pp. 243–51).

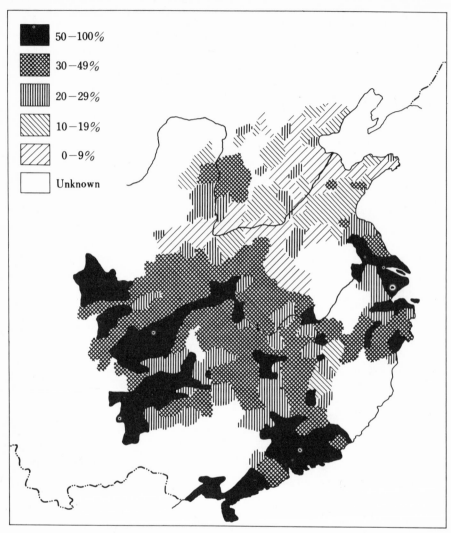

Map V. 1
Tenancy in the Twentieth Century
(tenant families as % of all farm families)

NOTES

SOURCES: This map is an impressionistic rendering of data in several sources. No attempt was made to accurately record each *hsien* in every province. Instead, the map gives a picture of the dominant level of tenancy in a given area. Thus, if one or two *hsien* in the southern section of a province had low tenancy, whereas ten others had rates of 60 or 70 per cent, the whole area is represented as being over 50 per cent. Where several sources of data were available for the same area and they were not consistent with each other, I relied on the one that was most consistent with data in Map V.2 and with other impressionistic evidence for the area. Although most of the data are for the 1930's, I resorted to using 1918 data (*NSTCP*) for parts of Kiangsu, Shansi, and Shensi provinces.

Most of the surveys used were conducted by the Ministry of Industries (*Shih-yeh Pu*) or the Ministry of Agriculture and Mining (*Nung-kuang Pu*). These surveys and others can be found in the following sources:

1. *Chung-kuo ching-chi nien-chien*, Vol. I, pp. F, 29–70.
2. *Chung-kuo shih-yeh chih (Kiangsu Sheng)*, pp. 27–32.
3. *Chung-kuo shih-yeh chih (Chekiang Sheng)*, pp. B, 31–36.
4. *Chung-kuo shih-yeh chih (Shantung Sheng)*, pp. B, 53–60.
5. *Chung-kuo shih-yeh chih (Hunan Sheng)*, pp. B, 43–47.
6. *Hupei sheng nien-chien*, pp. 146–147.
7. *Kiangsi nien-chien*, pp. 632–634.
8. *Kweichow ching-chi*, pp. F–14.
9. *Szechwan ching-chi ts'an-k'ao tzu-liao*, pp. M, 17–20.
10. *Szechwan nung-ts'un ching-chi*, pp. 177–181.

I also referred to data in Buck, 1937 (Statistical Volume), pp. 57–59 to check for consistency. By any standard, there is considerable inconsistency among the various surveys. In part this may have resulted from the use of differing definitions of what constituted a tenant as against a part-owner. The Ministry of Industries survey of Kiangsu province, for example, must have used a definition that excluded large numbers of people who most other surveys would have classified as tenants. In many cases, however, the inconsistency must have resulted from errors in one or all estimates for a particular area. Many individual *hsien* estimates probably represented little more than wild guesses.

There are 1918 data available for a number of the areas left blank, and even some 1930's data (e.g., for Fukien). The Fukien figures, however, indicate that tenancy even along the coast was only moderately high (10 to 40 per cent) which does not jibe with impressionistic material that indicates that tenancy on the Fukien coast was very high.

Where the map does indicate that a particular area has a certain level of tenancy, it does not follow that data are available for every *hsien* in the area. It only indicates that enough data were available to give an impressionistic picture of the level of tenancy in the area.

cent of the total cultivated acreage.[2] This figure is presumably only a rough estimate, but it is consistent with the figures on the number of tenant families together with the knowledge that the percentage of land rented was a bit higher than the percentage of tenant families.[3]

Second, the figures clearly show pronounced differences in tenancy among regions. The principal pattern is one of low tenancy in the north, high tenancy in the south. In fact, in large parts of north China there was little landlord-owned land at all. This basic pattern is well known. Equally interesting are several of the deviations from this basic pattern—the high rates of tenancy in the mountains of Shensi (NW) and in Manchuria (NE) and the low rates in Kwangsi (SE) and parts of Yunnan (SW) in the south.

With these patterns in mind, it is possible to begin an analysis of the causes of land tenancy. The subject has received much attention in the literature of the past several decades. For the purposes of this analysis it is desirable to begin

2. I used the cultivated acreage figure for 1952 in calculating this percentage. If I had used 1957 land figures, the percentage would have been 42 per cent. Pre-1952 figures undoubtedly understate the amount of acreage under cultivation. The source of the figure for land given away is Hsueh Mu-chiao, *et al.*, 1960, p. 87.

3. Data on both the percentage of rented land and of tenant families are available for sixteen of the villages recorded on Map V.2. In only one of the villages is the percentage of tenant families higher than that for rented land. In the other fifteen, the percentage of rented land varies from 2 to 28 per cent higher than the percentage of tenant families, averaging 14 per cent or 12.5 per cent if the sixteenth village is included. For what it is worth, 30 per cent plus 12.5 per cent is 42.5 per cent, roughly the same as the figure given by the Communists.

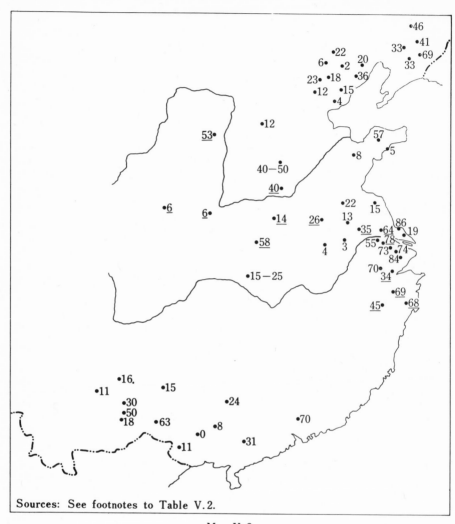

Sources: See footnotes to Table V.2.

Map V.2 ·
Land Tenancy (2)
(Tenant families as % of all families or in
the case of the underlined figures: rented
land as a % of all cultivated land)

with a general discussion of the major elements that determined whether a given area had a high or low rate of tenancy. The elements involved were of two types. First, were the conditions that caused an individual to want to sell his land; second, were the conditions that led other individuals to want to purchase that land.

Most discussions of land tenancy in China properly begin with a description of peasant attachment to the land and how only extreme hardship led them to give

TABLE V.I. TENANCY (TENANT FARM FAMILIES
AS A PERCENTAGE OF TOTAL FARM FAMILIES)

Province	1912[a]	1917–1918[b]	early 1930's[c]		1931–1936[a]
NW					
Chahar	30	16	—		35
Suiyuan	36	23	—		26
Ningsia	—	—	3	(1)	27
Tsinghai	18	—	73	(2)	21
Kansu	16	18	26	(6)	22
Shensi	21	23	16	(20)	23
N					
Shansi	19	16	25	(4)	17
Hopei	13	13	12	(6)	12
Shantung	13	14	10	(15)	12
Honan	20	27	23	(8)	22
E					
Kiangsu	31	31	46	(6)	33
Anhwei	43	33	65	(2)	44
Chekiang	41	36	51	(14)	47
C					
Hupei	38	36	34	(5)	40
Hunan	48	70	57	(13)	48
Kiangsi	41	30	33	(7)	41
SE					
Fukien	41	34	15	(1)	42
Kwangtung	52	37	49	(13)	52
Kwangsi	35	—	—		40
SW					
Kweichow	33	—	53	(6)	43
Yunnan	29	—	24	(8)	38
Szechwan	51	—	58	(3)	56
National Average (excluding Manchuria)	28	27	33	(146)	30

— Indicates data not available.

[a] *CKNY*, III, p. 728.

[b] *NSTCP* (1917, 1918). The figures for Hunan cover only a small part of the province. For both Hunan and Kwangtung, estimates are available only for 1917.

[c] Buck, 1937 (Statistical Volume), pp. 57–59. The figures in parentheses are the number of observations in each province. Buck also presents two other sets of data, but the rates of tenancy indicated by these figures appear to be much too low and hence I have not used them.

it up. Chinese farmers did not sell the land of their ancestors in order to obtain capital for speculative or commercial purposes or because they wanted a change of scenery. Although there are many variations on the main theme, most land alienation began with a peasant proprietor going into debt. Debts were seldom acquired to enable a farmer to increase the productivity of his farm except occasionally in newly settled areas where farmers used loans to tide them over the first few difficult years. Usually sickness in the family, a year or more of famine, or a family wedding or funeral exhausted the peasant's savings, if he had any, and forced him to borrow from a moneylender. The rates of interest on such loans were commonly 30 or 40 per cent per year and more. If the initial loan were large or if it were not quickly repaid, the peasant found himself increasingly in debt. Eventually the land which he had used to secure his loan would be surrendered to pay off all or a part of his obligation.

If the above picture constituted a complete explanation of the causes of tenancy, then it would follow that land alienation would be greatest where natural and man-made disasters were most frequent or where poverty was the greatest. Since most farmers were poor and frequently in need of credit, there would be a steady rise in the rate of tenancy over time everywhere. The only check on such a rise would be the Chinese practice of dividing the family inheritance equally among all the sons, a practice that tended to break up large accumulations of wealth.

It would also follow that tenancy would be highest in north China, because that is where natural disasters were most severe. Due to the lack of irrigation in much of north China and the frequent flooding of the Yellow River, crop yield fluctuations were much greater in that area than in, say, the region of the Yangtze River. Farmers were thus more often reduced to famine conditions in the north, hence more likely to resort to credit to tide them over, and thus more likely to lose their land. Yet it is in north China where tenancy is lowest.

To understand how this situation could prevail, one has to look closely at those who bought land and their motives for doing so. Who were they, how did they make their money, what kind of land did they buy, and why did they buy that kind of land?

Some landlords, of course, were not wealthy at all. Widows, orphans, and teachers might possess small plots and yet be unwilling or unable to farm those plots themselves. Only a small portion of the total amount of land rented out, however, was owned by such people. A somewhat larger but still small portion was publicly owned and the rents from this land were used to support local schools, pay for traditional religious rites, and the like.

The remaining rented-out land was either owned by individuals or clan organizations within the village or by absentee landlords, that is, individuals or groups outside the villages. About one-quarter of this land was owned within the village, three-quarters by outsiders (see Table V.2).[4] Clan land differed from individually owned land in that it was sometimes rented out to clan members on more

4. In 34 of 37 villages whose survey results appear in Table V.2, an average of 41 per cent of all cultivated land was owned by someone other than the individual who cultivated it. Thirty-two per cent of all cultivated acreage, or about three-quarters of all rented land, was rented from outsiders. I have eliminated the three villages in the table where residents of those villages rented out large amounts of land to farmers in other villages because their inclusion would bias the percentages downward. If instead I had assumed that these negative figures meant in effect that no land was rented from outsiders, then the percentages for the 37 villages would be 42 and 30 per cent instead of 41 and 32 per cent.

favorable terms than was the case with other land, but this was by no means always true.[5]

The principal problem, clearly, is to explain the nature and motivation of the absentee landlords, since they owned three-quarters of all rented out land. All available evidence suggests that these landlords attained their initial wealth from some source other than farming. In a survey of Kiangsu (E) in the 1930's, for example, of 374 landowners who possessed over 1,000 *mou* of land, 166 were military or government officials, 129 were moneylenders, and 89 obtained their initial wealth from commerce and industry (*CKNY*, III, p. 365). Of 131 landlord households in north China in the 1890's for which information was available, 8 had been officials, 64 merchants, and 59 had started as wealthy peasants who had gone into money lending.[6] In Hunan (C) after the Taiping rebellion, large tracts of land were bought up by Ch'ing generals,[7] and elsewhere in the eighteenth and nineteenth centuries high government officials owned as much as one million *mou*, in at least one case over two million *mou* (Li Wen-chih, 1957, p. 609). A twentieth-century survey of Wuhu, Anhwei (E) found that 23 of 36 landlord families were in commerce, only 2 in farming. Of 191 landlords surveyed in Kwangtung (SE), 138 were in some kind of commerce.[8] These examples could be readily multiplied. Although these surveys only indicate the principal occupation of the various landlords at the time the survey was taken and not their occupation when they first became wealthy, it would seem likely that a survey of the latter aspect would present much the same picture.

Money to purchase land (or to lend out with land as security) was generally made outside the agricultural sector because profits from the most successful Chinese farms were low and even those were obtained only with years of laborious effort. Profits from land ownership, that is from renting out land, were also low when expressed as a percentage of capital invested. One estimate by Buck for the year 1922, for example, indicates that the landlord's return was only 2.5 per cent on his investment.[9] This figure may be somewhat low, since beginning shortly after the fall of the Ch'ing dynasty in 1911, land prices tended to be depressed which might indicate that returns on owning land had fallen. Prices paid to farmers, for example, generally rose much faster in the 1910's and 1920's than did land prices.[10] Still, the rate of return in the nineteenth century was

5. An example where easier terms were given on clan-owned land can be found in Fei and Chang, 1948, pp. 78–79. An example where clan land was rented out on essentially the same terms as individually owned land can be found in C. K. Yang, 1959, pp. 47–48.

6. This survey is reported in Ramon Myers, *The Chinese Peasant Economy: A Case Study of Agricultural Development in Hopei and Shantung between 1890 and 1949* (forthcoming).

7. Unpublished paper by Yeh-chien Wang, "Agricultural Development and Peasant Economy in Hunan During the Ch'ing Period."

8. The Anhwei survey was taken in 1922, that for Kwangtung in 1929 (*CKNY*, II, pp. 324–25).

9. This figure was based on a survey of farms in Wuhu, Anhwei and is referred to in Chung-li Chang, 1962, p. 139.

10. The relevant price indexes can be found in Buck, 1937, pp. 344 and 346. Although the relative decline in land prices would in itself keep the rate of return on new investment in land up, the decline was presumably an indication that the rate of return on previous investment in land had been falling.

TABLE V.2. ABSENTEE LANDOWNERSHIP (1930's)

Province	Locality	Rented[a] Cultivated Area	Area Rented[b] from Outsiders	Survey conducted by
		(As Percentage of Total Cultivated Acreage)		
Hopei (N)	Tsun-hua[1]	8	2	J
	Mi-yun[2]	36	−5*	J
	Feng-jun[3]	34	27	J
Shantung (N)	Tai-an[4]	23	12	J
	Tsing-tao[5]	14	3	J
	Wei[6]	78	63	J
Honan[7] (N)	Hsu-chang	14	12	RRC
	Hui	40	16	RRC
	Chen-ping	58	−53*	RRC
Shensi[8] (NW)	Wei-nan	6	3	RRC
	Feng-hsiang	6	5	RRC
	Suite	40	32	RRC
Kiangsu (E)	Tai-tsang[9]	93	91	J
	Chang-shou[10]	80	70	J
	Chang-shou[11]	82	69	RRC
	Sung-chiang[12]	87	85	J
	Wu-hsi[13]	31	19	J
	Nan-tung[14]	33	2	J
	Chi-tung[11]	64	62	RRC
	Yen-cheng[11]	28	28	RRC
	Pei-hsien[11]	50	46	RRC
Chekiang[15] (E)	Chung-te	34	16	RRC
	Tung-yang	69	67	RRC
	Lung-yu	45	−29*	RRC
	Yung-chia	68	43	RRC
Kwangsi[16] (SE)	Tsang-wu	34	18	RRC
	Yung-ning	5	5	RRC
	Liu-chou	15	13	RRC
	Kwei-lin	37	28	RRC
	Lung-chou	13	13	RRC
Yunnan (SW)	Kun-ming[17]	47	46	RRC
	Lu-feng[17]	29	14	RRC
	Yü-chi[17]	41	30	RRC
	Ma-lung[17]	26	23	RRC
	Kai-yuan[17]	90	88	RRC
	Yu-tsun[18]	44	29	Fei
	Lu-tsun[18]	35	13	Fei

* Negative numbers indicate that villagers owned more land than they cultivated (i.e.ᵛ they rented land to farmers outside the village).

J = Japanese village surveys conducted in the late 1930's—each survey was of a single village in a particular *hsien*.

RRC = Rural Reconstruction Commission surveys of several villages in each *hsien*, conducted in the early 1930's.

ᵃ Total cultivated acreage rented by villagers divided by the total cultivated acreage utilized by those same villagers.

ᵇ (1—total area owned by villagers/total area cultivated by villagers.) Where possible, "owned area" includes only cultivated acreage. Where it does not, the difference is not significant. The resulting percentage is the net area owned by outsiders.

SOURCES:

1. *Noson jittai chosa hokoku* (Hokushi kezai shiryo No. 27), pp. 72–82.
2. *Noson jittai chosa hokoku* (Hokushi kezai shiryo No. 29), pp. 24–36.
3. *Noka kezai chosa hokoku* (Hokushi kezai shiryo No. 5), pp. 73–74.
4. *Noson gaikyo chosa hokoku* (Hokushi chosa shiryo No. 15), pp. 74, 82.
5. *Noson jittai chosa hokoku* (Hokushi chosa shiryo No. 7), pp. 15, 25.
6. *Noson gaikyo chosa hokoku* (Hokushi chosa shiryo No. 17), p. 127, tables.
7. Rural Reconstruction Commission, *Honan-sheng nung-ts'un t'iao-ch'a*, pp. 22, 24–25, 64, 65.
8. Rural Reconstruction Commission, *Shensi-sheng nung-ts'un t'iao-ch'a*, pp. 24–25, 65, 99.
9. *Noson jittai chosa hokoku* (Shanghai man-tetsu chosa shiryo No. 35), tables.
10. *Noson jittai chosa hokoku* (Shanghai man-tetsu chosa shiryo No. 34), tables.
11. Rural Reconstruction Commission, *Kiangsu-sheng nung-ts'un t'iao-ch'a*, pp. 51–52.
12. *Noson jittai chosa hokoku sho* (Shanghai man-tetsu chosa shiryo No. 48), pp. 50–51, tables.
13. *Noson jittai chosa hokoku sho* (Shanghai man-tetsu chosa shiryo No. 50), tables.
14. *Noson jittai chosa hokoku* (Shanghai man-tetsu chosa shiryo No. 51), tables.
15. Rural Reconstruction Commission, *Chekiang-sheng nung-ts'un t'iao-ch'a*, pp. 34, 89, 128, 139, 143–44, 188.
16. Rural Reconstruction Commission, *Kwangsi-sheng nung-ts'un t'iao-ch'a*, pp. 49–50, 90–91, 106.
17. Rural Reconstruction Commission, *Yunnan-sheng nung-ts'un t'iao-ch'a*, pp. 96–97, 106–107, 199, 235.
18. Fei Hsiao-t'ung and Chang Chih-i, *Earthbound China*, pp. 76, 222–23, 237.

probably little if any more than 5 per cent on most land.[11] By contrast, the rate of return on commerce and moneylending was often 10 or 20 per cent or more of capital invested. Investment in education if it led to high official posts also paid off handsomely.

Rent was paid in grain, or peasants sold their grain or other products and paid cash. Either way, a large landlord living in a town or city had eventually to convert most of his rental income into money, there being a limit to what he and his family could eat themselves. For a substantial number of landlords to exist in a

11. For example, the rate of return on five pieces of land in Fukien province for various years between 1782 and 1864 ranged between 5 and 10 per cent (average of 8 per cent) before taxes and other deductions. Further this figure probably represents the return in a year when the harvest was reasonably good. During poor years, little or no rent could be collected. These percentages are based on rent and land price data in Fu I-ling, 1961, p. 24. I have assumed that the price of unhusked rice in 1782 was 0.75 *liang* per *shih* and for the remaining years 1.0 *liang* per *shih*. Data in *CKNY*, III, pp. 247–48, indicate that money rents in the 1930's averaged 10 to 12 per cent of the price of land (with a range of from 5 to 25 per cent depending on the province and the quality of land). To obtain average net profits, one has to subtract taxes, rent collection costs, and deductions for poor harvests, among other things.

particular way, therefore, there had to be a well-established market for grain. Such a market, as will be indicated in Chapter VII, was limited to areas where there was good water transport. For example, one hundred thousand farm families, 80 per cent of whom were tenants, might easily pay one million *shih* in rent to large landholders living outside the village, or enough to feed a city of 250,000 persons (or nearly 50,000 families).[12] If there were no such large non-farm population near enough to be accessible at a reasonable transport cost, the grain would have to be sold back to the farmers themselves, but then the question becomes, in exchange for what?

Farmers in north China could produce cash crops which they could sell in distant markets, but even this was difficult where transport costs were high. An area where the percentage of agricultural produce marketed was low, therefore, was an area where the rate of return on investment in land would fall the more land tended to become concentrated in the hands of a few non-resident owners who had no use for the excess grain themselves and could not afford to ship it elsewhere because of high transport costs.

It is in this sense, I believe, that Tawney's statement (1932, p. 37) that "the yield of the soil [in the north] is too low to make it an attractive investment to the capitalist," must be understood. Landlords in north China had probably accumulated land up to a point where the rate of return had been driven below acceptable levels.[13] Thus the lack of highly developed commerce in a region worked in two ways to reduce tenancy. On the one hand, there were fewer rich merchants demanding land while, on the other, there was less incentive for existing merchants to invest in land. Neither of these propositions can be proved conclusively. Perhaps the most that can be said is that they appear to be key elements in any explanation of the high rates of tenancy in the Yangtze valley and along the southeast coast as contrasted to low rates on the North China Plain.

It is also clear that the above analysis does not explain all variations in rates of tenancy. In Shantung (N) Province, for example, some of the highest rates of tenancy were in the highly commercialized regions around the cities of Tsingtao and Tsinan, but then there was also relatively high tenancy in some of the more mountainous *hsien* in the center of the province.[14] In Shensi Province in the northwest, the comparatively rich plain around the city of Sian had little tenancy, but the mountainous regions in the north were areas where in some cases a high proportion of the land was rented. These northern Shensi (NW)

12. If one assumes that each tenant family worked 15 *mou* of land and that land yielded 2 *shih* of grain, half of which, 1 *shih*, was paid to the landlord, then 80,000 families would pay 1.2 million *shih* in rent. If the land's yield were 3 *shih*, total rent payments would be 1.8 million *shih*. Three-quarters of these amounts (that controlled by absentee landlords) would be 0.9 or 1.35 million *shih*.
13. There remains the problem of explaining why the price of land didn't fall far enough to make it profitable for landlords to accumulate more land. Probably peasant farmer demand for land kept its price above such levels. That is, where marketing was less developed, the value of the output of the land was higher (in money terms) for the peasant than for the absentee landlord.
14. Refer to Charts V.1 and V.2.

areas were among the poorest and least commercialized regions of the country.[15] In Hunan (C) and Szechwan (SW), the highest percentages of tenants were mainly in commercialized regions with good access to the Yangtze River, but there was also high tenancy in some of the least accessible parts of each province (e.g., western Hunan (C) and northwestern Szechwan (SW)).[16]

There is some evidence to suggest that landlord–tenant relations in these backward mountainous areas were more feudal in character than those in the commercialized areas. Certainly this was the case in Hunan (C) in the early part of the Ch'ing dynasty. According to Atsushi Shigeta (1960), landlords in the rich commercialized areas of Hunan (C) at that time collected rent and nothing else, but in the backward mountainous areas all kinds of extra exactions were imposed. At the New Year, for example, the landlord expected gifts of cakes, meat, and chicken. When there was a wedding or funeral in the landlord's family, the tenant had to help out and was often little more than a servant.

The backwardness of these areas may have made it possible to impose greater control over the tenants. In addition, the lack of highly developed commercial relations meant that land that provided only rents in grain to the owners was of limited value. To obtain an adequate return on his investment, the landlord may have felt these added exactions were necessary.

A few highly commercialized areas had low rates of tenancy, principally southeastern Kiangsu (E) and northern Kiangsi (C). In these areas, the land had been laid waste during the Taiping rebellion and a more normal pattern had simply not had time to fully reestablish itself.[17] As early as 1920, however, many of the *hsien* in these areas had already reverted to being regions where most of the land was owned by non-cultivators.

Up to this point, the discussion has emphasized essentially economic factors as they key determinants of the pattern of land tenancy. A final element that was crucial for the existence of landlords and high tenancy was political-legal security. There had to be some way of ensuring that the farmers paid their rents. When such means did not exist, many tenants felt few compunctions about keeping the rent portion for themselves.

Prior to 1911, basic support for landlords came from the imperial government. One of the responsibilities of officialdom was to support the rights of landowners,

15. For eyewitness descriptions of this area, see Myrdal, 1965, and Burgess, 1957.

16. The low quality of the land-tenancy data makes it difficult to make these statements with much confidence. In Szechwan, for example, several different sources giving data on land tenancy for various years during the 1930's generally agree that tenancy in *hsien* near Chengtu and along the Yangte was very high, but there is less than complete unanimity about conditions in the northwest corner of the province. Sources include J. L. Buck, *Land Utilization in China*; *Szechwan ching-chi ts'an-k'ao tzu-liao*, pp. M17–20; Lü P'ing-teng and *Szechwan nung-ts'un ching-chi*, pp. 177–81. For Hunan, I used data in *Chung-kuo shih-yeh chih (Hunan Sheng)* pp. B 43–47.

17. For an interesting discussion of the immediate post Taiping situation in Kiangsu, see Yeh-chien Wang, "The Impact of the Taiping Rebellion on Population in Southern Kiangsu," *Papers on China*, Vol. 19, pp. 120–58. The various materials on tenancy in Kiangsu and Kiangsi are far from being completely consistent with each other.

who were themselves often officials or related to them.[18] But this support was not unqualified. Chinese courts were operated in a way to discourage most individuals, including landlords, from using them. In some areas officials made little or no effort to aid landlords.[19] Nor were the property rights of landlord families inviolate. The state often confiscated the land of wrongdoers, rebels, and the like.

In areas where commerce was highly developed, financial affairs generally were more regularized and this situation must have made rent collection simpler. Even in such areas, however, landlords found it convenient to turn responsibility for rent collection over to a "bursary." These bursaries were run by individuals with official backgrounds who, hence, were better able to call on support from the government when necessary.[20] At the other extreme in the most backward areas of China, landlords and officials apparently worked closely together, and in many cases the landlords were virtually a government unto themselves.

After 1911, the position of the various local and regional governments toward landlord–tenant relations varied considerably among regions and over time. Twentieth-century developments, however, are discussed at greater length below.

LAND TENANCY, RISING OR FALLING

If the above factors were the key determinants of land tenancy in China, then it is possible to begin to reconstruct a portrait of the changes in the rate of tenancy over the past several centuries. Unfortunately, data for the Ming and early Ch'ing periods are rather scarce and so the analysis cannot be carried out with precision.

In the Sung population records, families were classified as being either lords (*chu*) or guests (*k'e*). If one accepts the argument of some Japanese scholars that the lords were landowners and the guests, tenants, one can reconstruct a complete picture of land tenancy conditions in the latter part of the eleventh century.[21] At that time 34 per cent of China's 16.5 million families were tenants (or guests), about the same percentage that prevailed in the 1930's. The regional distribution differed somewhat from modern times, but the areas with the lowest tenancy rates were generally in the north in that period as well, although what is now Chekiang (E) and Kiangsi (C) provinces also had low rates of tenancy. It would, however, take us too far beyond the boundaries of this study to establish whether this regional pattern was determined by factors similar to those that were important several centuries later. There is also a problem with the underlying

18. See, for example, the discussion on this point in Kung-chuan Hsiao, *Rural China: Imperial Control in the Nineteenth Century* (Seattle: 1960), pp. 386–96.

19. The rich areas in Hunan, for example, are a case in point (Atsushi Shigeta, *op. cit.*).

20. Yuji Muramatsu, "A Documentary Study of Chinese Landlordism in Late Ch'ing and Early Republican Kiangnan," *Bulletin of the School of Oriental and African Studies*, Vol. XXIX, No. 3 (1966), pp. 566–99.

21. The statements in this paragraph are based primarily on Shigeshi Katō, "The Totals of Landowning and Tenant Households in the Sung Dynasty," *Shina keizai shi kōshō* (Tokyo: 1953), pp. 338–70.

data. Many "guests" may simply have been recent immigrants and not neces-sarily tenants.

There are no figures for the Ming that are comparable to those for the Sung. But it is known that the lands of large numbers of landlords who opposed Ming T'ai-tsu were confiscated and that these lands remained under the control of the government. The tenants simply paid their rents to the government instead of the landlords. Most of the confiscated land was located in what is today southern Kiangsu (E).[22] According to the land figures for the year 1502, 51 per cent of this area was still in official hands at that time.[23] When one adds the fact that there were a good many private landlords left, it is clear that tenancy in southern Kiangsu (E) in the fifteenth century was at least as great as in the nineteenth and early twentieth centuries. In 1393, this area alone contained 11 per cent of the total population of the empire.

The situation in the rest of China in Ming times is less clear. In north China, government-owned acreage was generally only 1 or 2 per cent of the total, as contrasted to 24 per cent in the south.[24] If privately owned and rented-out land were added to these percentages, I suspect that at least in the south the combined figure would be as high as that for the same area in the 1930's (a little over 50 per cent). It is less likely that tenancy in the north was as high as at some later date. The ready availability of unused and easily cultivable land in that area would have made it difficult for landlords to find tenants, but this is only speculation.

As one moves forward into the Ch'ing period, the key question is what hap-pened to the percentage of land cultivated by owners of that land in provinces such as Hunan (C) and Szechwan (SW), which were comparatively empty at the beginning of the Ch'ing dynasty. The massacres of Chang Hsien-chung had left both of these provinces with large amounts of land ready for cultivation. Scattered evidence suggests that in Hunan (C), and probably Szechwan (SW) as well, when the Ch'ing period began, tenancy was low, but that it rose rapidly to levels approximating those of the twentieth century. By the middle of the eighteenth century, a memorial could state that where previously the people had been landowners, now they were tenants with 50 to 60 per cent of the land having reverted back into the hands of wealthy families (Li Wen-chih, 1963, p. 88), a figure comparable to that of the 1930's. In Kwangtung (SE), the great political power of the landlords allowed them to keep a hold on their tenants even though there was much good uncultivated land available for those free to take it (Ho, 1959, p. 219).

22. These remarks are based on articles by Takanoku Terada "On the Agricultural Economy of the Soochow Plain under the Ming," *Tōyō shi kenkyū* (Vol. XVI, No. 1 (1957), pp. 1–25; and T. Nishiyama, "A Study of Landlords in *Chiang-nan* during the Ming Period," *Nōgyō Sōgō kenkyū*, Vol. 4, Special Issue, (March 1950), pp. 243–51.

23. The Ming land data for 1502 are given in Liang Fang-chung, 1935, p. 104.

24. The one exception in the north was Ta-ming prefecture, where 99.5 per cent of the land was official land. In calculating the percentage for the south, I excluded the figures for the relatively undeveloped regions of Szechwan, Yunnan, and Kweichow. It should also be noted that if Hukwang were excluded, the percentage of official land in the south would be much lower.

Thus in newly settled areas, where investment in land was attractive to the rich, high rates of tenancy either existed from the start or quickly appeared. In the older areas of the lower Yangtze and Southeast coast, tenancy was apparently high throughout the Ch'ing period and probably the Ming period as well (Ho, 1959, pp. 218–19).

A comparison of the late nineteenth century with the situation in the 1930's indicates that rates of tenancy either did not change much during that half-century or actually fell slightly. A detailed study by Ramon Myers of the rates in 22 *hsien* of Shantung (N) Province is one case in point. Of these 22 *hsien*, the percentage of tenants rose in nine and fell in thirteen between the 1890's and 1930's while the overall average rate fell from 18 to 11 per cent.[25] Figures for Kiangsu (E) and a few other areas of south China are presented in Table V.3 and tell a similar story. Between the late nineteenth century and 1918, for example, there was, according to the data in the table, a rise of tenancy in four *hsien*, no change in one, and a fall in three. If the 1930's figures are any guide, tenancy fell in most *hsien* between the late nineteenth century and the 1930's. The quality of these data, however, is so low that one must not draw firm conclusions from them standing alone.

In general, therefore, although land was often bought and sold, the basic pattern of low tenancy in some areas together with high tenancy in others changed little. In times of prosperity farmers bought back more land, while in times of hardship they lost it again. But no amount of prosperity seems to have much reduced the amount of land under landlord control along the Yangtze River and the southeast coast, and no amount of poverty appears to have greatly increased tenancy in the north. It was poverty that caused a peasant to mortgage his land, but where absentee landownership had little financial appeal a peasant family must have had difficulty obtaining credit and hence did not lose its land. If conditions were hard enough, family members lost their lives instead.

Even the disruption and warfare of the first half of the twentieth century, together with increasing crowding on the land, did not lead to more land under absentee ownership. Nor did the coming of the railroad and the consequent rise in rural commerce in the north (see Chapters VI and VII) increase tenancy in that area. In part, of course, the twentieth century saw many more lucrative areas for investment appear. But, perhaps more important, land was not a very safe form of investment in the twentieth century. Buck, for example (1937, p. 333), attributes the relative decline in land prices to "agitation against landlords" during the period. Even without agitation it was difficult to collect rents in periods of disruption. Buddhist monasteries, for example, had great trouble on both counts from the 1920's on and particularly after the Japanese occupation (Welch, 1967, p. 219). Thus, although times were hard during the eight years of war with Japan, the amount of land redistributed by the Communists was apparently about the same as that under landlord control in the 1930's.

25. Myers' 1890's data for Shantung are taken from, Ching Su and Lo Lun, *Ch'ing-tai Shantung ching-ying ti she-hui hsing-chih* (Shantung:1959.

TABLE V.3. TENANCY CHANGES (1870–1930'S)

Area	Year	Tenants as Percentage of all Farm Families	Percentage Tenants 1918[b]	Percentage Tenants 1930's[c]
Hopei (N)				
Hsi-ning	1873	33	—	—
Wu-ch'ing	1888	30	—	7
Wang-tu	1905	50	—	3
Shansi (N)				
P'ing-yang	1888	small	—	—
Kiangsu (E)				
Chin-shan	1877	65	95	—
Chiang-yin	1878	65	50	16
Soochow	1884	80–90	85	5
Hsing-hua	1888	70–80	35	20
Chiang-nan	1888	10	—	—
Ch'en-chiang	1888	small	—	15
K'un-shan	1905	57	46	20
Nan-t'ung	1905	57	60	58
Anhwei (E)				
Su	1905	18	29	—
Chekiang (E)				
Hangchow	1888	50–60	63	20
Kiangsi (C)				
Hsin-ch'eng	1871	70	—	—
Hupei (C)				
Kwang-chi	1888	70–90[a]	—	60
Hunan (C)				
Pa-lu	1891	60	—	—
Hsiang-tan	early 19th cent.	high	—	49
Fukien (SE)				
Foochow	1888	50[a]	—	—
Kwangtung (SE)				
Ch'eng-hai	1888	70	—	—
Kweichow (SW)				
Kweiyang	1888	small	—	80

[a] These figures appear in *CKNY*, I, pp. 195–96 and were originally taken from various *hsien chih* and a report of the Royal Asiatic Society (1888).

[b] *NSTCP* (1918).

[c] Many of the Kiangsu figures for the 1930's are clearly too low and probably reflect the use of a rather exclusive definition of tenancy. Data are taken from the same sources as were used to construct Chart V.1, principally the surveys of the *shih-yeh pu*.

TENANCY AND FARM PRODUCTIVITY

If the above analysis that the rate and pattern of tenancy changed little over the six centuries with which we are concerned is correct, then the explanation of the rise in land productivity cannot be made in terms of an improving or deteriorating land-ownership situation. Nor does the pattern of tenancy give much support to the belief that landlords had much effect on productivity one way or the other.[26] Productivity per unit of land in the north with low tenancy appears to have grown no more rapidly than that in the south.

The most surprising result would have been one where there seemed to be a substantial correlation between high tenancy and a rapid rate of increase in productivity, but this is not the case in China either.[27] Landlords in other countries have on occasion been able to bring about agricultural improvements, but these landlords have generally been resident in the farming area. The high degree of absenteeism in China, together with such institutions as bursaries, would have made it difficult for landlords to make any positive contribution. To landlords, the holding of land was mainly a reasonably safe and convenient way of holding wealth already acquired. It was not the major source of that wealth in the first place. The rate of return on investment in land was too low for such investment to be a major path to riches.

To understand why the existence of widespread tenancy where it existed was not a major deterrent to increased yields on the land, however, it is necessary to look in some detail at the nature of the landlord-tenant contract. This subject is so complex and the literature on it so vast that I shall make only a few general and rather superficial remarks. Further, I shall deal only with the two aspects of the landlord-tenant relationship which could have significantly influenced land productivity, the length and security of the tenant's right to cultivate a particular plot of land, and the method by which this rent payment was calculated.

In the first decades of the twentieth century and during the Ch'ing period, the length and security of a tenant's contract varied both within and among regions. In some areas a tenant could be evicted at will or on the slightest pretext, whereas in others he had a permanent right to cultivate the land and to pass that right on to his sons, losing that right only if he failed to pay his rent, and not always even then.

Although these various systems of tenure appear to have existed side by side in many regions, scattered evidence suggests that certain systems tended to predominate in one area but not in another. If these materials are not misleading, tenure "contracts" of long or permanent duration were a common and perhaps dominant feature of the high-tenancy areas of the lower Yangtze and such other highly commercialized regions as coastal Fukien (SE) and the main rice surplus areas of Hunan (C). Yuji Muramatsu's study (1966) of bursary records for

26. For a rough picture of the province by province rise in productivity, refer back to Table II.3.

27. Even if there were a substantial degree of correlation between high tenancy and a rapid rate of increase in productivity, there would not necessarily, of course, be any causal relationship.

southern Kiangsu (E) provides some of the best evidence available that rented land was often passed on by tenants to their sons and that changes in tenants in general were not very frequent in the late nineteenth and early twentieth centuries. Fei Hsiao-t'ung (1946) provides similar first-hand evidence from his study of a village near the Kiangsu–Chekiang border. As Fei points out, even if a landlord wanted to change tenants, he had to find a tenant willing to go live in a village where he could expect local hostility as a result of his replacing one of the village's own. The evidence for Fukien (SE) (Shimizu, 1954) and Hunan (C) (Shigeta, 1960) is less conclusive, but it does indicate that permanent tenant control of the land was a common feature in both provinces. In Fukien (SE) at least, this right of tenancy could be bought and sold by the tenant. A survey of eight provinces in the early 1930's gives some support to the relative permanence of tenure in these highly commercialized areas, but the data are not ideal for the purposes of this study because they include a large category of "no fixed period of tenure."[28]

In north China (except Chahar and Suiyuan), by contrast, tenancy contracts were generally short, frequently for no more than a year's duration.[29] Other areas where tenure was short included Kwangtung (SE) (C. K. Yang, 1959, p. 48) and the mountainous areas of Hunan (C) (Shigeta, 1960).

There is little direct evidence which explains why this pattern prevailed. An important factor influencing the length of a contract, however, must have been the degree to which productivity on a particular piece of land could have been raised. Thus, while in Kwangtung (SE) tenure was generally short, still it was commonly three years rather than one. Any shorter period would have led the tenant farmer to plant crops in ways that would greatly reduce the productivity of the soil over time. The proper rotation on the Canton delta was three years in length and hence so were most contracts (C. K. Yang, 1959, p. 48).

Areas where elaborate irrigation works existed, as in most of the highly commercialized areas of the Yangtze River, must also have encouraged long tenure. Otherwise the tenants would have been greatly tempted to raise their own income by depreciating the landlord's capital. In the north, in contrast, fixed capital inputs were less significant.

There may also have been non-economic factors influencing the pattern of tenure. Some areas, for example, might have been more willing to accept newcomers than others, thus making it easier for the landlord to change tenants. In other regions, landlord political power may have been such as to prevent tenants from attempting to maximize their gain from a short-term arrangement. Whatever the case, wherever there were compelling economic reasons for a longer tenure, it was in the long-run interests of both lord and tenant to make such an arrangement and generally they appear to have done so. Thus tenure was com-

28. *CKNY*, III, p. 251. See also Land Committee, 1937, p. 45, in which it is stated that 86 per cent of the rented land in Fukien and 99 per cent of the rented land in Hunan is rented with "no fixed period of tenure," a catchall phrase apparently covering almost everything that is not "perpetual" or clearly of "fixed tenure."

29. *CKNY*, III, p. 251, and Myers. According to Land Committee, 1937, p. 45, in Chahar and Suiyan most rent contracts were permanent.

monly set in such a way as not to interfere with tenant efforts to raise productivity. It is reasonable to assume, however, that the degree to which such adjustments were made was far from perfect and that tenants would have had an even greater incentive to improve and invest in the land if they had owned it outright.

The method by which rent was paid was also designed so that a tenant farmer had an incentive to raise output. The system with the least incentive would have been one where a peasant was allowed a certain fixed income, the surplus to go to the landlord. Hiring labor at a fixed wage was an arrangement of this type, but where this was done the landlord generally managed the farm directly himself.

Most land, however, was leased with rent set at a fixed amount in cash or kind, or at a percentage of the harvest. All three systems led to a rent which in absolute terms amounted to about half the annual harvest of the main crop,[30] but each had a somewhat different effect on the incentive to raise productivity. Approximately half of all leased land in China in the 1930's paid a fixed rent in kind, with the other half more or less evenly divided between a fixed money rent and a percentage share of the harvest.

Data collected by the Economic Research Office of Academia Sinica (Peking) indicates that the national average share and regional distribution of the various rental systems changed little between the Chia-ch'ing period (1796–1820) and 1934. The relevant data are presented in Table V.4. In the original source, the figures for 1796–1820 were presented in separate tables with no apparent intention that they be used to compare the regional distribution of rental systems.[31] It is not unreasonable to assume, therefore, that these 139 citations were randomly collected from gazetteers and similar sources. Of the sixteen provinces for which Chia-ch'ing data were available, in ten the relative rank of the three rental systems was identical in 1796–1820 and 1934. In five of the remaining six provinces, either the highest or the lowest ranking system was the same, but not both.[32]

A fixed rent in kind was the dominant system in all provinces except for several in the north (and Kweichow in the southwest). Under this system, a farmer paid his landlord a fixed amount of grain in good years and bad. In particularly poor years, of course, even this system generally made some allowances, either by reducing the rent or postponing payment. Although rent calculated in this way was not always ideal from the point of view of the health and welfare of the tenant, when combined with a long-term contract, it did provide the maximum incentive. Improvements in productivity redounded to the farmer's benefit. Over the longer run, the landlord also gained because he could, when the contract ran out, raise the rent.

Fixed money rents had much the same effect on incentives as fixed rents in

30. For survey data on this point for the whole country in the 1930's refer to *CKNY*, III, pp. 247–48.

31. These figures appear to have been collected principally for the purpose of indicating the level or burden of rent payments in various regions.

32. The sixth province was Honan. For Honan there were only two citations for the years 1796–1820.

TABLE V.4. RENTAL SYSTEMS

	FIXED (IN KIND)		SHARE (% OF HARVEST)		MONEY	
Province	*C. 1800*	*1934*	*C. 1800*	*1934*	*C. 1800*	*1934*
	no.	*%*	*no.*	*%*	*no.*	*%*
NW						
Shensi	4*	59*	3	26	2⁰	15⁰
N						
Hopei	1⁰	22⁰	4	26	10*	52*
Honan	1	40	—⁰	44*	1	17
Shantung	—⁰	31	3*	39*	2	30⁰
Shansi	4*	46*	—⁰	27⁰	1	27
E						
Kiangsu	5	53*	—⁰	19⁰	6*	28
Anhwei	1	53*	6*	33	—⁰	14⁰
Chekiang	13*	66*	5⁰	7⁰	12	27
C						
Kiangsi	7*	80*	3	13	—⁰	7⁰
Hunan	2*	74*	—	18	—⁰	7⁰
SE						
Fukien	5*	56*	3	25	—⁰	19⁰
Kwangtung	18*	58*	—⁰	18⁰	3	24
Kwangsi	3*	65*	2	29	—⁰	6⁰
SW						
Szechwan	4*	58*	2	16⁰	—⁰	26
Yunnan	—	61*	2*	25	—	14⁰
Kweichow	—	40	1*	51*	—⁰	10⁰
Total	68	51	34	28	37	21

* Dominant system in province in period designated.
⁰ Least significant system in province in period designated.
SOURCES: The Chia-ch'ing (1796–1820) data are reported in Li Wen-chih, 1957, pp. 613–14. The 1934 data are in *CKNY*, III, p. 245. The "total" figures for 1934 are an average which includes percentages for Hupei, Ninghsia, Suiyuan, Chahar, Kansu, and Tsinghai as well as the provinces listed in the table. Generally similar (but not identical) figures can be found in, Land Committee, 1937, p. 43. The greatest discrepancy between the two sets of data is for Honan province (except Kiangsi, where the discrepancy appears to be due to a typographical error in Land Committee). The national averages in this latter source are 60 per cent (fixed rent in kind), 15 per cent (share), and 25 per cent (money).

kind. Unlike what one might expect, money rents were used mainly where the land was poor or the landowner was a public body rather than a private individual.[33] Crops grown on poor land were often not suitable for marketing, and hence a share of that land's produce was of limited use to the landlord. Public bodies do not appear to have been well equipped to market grain themselves, whatever its quality. In contrast, landlords or their agents in highly commercialized areas such as the Yangtze delta often preferred to be paid in kind so that

33. Such at least was the case on public land in Hopei and Shantung (R. Myers); and to a lesser degree in Yunnan (Fei and Chang, 1948, p. 226).

they, rather than the tenant, could gain whatever advantages were to be had on the market.[34]

Share rents were most common in the north, where security of tenure was also short. Crop yields in the north fluctuated much more than those in the irrigated rice lands of the south. On poor-quality land in the north, a peasant who agreed to a rigid fixed rent might be gambling his family's existence on a good harvest. With a percentage rent, the landlord had to share the risk, but it meant that the landlord also shared in any increases in productivity brought about by tenant investment in the land.

Thus in areas where tenancy was widespread, any retarding effects on productivity which absentee landownership might have had were muted by leases which called for long tenure and fixed rents. In the north, contract conditions were less suitable for encouraging farm improvements by the tenant, but then tenancy in the north was much less prevalent. Further, production in the north did not depend as much on long-term capital investment as in the south. Thus incentives in the north may still have been adequate from the point of view of the need to raise productivity.

The above portrait is, of course, greatly simplified. Reality in China was more complex. The sanctity of contracts, for example, was often held in low esteem by tenants and landlords alike, with the result that tenure and rent payment conditions were sometimes determined as much by political conditions in an area, or by the degree of personal rapport between landlords and officials, as by the contract. The contracts themselves were also more complex than I have indicated. I have ignored such items as rent deposits or three-tiered land ownership, for example. Still, the picture painted above does, I believe, capture the essence of the system as it existed in China in the Ch'ing period and the first half of the twentieth century.

INEQUALITIES IN THE DISTRIBUTION OF FACTORS PER FARM

The existence of tenancy did not result in a situation where all individuals or families managed farms of similar size. Instead, among those who farmed, income and cultivated acreage per capita and per farm were very unequal. Leaving landless laborers aside, the amount of crop area per person on "large" farms (Buck's classification) was two and one-half times that on "small farms" in both the wheat and rice regions.[35] Tenancy, interestingly, was not necessarily a condition of poverty. According to Buck's estimates (1937, p. 194), "large" farms rented virtually the same percentage of the land they cultivated as did "small" farms. Farmers in areas of high tenancy probably on the average had slightly lower incomes than those living in such low-tenancy areas as the North China

34. See, for example, the discussion in Shen, 1951, pp. 98 and 103. It was also common in the Yangtze area for rent to be calculated in kind, but paid in money. In this case, payment in kind amounted to little more than a way of protecting the landlord against inflation.

35. Buck, 1937, p. 279. Farm size varied even more than this, but larger farmers tended to support more people per family.

marginal productivity of capital.

Plain, although the differences do not appear to have been pronounced.[36] From a welfare point of view, however, farmers in southern Kiangsu (E), where tenancy was extremely high, may have been better off than those in say Hopei (N), because of the greater danger of complete crop failure and famine in the latter area.[37]

From the point of view of this study, the key issue is whether inequalities in income, cultivated acreage and the distribution of other factors of production reduced or enhanced farm efficiency. From what little data are available to deal with this question, it would appear that such inequalities reduced the overall average productivity of land in China, but not by very much.

The smaller the farm and the more fragmented its individual plots, for example, the greater was the amount of land used up by boundaries, but at the worst such boundaries occupied only a small percentage of the cultivated land. On acreage that was under cultivation, the yields per unit of land were virtually identical for all sizes of farms (Buck, 1937, p. 273).

Generally, smaller farms had more labor power per acre, while larger establishments were able to apply more capital. If this was in fact the case, then the average productivity of all land could probably have been raised by a more even distribution of labor and capital per acre.[38]

It is easier to demonstrate that there was more labor per acre on small farms than that there was more capital per acre on large farms. Small farms had almost twice as much labor per acre as large farms and, where weather allowed, this extra labor made possible more double cropping than on the larger establishments (Buck, 1937, pp. 274–76). On the other hand, large farms had more labor animals per acre than small farms, although ownership figures tend to exaggerate the difference because those without labor animals could usually rent them from others. Further, larger farms applied slightly more fertilizer than did small farms, although here again the difference was not great (Buck, 1937, p. 259).

What these figures seem to indicate is that either the marginal productivity of labor was very low and declining hence the small farms obtained only a limited advantage from large amounts of additional labor,[39] or that the productivity of traditional forms of capital was high, or that richer farmers were technologically superior to those poorer than themselves. If the third possibility was pronounced, that is, if richer farmers were better farmers or if there were economies of scale

36. Buck, 1937, p. 282. Output per person was higher in the south, but rent payments to landlords were a much larger share of output than in the north. South as used here excludes the southwestern provinces where output per man was much higher than in the lower Yangtze region and where tenancy was less common.

37. Farmers in Kiangsu also had access to a much more highly developed market.

38. This statement assumes, among other things, that there was a diminishing marginal rate of substitution between capital and labor, and that technological conditions on all farms were similar. The latter assumption will be qualified below.

39. It is interesting to note, however, that the number of idle months per able bodied man on small farms was actually slightly less than on larger farms (Buck, 1937, p. 295). But the marginal product of labor on these smaller establishments could still have been low and sharply declining. Poverty alone could drive workers on poorer farms to work at tasks that no one on a larger farm would consider worth the effort.

for larger-size farms, then land redistribution would not necessarily raise productivity if in the process of redistribution, land formerly rented by large farmers was given to small farmers or landless laborers. The limited amounts of relevant data, however, do not allow firm conclusions on any of these points.

LAND REFORM, COOPERATIVES, AND COMMUNES

The above described land-tenure system came to an abrupt end under the impact of the Communist land reform of the late 1940's and early 1950's. Most of the world's great land reforms have been undertaken primarily for political not economic reasons[40] and in this respect the Chinese reform was no exception. The landlord class was eliminated and the power of the Chinese Communist Party in rural areas was consolidated. That land redistribution was not looked on as a long-run solution to either rural China's economic or political problems was clearly demonstrated a few years later in the winter of 1955–56 with the collectivization of agriculture.

Two features of land reform may have had a negative impact on production. First, the land was given to the poorest classes, including landless laborers who on the average were probably not the best farmers and were too poor to invest much in the land. Second, well-to-do farmers, although left alone to farm their land, were in a politically vulnerable position that must have reduced the interest of some of them in becoming any better off in economic terms. My own guess, however, and it is no more than a guess, is that these influences were probably outweighed or at least matched by the elimination of rented land held under conditions of insecure tenure and other undesirable contractual arrangements.

It is impossible to measure the impact of this land redistribution in any quantitative way, precise or otherwise. The completed reform remained in effect for too short a period (1953–1955), the reliability of the statistics for these and earlier years are still in dispute, and factors affecting land productivity are extremely complex.

One feature of Chinese agricultural policy prior to collectivization must have had some negative impact on farmer incentives. Compulsory grain quotas were introduced in November 1953, and, during their first year were both high and unpredictable. Many farmers must have feared that any rise in their productivity would simply be taken by the state at prices well below those necessary to encourage voluntary grain sales in that amount. Prior to the introduction of compulsory quotas, there were compulsory deliveries in the form of an agricultural tax, but tax quotas were, in effect, a fixed and unchanging quantity, and hence did not interfere with incentives to raise output. In 1955, the government introduced a similar feature into the sales quotas. Quotas were set on the basis of "normal yield" and were to remain unchanged for three years.[41]

40. That, at least, is the conclusion of E. H. Tuma, 1965, Chapter XII.
41. For more details on the nature of agricultural quotas and taxes and other aspects of Chinese Communist agricultural policy relevant to this discussion, see Perkins, 1966, chaps. III–IV.

The amount of the tax and sales quota taken together (40 + million tons) (Perkins, 1966, p. 248) may have been slightly higher than rent payments in the 1930's (perhaps 30 + million tons),[42] but in the 1950's the farmer received some payment for a part of his deliveries.[43] Further, in 1955 at least, the system may have appeared somewhat less arbitrary than previous landlord-tenant contractual relations.

This appearance of stability, however, did not last long. Collectivization in the winter of 1955–56 radically altered the relationship between individual peasants and what they produced. This is not the place to analyze all aspects of the Chinese cooperatives of 1956–57, or the various types of commune organizations that have been tried since 1958. But the above discussion of the relationship between land tenancy and productivity does have particular relevance to certain aspects of the cooperative and commune organization.

For example, the analysis of tenant-landlord relations emphasized the importance of a degree of stability and predictability in that relationship, particularly where long-term capital investments might be involved. The agricultural policies of the Chinese government during the past fifteen years, however, have been anything but predictable. Land reform had no sooner been completed than collectivization was carried out. Two years later the cooperatives were completely reorganized into communes (1958), which were in turn progressively reorganized in 1961 and 1962, and then in 1966 the "cultural revolution" and Red Guards erupted with accompanying instability and uncertainty. In between these major changes there were numerous lesser but still important adjustments. In 1957, for example, the "three-fix" grain quota policy was virtually abandoned and for the next two years deliveries rose sharply until the agricultural crisis of 1959–1961 forced a reduction. The negative impact of this instability has probably been reduced, but not eliminated, by the fact that most important decisions, particularly those related to capital investment, have largely been in the hands of cadres responsive to the state rather than the individual peasant farmers.

Perhaps most important, the cooperatives and communes have partially separated farm effort from reward. Instead of receiving one's produce directly, a farmer now receives work points which are later converted into food and money. At times, elaborate steps have been taken to ensure that these work points reflected individual effort and productivity, while at other times, as during the early stages of the commune movement, few such steps were taken. At best, however, the relationship between creative effort and reward is less certain than when the peasant owned the land himself. Whether the work-point system provided a greater incentive to raise productivity than a typical tenancy contract cannot be determined with evidence now available. For what it is worth, however, it should be noted that in 1961 the Chinese government

---

42. Tung Ta-lin, 1959, p. 7. This figure is probably little more than a crude guess at the actual total.

43. The portion that was not a tax was paid for at the price level existing prior to the introduction of compulsory quotas.

instituted the "responsibility farm system" in an attempt to increase peasant incentives. Under this system, the state on some land in effect substituted a rental contract for the work-point method of maintaining incentives.[44]

What the overall effects of cooperatives and communes on productivity have been, of course, involves much more than the question of their effect on individual incentives. I have also purposely stayed away from the whole issue of the effects of these organizations on peasant welfare, material or psychological. Even what has been said about the effects of the cooperatives and communes on individual incentives does not allow one to draw any firm conclusions about the magnitude of these institutions' influences on productivity. The pre-1949 landlord-tenant system does not appear to have had much of a negative impact on the pace of the rise in yields from the fourteenth century on. Perhaps relatively modest cooperative forms of agricultural organization such as those prevailing in 1956–1957 or from 1962 through 1968 may not have much of a negative influence on farmer incentives to raise productivity either, but it is too soon to tell.

44. Under this system, in 1962 land was apparently given to individual peasant households after they signed a contract (presumably guaranteeing deliveries to the state). If the self criticism of Liu Shao-ch'i is genuine, Teng Hsiao-p'ing was an advocate of extending this system to the whole country (*Mainichi* [Tokyo], January 28, 1967).

CHAPTER SIX

Rural Marketing and Its Impact on Farm Output

A Chinese farmer had little direct contact with the world outside of his village or market town. In times of famine he might wander to some distant place in hopes of finding work and food or he might leave his ancestral home to start over again on new lands in the southwest or northeast. Most of the time even government officials did not intrude into the life of the rural village except to collect taxes or to settle disputes and breaches of public order on the rare occasions when these could not be handled by the village's own elders.

As a result, a peasant farmer's involvement with and knowledge of other areas besides his own was mainly through the vehicle of commerce. In the markets that he frequented there were goods produced not only in neighboring villages, but also in distant provinces and foreign lands. Goods from far-off regions were probably the most common channel of new ideas and techniques into the village. New seeds and new crops presumably made their way across China in the holds of merchant junks or on the backs of mules. But in the fourteenth through nineteenth centuries, as indicated in Chapters III and IV, there weren't many techniques for raising grain other than new seeds and new crops that were not already known in many or most areas within China. It was not until the rise of large-scale foreign trade in the late nineteenth and early twentieth centuries that commerce again brought innovations which had a major impact on agricultural output, particularly the output of cash crops.

Although trade was a vehicle for spreading improvements in technology when there were improvements to spread, most of what one can say on this subject has to do with the new techniques themselves, and not with the particular role of commerce. The focus in this chapter and the next, therefore, is on another way in which commerce influenced grain output and agricultural productivity in general. Commerce made it possible for an individual farmer to concentrate on crops (or handicraft products) suited to his soil or his skills. He did not have to produce everything he needed for himself but could sell the surplus of his speciality in exchange for these other items. Specialization increased his efficiency. Otherwise there would have been little point in specializing.

The issue that concerns us here is whether, during the six centuries with which we are concerned, there were any fundamental changes in the nature of Chinese commerce that might have contributed to the rise in grain yields or to increases in agricultural output in general. It must be stated at the outset, however, that the discussion of non-grain crops in this chapter is rather impressionistic. A full analysis of the performance of these crops would require an effort comparable to that reserved in this book for the study of grain. Most cash crops, in fact, could not be properly dealt with except in conjunction with an analysis of handicrafts and the rise of the modern agricultural processing industries. But one cannot deal with the impact of commerce on grain output without also covering what happened to cash crops. The discussion in this chapter, therefore, looks at the performance of commerce and its impact on agricultural production in general as well as grain in particular. Chapter VII is devoted to an analysis of the grain market alone.

For the discussion in this chapter, one must begin with some notion of the size and nature of China's internal commerce before attempting to appraise its impact on agricultural output. From the outset it is important to differentiate the various kinds of Chinese commerce. The key distinction in this study is between trade that takes place between distant points as against trade within a given rural market-town area.

There is also a third kind of trade, namely that which involves exchanges between cities and the immediate surrounding countryside. This trade has much in common with long-distance commerce except that the goods are transported over only short hauls and hence often not taxed or otherwise recorded. For the 1950's this situation does not present a major problem because some data pertaining to this third kind of trade are available. But for the 1930's and earlier such is not the case. As a result, I have assumed trends in trade between distant points to be a proxy for the broader category that includes short-haul rural-urban exchange as well, making qualifying remarks where necessary.

Prior to the advent of modern industry, the bulk of Chinese trade took place within the market town or within a somewhat broader area encompassing other nearby rural areas as well. What little I can say about this important subject is dealt with in the first section of this chapter. Long-distance trade, that is, trade across provincial boundaries and between markets hundreds of miles apart (and much short-haul rural-urban exchange), was small and confined to a few key commodities. With the coming of the steamship, the railroad, and industrialization, the relative importance of these two kinds of commerce began to shift until by the 1950's long-distance trade matched or exceeded that between neighboring farms and villages. The next sections of this chapter, therefore, are devoted to an analysis of the size and commodity composition of long-distance trade and changes in that trade after 1910. Before 1910 interprovince or long-distance trade dealt mainly in luxury products and was dominated by the official and landlord classes, although in terms of quantities there were fairly large shipments of grain as well. From the point of view of the individual peasant farmer, much of this trade was in one direction only. Goods left the farm for the cities but little came back from those cities except to the wealthy landholder. By the middle of the twentieth century, however, more and more farmers were sending their produce to modern factories where it was processed and a part returned to the rural areas. The remainder stayed in the cities where it fed and clothed the rising urban population.

In the 1950's, the increasing demands of industrialization together with a burgeoning urban population began to strain the ability and willingness of the farmer to meet that demand. Much was being asked of agriculture, but too little was being given back to it in exchange. It was not until after the crisis years of 1959–1961 that major steps were taken to supply the farmer with adequate compensation for his surrendered produce. This compensation came in the form of a great increase in the supply of producer goods to the farms, principally chemical fertilizers.

China's foreign trade will be dealt with in the final section of this chapter as an adjunct of interprovince trade. Initially the commodities traded in both domestic (long-distance) and international commerce were the same. Even in the 1950's goods leaving the rural areas for the cities and those going abroad to pay for imports of machinery were similar in their composition. Equally important, both sets of goods took more and more from the farmer without a commensurate increase in commodities returned to the countryside.

TRADE WITHIN THE MARKET TOWN

For many centuries there has been a high degree of specialization in rural China. Farmers have not tried to produce everything they needed at home. Instead they concentrated on a few key items and traded for the remainder. Prior to the twentieth century, the bulk of this trade occurred in the rural market towns.

Although it is possible to define a rural market town with some precision, this precision is of less value in a discussion of commerce than it is in an analysis of rural society. A peasant might purchase and sell many of his goods in his own market town, but the goods themselves might be destined for or have come from a distant place. When I speak of trade within a marketing region, therefore, I am referring to trade of goods produced and sold within a market town or in market towns several tens of miles distant (including much inter-*hsien* trade), but not regions or markets hundreds of miles away. This definition includes most trade within the agricultural sector and excludes most trade between agriculture and urban areas, particularly the modern industrial sector. Even this demarcation, however, is imprecise, primarily because the data I shall be using do not fit into a more exact division.

Unfortunately, there is no reliable way of estimating trade within a rural marketing region in the late nineteenth century. In the 1950's, farmers marketed about 38 per cent of their produce.[1] A survey (Buck, 1937, p. 84) for the years 1921–1925 indicates that 58 per cent of an average farmer's income was in cash. But this survey was biased toward regions that marketed a high percentage of their produce. In central and south China, for example, where an estimated 66 per cent of all income was cash income, all eight regions surveyed were on or very near to major water transport routes. Four of these areas were within thirty miles of Nanking (E), and one each was within a few miles of Ningpo (E), Foochow (SE), and Wuhu (E), all major commercial centers. Other surveys for particular regions in the early 1920's and 1930's give figures falling in between 38 and 58 per cent.[2]

It is not possible to derive an exact estimate of marketed agricultural produce in the 1920's, 1930's, and 1950's from these figures, but the average probably fell somewhere between 30 and 40 per cent, with many regions, such as those along the Yangtze, over 50 per cent.[3] But how much of this produce ultimately ended up in the hands of farmers in nearby regions and how much entered long-distance trade? For the 1950's it is possible to derive an estimate that suggests that about half of all marketed farm produce was ultimately sold to other farmers without being processed in urban industries in between. That is, about 15 to 20 per cent of agricultural output was sold in this manner, most of it probably in areas near to where it was produced.[4] There was, of course, great regional variation, but this variation probably had a greater effect on the farmer's degree of reliance on distant sources of supply, although this is difficult to prove. Chekiang (E) farmers, for example, sold a higher percentage of their produce on the market, but they also were probably much more dependent on distant markets and sources of supply. Hence the percentage traded with neighboring areas may not have been much higher than in, say, Yunnan (SW) Province.

Prior to 1900, long-distance trade was a much smaller share of all rural trade than in the 1950's, as will be clearly demonstrated below. It is reasonable to assume, but difficult to prove, that some of the increase in long-distance trade was at the expense of trade within a given region. As I shall state several times

1. This is the figure for 1957 (gross value of agricultural output divided by purchases from agriculture, both in 1957 prices). The 1957 gross value figure excludes rural output of processed industrial products. If one eliminates this category from the 1954 data, one also arrives at a marketed percentage of 38 per cent. For sources, see *TGY*, pp. 118 and 168; and Chao Chin-hsing, 1956, pp. 26–27.

2. Surveys of parts of Szechwan (SW), Suiyuan (NW) and Manchuria (NE) appear in *CKNY*, Vol. II, p. 271. For the 1930's, data for Chekiang (E) and Kweichow (SW) appear in *CKNY*, Vol. III, pp. 312 and 315.

3. The figures for 1954 and 1957 are significantly higher than those for, say, 1952 prior to the introduction of compulsory purchase quotas. But compulsory quotas probably did little more than offset the impact on marketing caused by the elimination of the landlord class, thus a figure a little below 40 per cent appears plausible for the 1920's and 1930's as well.

4. This figure includes a limited amount of grain that did undergo some processing, i.e., milling. For further discussion of this figure, see Appendix I.

in the course of this chapter, no definitive estimate of what happened in this regard can be made without a thorough study of the performance of rural handicraft industries, a study that is another book in itself. All that can be done here is to state that farm sales within a limited region a few tens of miles in diameter probably amounted to between 20 and 30 per cent of farm output. Prior to 1900, as will be demonstrated, only about 7 or 8 per cent of all farm output entered into long-distance trade.

There are several questions that pertain to this study that can be asked about intrarural trade in China, although they cannot be so readily answered. The first is whether there was any increase in per capita trade over time. The second is, why wasn't the percentage of agricultural produce marketed larger? And the third is, what effect did marketing have on grain output and farm productivity, either per capita or per acre?

I shall not even try to answer the first question. William Skinner's work is the first step in the direction of an answer,[5] but—as Skinner points out—demonstrating a relationship between the density of population and the number of market towns, as he does, is not the same thing as establishing a relationship between the density of population and the amount or value of trade in those markets. It is to be hoped that someone will soon undertake a study of this question. Here suffice it to say that there could not have been a dramatic increase in this trade in the centuries immediately prior to 1900. The size of such trade in 1900 was not very large and there is ample qualitative evidence to suggest that rural marketing appeared about the same to an observer in, say, the fifteenth century as to one in the nineteenth.[6]

There were two principal reasons why this rural trade was not larger. First, for the farmer to trade, he had to gain something from that trade. If, for example, he took his grain to a mill to be processed, the labor time and capital saved had to find some alternative occupation which paid more than the milling charges. For many farmers, milling, weaving, and other such occupations were carried on in off seasons when there was comparatively little else to do. If the farmer ceased doing his own milling, he might only gain more leisure time at the expense of net income. Handicraft processing enterprises sometimes were not much more efficient than what the farmer could do for himself. Handicraft enterprises that were significantly more efficient were still rather small in scale and could be located near their raw materials, so that they often did not generate much trade or specialization. Modern industrial processing, by contrast, was much more efficient than that done in the home, or in handicraft enterprises, and was generally located in large urban centers.[7] A modern edible oil extraction

5. See G. William Skinner, 1964–1965. Skinner does not primarily concern himself with this question, but his data are relevant to it.

6. See, for example, John Meskill, 1965, pp. 109–11 and 115–56. Foreign travellers were most impressed by long-distance commerce, but their comments also apply to local trade as well.

7. A large urban grain mill, or textile mill, would, for example, require a substantial commercial network simply to provide its workers with food. A local mill owner could grow his own food or take a share of what he processed. In any case he wouldn't have to provide for a large staff.

plant, for example, could extract anywhere from 2 to 16 per cent more oil from a ton of beans or other seeds than a handicraft plant, and at a lower cost.[8] The examples could be readily multiplied.

The second major reason why farmers did not want to market more of their produce was that a serious risk was involved. As will be argued at greater length in Chapter VII, excessive dependence on the market for one's grain supply carried with it the threat of possible starvation. It was safer to ensure minimum requirements on one's own land, even when that land was better suited for some cash crop which would normally return a higher income. It does not follow that farmers never took risks, but there was certainly less specialization and trade than would have occurred if such risks had not existed.

There is little reason to doubt, however, that the marketing that did take place raised per capita farm incomes over what they would have been if Chinese peasants had really depended entirely on their own resources. There is also a basis for believing that marketing raised per acre yields—but primarily the yields of cash crops and only to a lesser extent grain. Certainly if everyone had had to grow their own cotton requirements, much cotton would have been planted on land ill-suited for the purpose and the same would hold true for many other crops as well. Since three-quarters of the sown acreage was in grain, however, grain had to be grown on all kinds of land anyway. Still there was some room for specialization, even for grain, and it is reasonable to assume that this division of labor had a positive impact on grain yields. What appears less likely is that there was any major increase in the degree of specialization in rural areas between the fourteenth and nineteenth centuries that would have accounted for the rise in yields described in Chapter II.

To prove the thesis that cash-crop yields were raised by specialization, one would have to find a period when specialization was less than in, say, 1900. The next step would be to obtain yield data and then prove that any increase could not be explained in some other way, an impossible task.

THE SIZE AND COMPOSITION OF LONG-DISTANCE TRADE (BEFORE 1910)

There is no precise point where a good becomes a part of long-distance trade as against trade within a rural marketing region. To a significant degree, however, China's provincial boundaries separate and delineate geographic and economic regions. For many centuries emperors of China found it both desirable and possible to set up tax stations on the trade routes connecting provinces and major centers of trade. These tax stations provide us with at least some notion of the size of China's internal long-distance trade.

Unfortunately too little work has been done on many of the tax figures available in original sources for them to be of use to this study. Etienne Balazs (1957, p. 589) published an estimate of internal trade in the Sung period (for A.D. 1077) based

8. See Ministries of Light Industry, Local Industry, Commerce and Grain and the General Office of Supply and Marketing Co-operatives, "Plant Oil Processing Methods," *Chung-hua jen-min kung-ho-kuo fa-kuei hui-pien*, No. 1, p. 328.

on tax revenue figures. At that time, revenue from the two principal forms of commercial tax, amounted to 6,918,159 strings of *cash* (*kuan*) which Balazs estimates correspond to 5–10 per cent of the value of merchandise traded. Thus total taxed trade ranged in value somewhere between 70 and 140 million strings. If one assumes that per capita farm output in real terms was not much different than in, say, 1933, then this trade represented about 20 to 30 per cent of total farm output in 1077.[9] Unlike the late Ch'ing figures, this estimate does include short-haul rural-urban exchange. The Sung commerical tax was paid not only by traders in transit but by shops in cities as well. But the advantage of the greater coverage of the Sung figures is offset by the difficulty of establishing the reliability of the data and of obtaining an estimate of Sung agricultural output within some useful margin of error. From the eleventh century through the first half of the nineteenth century, there were other taxes on commerce, but much more needs to be known about the institutional basis underlying these taxes before one can use such data to estimate the size of trade.[10]

For the late nineteenth and early twentieth centuries, it is possible to estimate long-distance trade (but not short-haul rural-urban exchange) within a narrower margin of error. This narrower range is feasible because more is known about late Ch'ing commercial taxes, and because there are several alternative methods of arriving at an estimate of long-distance trade in this period. These estimates are discussed in detail in Appendix I, and only a brief summary of the findings in that appendix is presented here.

The most direct sources of information on long-distance trade between 1870 and 1908 are the *likin* (commercial tax) revenue figures. The *likin* tax was a percentage of the value of commodities passing a particular tax station, the precise percentage varying between and even within provinces. These percentages together with revenue data can thus be used to estimate the value of commerce passing the tax stations (see Table VI.1). As the discussion in Appendix I points out, estimates from *likin* data may understate the true value of internal trade because of smuggling, bribery of tax officials, or misuse of transit passes.[11] On the other hand, there may also be some overstatement arising from the fact that a single commodity was often taxed several times en route to its destination.

9. If one assumes that the number of families recorded in 1080 accurately reflects the population of Sung at that time when multiplied by 5.5, then population in 1077 was 16 per cent of that in 1933 (80 million versus 500 million) (see Tables A.1 and A.5). Taking 16 per cent of my estimate of the gross value of farm output in 1933 (in 1933 prices), one arrives at an estimate for 1077 of 2.5 billion *yuan*. The more serious problem is converting this figure into strings of *cash* in 1077 prices. For the years 1156, 1167, and 1179 I have prices per *shih* of husked rice of 1.5, and 1.3 and 1.5 strings of *cash* respectively (*Sung hui yao chi kao*, pp. 4,890, 5,523, and 6,057). At least two of the three citations are for normal (i.e., not famine) years. Prices of husked rice in 1933 per *shih* (of 150 catties) were about 10 *yuan* or seven times the level of 1156–1179. If one assumes prices in 1077 were similar to those in 1156–1179, one arrives at a figure of 350–400 million strings for the gross value of farm output in 1077. Further work could undoubtedly improve on this figure.

10. A discussion of some relevant aspects of the Ming commercial taxes can be found in E. Sakakida, 1967, chap. III.

11. Transit passes were desired to facilitate foreign trade, but much purely domestic trade apparently was able to travel under such passes. See Appendix I for further discussion.

There is no way of telling from institutional analysis alone, however, whether the trade figures derived from *likin* data are overestimated because of multiple taxation or underestimated due to smuggling and bribery.

Fortunately, it is also possible to estimate internal commerce from the reports of the Imperial Maritime Customs. Unlike most countries, the customs recorded not only international trade, but commerce between China's river and coastal ports as well. Prior to the construction of railroads, most of China's long-distance commerce took place between these ports. According to the estimates based on *likin* receipts, the trade of such interior provinces as Kansu (NW), Shensi (NW), Shansi (N), and Honan (N), none of which were serviced by treaty ports, amounted to only 8 per cent of all long-distance trade in the decade 1890–99.

The great advantage of the Maritime Customs Reports is that the officials who handled and compiled the reports were both thorough and honest. A disadvantage is that prior to 1902, only goods shipped on foreign ships and Chinese-owned steamships were recorded. The junk traffic was generally outside the control of these customs officials until after the Boxer Rebellion (1900), when all traffic between treaty ports was put under their jurisdiction. A second disadvantage is that traffic involving no treaty port or only one was not recorded except in the case of foreign trade.

Estimates of domestic trade (plus foreign exports) obtained from the two sources are presented in Table VI.1. It is clear from this table that between the 1880's and the first decade of the twentieth century, as the coverage of the maritime customs data increased, the gap between them and the *likin* trade estimates closed, but not completely.[12] Various other consistency checks are run in Appendix I. Although there are many discrepancies, there appears to be a sufficient degree of consistency between the two sets of figures for them to provide a starting point for an estimate of interprovince trade.

The coverage of neither set of figures is complete, however. If one makes allowances for this incomplete coverage, it is possible to arrive at an estimate of interprovince trade in domestically produced goods of 600–700 million *taels*, over one billion *taels* if foreign imports are included.[13]

A third method of estimating long-distance trade is to start from the knowledge that only a few kinds of commodities were generally transported over any any distance: cotton and cotton textiles, silk, salt, sugar, beancake, tea, and tobacco, to name some of the most important (see discussion below for further elaboration on the kinds of commodities traded). The gross value output of these items in 1931–1937 (in 1933 prices) can then be obtained and converted

12. In Table VI.1, two different maritime customs estimates are presented. The higher figure double-counts trade by recording each item at both its point of origin and at its destination. The lower figure only includes goods recorded at their destination. A figure comparable in coverage to the *likin* estimates would probably fall somewhere in between. That is, some *likin* trade is double-counted (if it paid taxes in more than one province), while other *likin* trade is not double-counted.

13. See Appendix I for the precise nature of the adjustments made to achieve more complete coverage.

into the prices of 1900–1909. If various assumptions are then made about the percentage of each item marketed, one arrives at a figure of around one billion *taels* (excluding foreign imports). This method is extremely crude, but it would seem to indicate that the *likin* and customs figures underestimate the size of trade even after allowances are made for incomplete coverage.[14] I have, therefore, decided to use a figure of 800–1,000 million *taels* as a better estimate of the size of interprovince trade in Chinese products (including exports abroad).

TABLE VI.I. ESTIMATES OF INTERNAL TRADE
(1,000 *Taels*—Annual Averages)

	FROM MARITIME CUSTOMS DATA		FROM LIKIN TAX DATA
	(1)	(2)	(3)
1870–1879	—	—	417,340
1880–1889	135,180	182,470	420,180
1890–1899	221,540	288,150	420,180
1900–1908	—	—	516,860
1900–1909	387,770	515,170	—
1910–1919	667,340	884,420	—
1920–1929	1,337,530	1,916,670	—
1930–1936	1,470,370	2,316,010	—

SOURCES: See Table I.8.
(1)—Foreign exports plus interport trade in domestic goods, imports only.
(2)—Foreign exports plus interport trade in domestic goods, both exports and imports.
(3)—See discussion in this chapter and Appendix I on the coverage of the *likin* data.

This figure of nearly one billion *taels* comes to under 20 per cent of the gross value of farm output at the time.[15] If exports abroad are excluded from these totals, purely domestic trade amounted to only about 700–800 million *taels*. The addition of imports from abroad together with exports would bring the total to about 1,200–1,400 million *taels*.[16] The 700–800 million figure represents only about 12–14 per cent of the gross value of farm output. Shipments of agricultural products out of rural areas to domestic and foreign markets thus probably amounted to about 400–500 million *taels*, or under 7–8 per cent of farm output.[17]

Therefore, long-distance trade in the late nineteenth and twentieth century was quite small when compared with agricultural production, even smaller if compared with total Chinese GNP at the time. Nor does this trade appear to have increased much in the decades immediately prior to the twentieth century.

14. See Appendix I for further discussion of this point.
15. An estimate of the gross value of farm output in 1914–1918 in 1933 prices can be found in Appendix D. This figure is converted into 1900–1909 prices using the price index in Appendix I. The figure so obtained is 5,700 million *taels* ($\frac{1}{3}$ of 17 billion *yuan*).
16. Imports from abroad were not taxed by the *likin* stations, but exports abroad were.
17. Total trade in each direction was about 600–700 million *taels* ($\frac{1}{2}$ of 1,200–1,400). Of this amount, probably 70–80 per cent was agricultural output, or 420–560 million *taels* as outer limits.

The rise in *likin* revenues was more than matched by a rise in prices. A 600 million *tael* figure, for example, is roughly the same in real terms as a 400 million *tael* figure for the 1870's and 1880's. If the Sung figures can be believed, there was not much change in the size of long-distance trade, expressed as a percentage of national or farm product, as much as eight centuries ago (although there could have been many fluctuations in between).

The argument that the share of long-distance trade is not likely to have increased much prior to the twentieth century can be bolstered with two other lines of argument. First, given that only about 7 or 8 per cent of all farm output was shipped out of the agricultural sector, it is difficult to see how such trade could have been much smaller in centuries past unless there was almost no trade of this type at all. But it is known from large amounts of qualitative (and quantitative) evidence that the tea and silk trades, among others, have been thriving for many centuries.

A second way of establishing that the share of long-distance trade did not change much over time is to look at the reasons why long-distance trade took on the configurations it did. The key determinants of the location of major trade centers and of the amounts and kinds of goods traded were transport costs, income distribution (particularly the amount of land rented to tenants), and climate and soil conditions in various regions of the country.

The principal limitation on long-distance trade was the high cost of transport. On land routes this high cost effectively eliminated low-price, bulky goods from interprovince commerce. Grain, for example, when carried on the back of a pack animal, cost as much to transport 200 miles as it did to grow it in the first place.[18] Transport on easily navigable waterways was, of course, less expensive. Yangtze River freight rates were one-third to one-fifth land rates in Hopei (N) and Shansi (N). Still, to carry grain from a rice surplus area such as Hunan (C) to the deficit regions of Kiangsu (E) and Chekiang (E), a distance of 1,000 miles, cost as much as the original price of the grain.

If one substitutes coal for grain in the above calculations, the dominant role of transport costs in limiting long-distance trade is even clearer. The cost of mining coal was about one-tenth to one-twentieth the cost of raising grain, yet transport costs were roughly the same.[19] Thus the real cost of coal doubled as little as twenty miles from the pits. Not surprisingly, coal was a negligible item in long-distance transport prior to the twentieth century.

At the other end of the scale were such luxury items as tea, silk, and precious

---

18. This statement is based on the assumption that the price of grain where it was produced was 1.5 to 2.0 *taels* per 100 catties. Transport costs over land in such northern provinces as Shansi, Hopei, and Shantung were between 0.25 and 0.3 *taels* for 100 catties per 100 *li* (one *li* = 0.36 mile). Source: Royal Asiatic Society, "Inland Communications in China," in *Chinese Economic and Social Life*, Vol. 2, pp. 175–76.

19. In the 1950's, the price of wheat was about 160 *yuan* per metric ton (Liu-Yeh, 1965, p. 376). In 1955, China produced 98 million tons of coal valued at 1,280 million *yuan* for an average value of 13 *yuan* per ton. This value figure, however, presumably includes coke and other high-priced items. The actual average price of soft coal was probably closer to 10 *yuan* per ton. The 13 *yuan* figure is derived from data in *Wo-kuo kang-t'ieh, tien-li, mei-tan, chi-chieh, fang-chih, tsao chih kung-yeh-te chin-hsi*, pp. 95–96.

metals. A hundred catties of tea, for example, was four or five times as expensive as an equivalent weight in grain. Raw cotton was slightly more expensive than tea.[20] A shipment of cotton from Hankow (C) to Shanghai (E), therefore, would only raise its cost by 10 to 15 per cent.[21]

Even a markup of several tens of per cent is not negligible, however. For the consumer to pay the additional sum, there had to be something gained in return. Otherwise that consumer would patronize nearby sources of supply.

In a modern industrial society, economies of scale often make it necessary to manufacture items at distances far from where they will be consumed. But there were few economies of scale in China's pre-modern industry. Handicraft firms could operate efficiently with small numbers of workers and limited output. Thus these firms could readily be located near their markets.

Climate and soil conditions, however, made it impossible to produce certain products everywhere. Sugarcane, for example, was largely confined to Kwangtung (SE), Fukien (SE), and Szechwan (SW) provinces (and Taiwan). Tea and mulberry leaves (for silkworms) could best be grown in a limited number of regions, particularly Chekiang (E) and southern Kiangsu (E). Salt and precious metals could be economically extracted in only a few areas. In fact, a brief glance at the major items entering long-distance commerce in the late nineteenth and early twentieth centuries (see Table VI.2) is enough to establish the predominance of commodities which could only be grown or extracted under specialized conditions. The data in Table VI.2, however, must be used with care.

TABLE VI.2. COMMODITY COMPOSITION OF
MARITIME CUSTOMS TRADE (1908)
(Million HK *taels*)

	Exports Abroad	*Domestic Trade*
Silk	83.0	14.1
Tea	32.8	4.1
Cotton and cotton textiles	12.9	5.4
Grain and flour	—	23.9
Beans and beancake	23.4	15.2
Oils and seeds	15.1	11.1
Tobacco and cigarettes	2.7	6.5
Sugar	1.4	5.2
Opium	0.9	11.7
Other	104.5	64.9
Total	276.7	162.1

SOURCE: See Table I.12.

20. See Table D. 31.

21. A *picul* of cotton cost 31 *yuan* in 1933, or about 15 *taels* in the prices of 1890, and the cost of transport by large junk was 0.15 *taels* per 100 miles (converted from data in Royal Asiatic Society, "Inland Communications in China," p. 137). From Hankow to Shanghai was a distance of about 700 miles (by water) or a cost of 1.05 *taels* per *picul*. If one adds loading and other costs, a total transport cost figure of 1.5 to 2.0 *taels* per *picul* appears reasonable.

They are taken from the Maritime Customs Reports, which undoubtedly under-state the amount of trade in such items as domestically produced textiles.

One can, of course, overemphasize the importance of climate and soil in determining the comparative advantage of China's various regions. The pre-dominance of southern Kiangsu (E) and northern Chekiang (E) in the silk trade was probably in part a result of this region's headstart over other suitable areas. Once the region had become a major center, there were many external economies which made it economical for new firms to continue to locate there. The presence of large pools of skilled workers, for example, would be one such economy. The existence of channels for marketing the finished silk all over the empire would be another.

Thus for a variety of reasons most of China's long-distance trade involved the exchange of a small number of goods which could be readily produced in only a few regions. Because trade between regions had to balance out (with exceptions to be noted below), an area with no particular climate or soil advantages sufficient to overcome the costs of transportation simply did not trade very much. North China, for example, with over 30 per cent of the population of the empire accounted for only a little over 10 per cent of all long-distance trade.[22] Kiangsu (E), by contrast, with less than 7 per cent of the population, accounted for nearly 15 per cent of all trade, at least if the *likin* data can be believed.

A third determinant of the configuration of China's long-distance trade was the level and distribution of income within a given area, particularly the dis-tribution. There is no precise way of measuring the degree of inequality in income distribution in nineteenth-century China. One can, however, argue that inequality in income distribution must have been positively correlated with the percentage of land in the hands of landlords.

The importance of income distribution to long-distance commerce arises from the fact that many of the products entering this trade were for luxury consump-tion only. Silk, for example, was mainly worn by the rich. Tea, considered the national drink of China, was consumed in great quantities by the rich. The poor more often than not substituted hot water. Pottery was produced throughout the empire, but only Kiangsi (C) pottery was shipped long distances, and Kiangsi (C) pottery was a luxury item.

One cannot explain all interprovince trade in this way. Salt was basic to the diet of all. Cotton textiles could not generally be classified as a luxury item. Still, the share of this trade accounted for by the requirements of the landlord and gentry class must have been large. Chang Chung-li (1962, p. 327) estimates that gentry income in the 1880's amounted to 675 million *taels*. The inclusion of other well-to-do individuals who were not classified as gentry would raise the figure. Without a detailed analysis of gentry expenditures, it is not possible to estimate precisely how much of this money was spent on commodities involved

22. North China as used in this sentence includes Shensi (NW) as well as Shansi, Honan, Shantung, and Hopei provinces. The trade data are derived from *likin* figures (see Table I.5) and are subject to a wide margin for error. The population figures are those for 1893 in Table A.5.

in long-distance trade. Certainly, however, it can be safely stated that the needs of China's upper classes dominated long-distance domestic trade.[23] Much of the trade activity along the Yangtze and elsewhere was therefore, in the service of only about 10 million of China's 400 million people.[24]

It is, however, difficult to separate out the effects of income inequalities from those of transport costs and special regional advantages. Most of the areas of high tenancy were also regions well served by water transport and possessing special climatic conditions [e.g., Kiangsu (E), Chekiang (E), Fukien (SE), and Kwantung (SE)].[25] The degree to which there was a causal relationship between high tenancy and a high level of commerce was discussed in Chapter V.

Prior to the twentieth century, therefore, China's long-distance commerce was small relative to the size of agricultural output for a number of quite specific reasons. It is not easy to see how, given these conditions, trade could have been much larger in the past. On the other hand, there is no reason to believe that tenancy was much lower in the Ming or early Ch'ing period (see Chapter V) or that transport costs were much higher. Perhaps government policy was more anti-commerce in its orientation in past periods,[26] but generally conditions would seem to have favored trade more or less on the scale of that in the nineteenth century (when expressed as a percentage share of farm output).[27]

Given the lack of much change in the share of long-distance trade in farm output, it does not appear likely that an increased division of labor stimulated by an expanding commerce had much to do with the slow rise in grain yields after the fourteenth century. This conclusion is reinforced by the above analysis of the commodity composition of that trade and of who benefited most from it.

From the above discussion it is apparent that the agricultural sector provided much of the income that went to support inter-province trade through rent paid to landlords, and only farmers and handicraftsmen who produced commodities such as tea and silk received from this trade a large share of the goods which they consumed. Tea and silk cocoon production did provide part- or full-time employment for several million farm families.[28] Further, without a nationwide trade network, production and employment in these activities would have been

23. If one-quarter of gentry income was spent on goods in long-distance trade or perhaps 200 million *taèls*, then the amount of trade to and from landlord gentry would be 400 million *taels*. The one-quarter figure was arbitrarily picked for purposes of illustration.

24. Chang Chung-li (1962, p. 327) gives a figure for gentry and their families of 7.5 million. There must have been several million non-gentry landlords and other wealthy persons in addition, hence the 10 million figure. Careful research could improve on this figure.

25. The same statement can be made about Szechwan (SW) and Hunan (C). There were a few areas of high tenancy that were poorly served by water transport—e.g., northern Shensi (NW) and parts of Yunnan (SW).

26. See, for example, the discussion in Ping-ti Ho, 1962, pp. 77–83.

27. Among other reasons, during the early Ming, China's population was concentrated in areas with readily available and cheap water transport.

28. An estimate for 1915 puts the number of families involved in growing tea as 1.5 million (Wu Chüeh-neng and Hu Hao-ch'uan, 1935, p. 30). According to another source, there were 124,000 families producing an average of 200 catties of silk cocoons in Wuhsin district, a major silk area (D. K. Lieu, 1941, pp. 8–9). If this average per-family production applied to the whole country, some two million families would have been employed part or full time in raising cocoons.

much smaller. Yet the total number of farm families producing commodities in significant quantities for long-distance trade of all kinds was probably only 15 to 20 per cent of all the farm families in the country.[29]

Whatever the precise number of families involved, this kind of long-distance trade could not have contributed much to the rising productivity of farm land planted in grain. Any influence on productivity was confined to the production of the luxury items themselves. Put in quantitative terms, if foreign and domestic long-distance trade in agricultural products taken together amounted to about 14 to 16 per cent of agricultural output, perhaps only 7 or 8 per cent or less involved trade that redounded to the benefit of the farm sector itself (excluding landlords). That is, excluding rent payments, farmers may have marketed 3 or 4 per cent of their output in distant regions and received 3 or 4 per cent of the goods which they consumed from such faraway areas.[30] These estimates could be subject to a considerable margin of error without much affecting the basic conclusions reached here.

INTERPROVINCE TRADE (1910–1960's)

If the above analysis is correct, for nearly one thousand years, China's long-distance trade changed little. The absolute amounts rose, but more or less along with the increase in population. China's farmers remained substantially cut off in economic terms from all but their immediate neighbors.

Then in the twentieth century modern industry and transport began to change this picture. By the 1920's interprovince trade in real terms was more than three times the levels of the late nineteenth century (see Table VI.1).

Not all of this increase in trade, of course, was in agricultural products. Railroads made it economical to ship large quantities of coal. Over half of the goods carried on Chinese government-owned railways in the 1920's and 1930's, for example, were mining products, principally coal.[31] But there was also a great increase in domestic and foreign trade in farm and processed farm products (e.g., textiles). Changes in the nature of foreign trade are discussed in the next section. Domestic trade is dealt with here.

The first problem is to describe changes in the size and nature of China's long-distance trade in agricultural products. This description is followed by an

29. Twenty per cent of all farm families would represent a total of perhaps 12 to 15 million families. To obtain an accurate figure, one would have to estimate the number of families producing cotton, sugar, and tobacco for the long-distance trade. It would also be necessary to establish some precise definition of "significant quantities." As used here, the term means that farmers received more than 5 or 10 per cent of their income from such trade.

30. No attempt was made to estimate these figures with any degree of precision. If the income of the gentry and non-gentry landlords and other wealthy persons was 800 to 1,000 million *taels* and one quarter of this income was used to purchase items in long-distance trade, then some 400 to 500 *taels* (2 × 200 or 250 million) of that trade was accounted for in this manner. That would leave 400 to 500 million *taels* (or 200 to 300 million *taels* each way) for the non-luxury farm trade (long-distance only).

31. See Yen Chung-p'ing, *Chung-kuo chin-tai ching-chi shih t'ung-chi tz'u-liao hsuan-chi* (Peking: 1966), p. 211.

analysis of why these changes occurred and the effect that they have had on farm output.

In describing changes in the size and nature of China's trade, the procedure followed is to look at the situation in the 1950's, then to compare it with conditions in the late nineteenth century, and finally to fill in what occurred in between these two periods and in the 1960's. A major problem from the outset arises from the fact that data on China's trade in farm products in the 1950's are not entirely comparable to figures given in the previous section for the nineteenth century.

The rural balance of trade for the year 1955 is presented in Table VI.3. The products included and the totals refer to commodities that were sold to or

TABLE VI.3. THE RURAL-URBAN TRADE BALANCE IN 1955
(In 1955 Prices)

Type	FARM PRODUCTS SOLD OUTSIDE RURAL AREAS[a] Amount (*Million* Yuan)	Type	NON-FARM PRODUCTS SOLD IN RURAL AREAS[a] Amount (*Million* Yuan)
Grain	510[b]	Cotton cloth	3,230
Cotton	2,010	Edible oils	800
Soybeans	1,520	Sugar	500
Edible Oil Seeds	590	Salt	590
Tea, Sugar, Tobacco	510	Kerosene	440
Silk, Hemp, etc.	260	Producer goods[c]	1,970
Meats, Eggs, Vegetables, etc.	1,600[d]		
Subtotal	7,000	Subtotal	7,530
Other	3,000	Other	2,500
Total	under 10,000[e]	Total	approx. 10,000[e]
		Total including Semiprocessed Farm Products	16,400[f]

[a] Except where otherwise noted, all data are derived from figures in Tables I.10 and I.11.

[b] This figure excludes tax grain and all grain processed and returned to rural areas. The value of this latter portion was assumed to equal 8.5 *yuan* times the number of *piculs* of grain sold in rural areas.

[c] I have assumed that 30 per cent of all producer goods sold to agriculture were handicraft manufactured in the rural areas. No precise figure is possible because 29.2 per cent of all producer goods sold to agriculture are subsumed under the category "other" (Chen, 1967, p. 401).

[d] Surveys of urban consumption in Shanghai indicate that 18.9 per cent of worker income was spent on these items. A survey of all urban workers suggests that their consumption pattern was not much different from workers in Shanghai. (For sources, see Chen, 1967, pp. 435–36). This percentage, reduced by 20 per cent to allow for transport costs and taxes, was applied to the 1955 official urban wage bill of 10 billion *yuan*. (For source, see Perkins, 1966, p. 255).

[e] These figures are guesses made on the assumption that most free-market sales were between rural producers.

[f] This figure can be derived from data in *T'ung-chi yen-chiu* data office, "Changes in 1957 Market Prices and Their Influence on the People's Standard of Living," *T'ung-chi yen-chiu*, April 23, 1958, p. 26.

purchased from urban areas or abroad. All goods traded within rural areas are excluded, including some which may have been transported a considerable distance. All goods sold outside of rural areas, of course, were not necessarily shipped to some distant point. Vegetables, eggs, and meat in particular were generally supplied to urban consumers from farms within a few miles of the city. Still the bulk of the goods appearing in Table VI.3 would have traveled far enough to have been taxed at *likin* stations or have been recorded by the Maritime Customs if either institution had existed in 1955.

Thus, long-distance trade in farm products in 1955 must have reached about 15 billion *yuan*. In real terms this figure was five times that of all long-distance trade in the late nineteenth century. Whereas in the late nineteenth century long-distance trade (each way) by the farmers themselves (excluding rent payments and the luxury trade) amounted to 3 or 4 per cent of gross agricultural output, by 1955 it amounted to nearly 15 per cent (each way).[32] In addition there were the rural tax payments to the government in 1955, but these were comparable in some respects to rent payments[33] and should not be compared to earlier trade estimates that exclude commerce in the service of the landlord class.

This rural urban trade was of two types. A part involved farm raw materials sent to the city, processed there, and returned to the countryside, after deducting urban consumption and exports. The second part was made up of an exchange of farm products for urban industrial goods using non-agricultural raw materials —everything from thermos bottles to chemical fertilizer.

A major source of increased long-distance trade involved the twentieth-century Chinese development of modern agricultural processing industries from cotton textiles to flour milling (Table VI.3 does not include processed grain which returned to rural areas). Some idea of the rapid growth of these industries can be seen from the figures in Table VI.4. By 1955, most cotton and tobacco were processed in modern enterprises, to name just two items.[34]

How much of the farm goods processed in the factories of Shanghai and Tientsin represented a net increase in output of these items, and how much simply represented a transfer away from rural handicraft firms cannot be estimated here. The subject is a basic one and worth a book in itself. Whichever the case, the rise of modern processing industries significantly increased the dependence of the countryside on distant sources of supply.

The second source of increased rural-urban trade was the exchange of farm products for industrial products not dependent on agricultural raw materials. In 1955, key industrial goods so exchanged included salt, kerosene, coal, and a variety of producer goods such as plows, insecticides, and chemical fertilizers.

32. The gross value of agricultural output in 1955 in 1952 prices was 55.5 billion *yuan* (*TGY*, p. 16).
33. By "comparable," I only mean that they involved a removal of goods from the farmer without compensation.
34. In 1955, only 12 per cent of the gross value output of the textile industry was produced in handicraft enterprises (for sources, see Chen, 1967, p. 226). In the 1950's, tobacco was not a major handicraft activity (see Chao Ching-wen, 1957, pp. 57, 193).

TABLE VI.4. THE GROWTH IN MODERN INDUSTRY

	Net Value Added— Selected Series (Millions of 1933 Prices)	Cotton Yarn and Cloth (Percentage of Total)
1912	60.2	22.6
1917	122.5	30.2
1921	163.4	45.2
1922	152.4	36.0
1926	240.2	44.0
1930	297.3	44.1
1933	369.5	41.4
1936	499.6	30.6

SOURCE: Chang, 1967, pp. 66, 69. The selected series represents between 40 and 60 per cent of the net value added of all factory production.

Of these items, only salt was of major importance in long-distance trade prior to the twentieth century.

Many of the changes apparent in the 1955 data had in fact occurred two and three decades earlier. Rural purchases of a few key items in both the 1930's and 1955 are presented in Table VI.5. The methods used in arriving at the 1930's figures and some of those for 1955 are sufficiently crude so that little faith can be placed in the indicated changes over time. What the data do show, is that in the 1930's farm purchases were much the same as in 1955.

This conclusion is not very surprising. By 1955 the Chinese Communists had had little opportunity to do more than bring about a recovery in the consumer goods industry to pre-war levels. Thus most of the changes that occurred between 1900 and 1955 probably were largely completed by the 1930's.

Two differences that did exist between the 1930's and 1955 involved the marked decline in the luxury trade[35] and an increase in the supply of modern producer goods to agriculture. The former was caused by the war, but was continued beyond that time by the policies of the government.[36] The latter was still in its beginning stages in 1955.

The causes of the changes in the rural-urban trade pattern are not difficult to pinpoint. Modern industries could produce many items much more efficiently than small handicraft enterprises, provided they could obtain raw materials (including food for their workers) cheaply. The key problems, as will be demonstrated in the next chapter, involved the transport of coal and grain, and these

35. Tea and silk, in particular, were down sharply (see Table D.32).
36. Land reform together with other policies effectively eliminated the landlord-gentry class (or its Kuomintang equivalent).

TABLE VI.5. RURAL PURCHASES OF
SELECTED COMMODITIES
(Unit: 1,000 Tons except for Cloth)

	1930's	1955
Grain (husked)[a]	19,150	20,680
Vegetable Oils[b]	720	669
Sugar[b]	445	359
Salt[c]	1,960	2,663[b]
Kerosene[c]	1,130	520[d]
Chemical Fertilizer[e]	neg.	1,255
Cotton Cloth (million meters)[f]	1,330	2,950

[a] The 1955 figure is an average of the drawback to rural areas in the grain years 1954–1955 and 1955–1956 (for sources of these data, see Perkins, 1966, pp. 248–49). The 1929–1933 figure is derived from data in Buck, 1937, p. 401 and (Statistical Volume) pp. 67–70. From this source one can derive a consumption per day figure for grain of 0.78 kilograms per adult equivalent. If one assumes the rural population was 80 per cent of the total and converts Buck's adult equivalent figure into a figure for the total rural population, one arrives at the estimate in this table. The total population figure used is 520 million and adult equivalents, according to Buck, equal 77 per cent of the total farm population.

[b] The 1929–1933 figures are derived from Buck in the same way as the figures for grain. The source of the 1955 figures which represent total sales by supply and marketing co-operatives can be found in Chen, 1967, p. 400.

[c] An estimate of the demand for salt and kerosene per farm family for the 1930's can be found in Tōa kenkyusho, *Shina nōgyō kiso tōkei shiryō*, p. 164. If one assumes there were 83 million farm families, one arrives at the figures in the table. One can also derive a sugar-demand figure of 282,000 tons.

[d] For the sources of data on kerosene consumption, see Table I.10, footnote g.

[e] For source, see Table IV.5.

[f] The 1955 figure is in *Wo-kuo-te kang-t'ieh, tien-li mei-tan, chi-chieh, fang-chih, tsao-chih kung-yeh-te chin-hsi*, p. 185. A recent study of Chinese cotton gives no information on how this figure was obtained (The Cotton Research Office of the Chinese Institute of Agriculture Science, *Chung-kuo mien-hua tsai-p'ei hsüeh*, pp. 20–21). For lack of a better alternative, however, I have used this figure.

problems were solved by the building of railroads. With these obstacles overcome, industry grew and, along with industry, the cities. By 1938, China's urban centers with populations over 100,000 persons had grown about 70 per cent over 1900–1910.[37]

This book, however, is about agriculture, not industry. The principal question that must be asked here is what effects these developments in rural-urban trade had on the agricultural sector, and grain output in particular. Even this question cannot be fully answered without a detailed study of what happened to rural handicrafts in this period, a study which as already indicated would take us well beyond the bounds laid down for this study.

To the degree that the rise of modern industry was a substitute for rural handicrafts, this development freed labor for work on the farm. But it is unlikely that the labor freed much increased the supply during periods of peak demand, as

37. See Table VII.2 and Appendix E.

at harvest time. Most handicraft activities were carried on during slack months. If the release of labor had any effect on farm output, it was on occupations that could be carried on during these slack periods. According to Buck, such subsidiary occupations occupied half the time of the average farmer. Buck's data also indicate that "rather important changes in subsidiary occupations have taken place during the memory of informants in 110 localities." [38] The principal changes he noted were a decline in weaving and spinning and a rise in hog and poultry raising.

If the increase in hog and poultry raising was in fact caused by an increasing supply of labor available to these occupations, this would constitute evidence that much of the rural population was not idle even during non-peak seasons. But such a conclusion cannot be backed up without further evidence. The rise in hog and poultry production may only have reflected increasing urban demand.

What the net effect of the rise of rural-urban trade and of changes in subsidiary occupations was on farm income cannot be estimated without further research. There is no reason, however, to believe that these changes had a significant influence on the per acre yields of major crops. The increase in labor came at the wrong time and modern capital inputs were not yet being supplied in great quantity (by 1955). The expansion of commerce did provide a vehicle for the more rapid transfer of new technology, but as indicated in Chapters III and IV, most of the worthwhile new techniques were only valuable when introduced in combination with modern capital inputs.

If the rise of rural-urban commerce did not have much of a positive effect on the output of major crops, by the late 1950's it would appear that urbanization and industrialization was placing increasing negative pressures on agriculture. Farm-product purchases by the state and others in real terms in 1955 were already 21 per cent above 1952. In 1956 they did not increase, but in 1957 they rose 5 per cent and in 1958 by another 10 per cent.[39]

Most of these increased deliveries went to supply the cities or were exported. Both of these developments will be discussed further in the next section and chapter. Here it is only to be noted that this increase took place without agriculture getting much in return, at least not in 1957. In 1958 there was a substantial rise in the amount of modern producer goods supplied to farmers.[40] The decline in industrial and agricultural output in the years 1959–1961 reduced deliveries both to and from the rural areas sharply. In the years 1962–1966, however, a rise in output (and presumably in deliveries) was accompanied by a great increase in the supply of chemical fertilizers and other modern producer goods (see Chapter IV). These increased supplies not only helped raise output, but probably also reduced the disincentive effects of the deliveries of farm products to the state. Still, there is every reason to believe that sales of agricultural pro-

38. These figures are all from Buck, 1937, p. 298.
39. Because of price increases, the rise in monetary terms was greater (*TGY*, pp. 168 and 172).
40. *TGY*, pp. 170–71. All 1958 data are suspect, but there is less reason to doubt the validity of these figures than, say, those for grain output.

ducts were greater than they would have been on a free market.[41] Producer goods, it would appear, were not from the peasant's point of view a completely satisfactory substitute for more food and other consumer goods. Further growth in urban centers without a rise in farm output sufficient to allow some increase in per capita food consumption in rural areas can only accentuate the existing strains.

FARM EXPORTS (1870–1960's)

The strain on agriculture caused by increased deliveries without adequate compensation is most apparent when one looks at foreign trade. To fully see the pressures placed on farmers from this source, it is desirable to look at the growth

TABLE VI.6. EXPORTS OF AGRICULTURAL AND
PROCESSED AGRICULTURAL PRODUCTS

	TOTAL EXPORTS		AGRICULTURAL AND PROCESSED AGRICULTURAL EXPORTS	
	(Current Prices)	*(1933 Prices)*	*(Current Prices)*	*(1933 Prices)*
	(1,000 *taels* or *yuan*)	(1,000 *yuan*)	(1,000 *taels* or *yuan*)	(1,000 *yuan*)
1870–1879	69,026	162,000	64,496	152,000
1880–1889	77,144	193,000	67,673	169,000
1890–1899	132,811	248,000	102,074	191,000
1900–1909	234,105	314,000	170,098	228,000
1910–1919	436,851	512,000	328,438	385,000
1920–1928	687,310	607,000	542,915	479,000
1950	2,030,000	—	1,841,000	864,000
1951	2,440,000	—	2,098,000	836,000
1952	2,710,000	—	2,225,000	879,000
1953	3,520,000	—	2,872,000	1,022,000
1954	4,050,000	—	3,078,000	1,062,000
1955	4,910,000	—	3,658,000	1,266,000
1956	5,689,000	—	4,204,000	1,415,000
1957	5,624,000	—	4,027,000	1,291,000
1958	6,748,000	—	4,892,000	1 534,000

SOURCES: The 1870–1928 current price data are derived from figures in, National Research Institute of Social Sciences, Academia Sinica, 1931, pp. 1–10. The current price data for the 1950's can be found in N. R. Chen, 1967, p. 406 and Dernberger, 1965, p. 439. The estimates in 1933 prices are obtained by using the Nankai Export Price index for the years 1870–1928 (see Table I.14) and official Communist government estimates of the index of farm purchase prices for the years 1933–1958 (see Table I.17). The resulting estimates in 1933 prices are thus only crude approximations, because the price indexes are not entirely comparable to the series which they were used to deflate. The problem is more serious for the 1950's estimates than for those of 1870–1928.

41. The continued existence of compulsory quotas for major crops together with rationing of major consumer goods is sufficient evidence of this. The grain supply curve was highly inelastic with respect to price once deliveries began to cut into what peasants considered an adequate level of consumption.

TABLE VI.7. EXPORTS OF SELECTED FARM AND PROCESSED FARM PRODUCTS

	Total Exports	TEA		SILK		BEANS, SEEDS AND OILS		GRAIN		TOBACCO		COTTON AND COTTON TEXTILES		OTHER AG. PROD.	
		Amount	%	Amount	%	Amount	%	Amount	%	Amount	%	Amount	%	Amount	%
1880–1889[a]	77,144	31,555	41	27,577	36	322	0.4	261	0.3	337	0.4	1,229	1.6	3,215	4
1900–1909[a]	234,105	27,361	12	74,134	32	17,801	8	1,756	0.6	2,497	1.1	14,598	6	31,951	14
1920–1928[a]	687,310	22,171	3	162,558	24	116,101	17	33,089	5	20,380	3	49,616	7	139,000	20
1955–1959[b]	6,124,000	86,880[c]	1.4	262,016[d]	4	824,000	13	466,000	8	158,000	3	942,500[e]	15	1,683,000	27

(Amounts in 1,000 *taels* prior to 1909 and 1,000 *yuan* after 1920.)

[a] The figures for 1880–1928 are taken from National Research Institute of Social Sciences, Academia Sinica, 1931, pp. 4–10.

[b] Except where otherwise noted, these data are taken from Dernberger, 1967, pp. 493–501. Because these figures had to be derived from external data, their coverage is not complete. But the figures do include most of China's major trading partners, including many Communist countries.

[c] To obtain this figure I use Dernberger's quantities and the tea purchase prices used in the construction of Table I.11 (footnote g).

[d] This is the average for 1955–1956 only and is taken from *Wo-kuo kang-t'ieh-tien-li, mei-tan, chi-chieh, fang-chih, tsao-chih kung-yeh-te chin-hsi*, p. 173.

[e] Dernberger gives figures for total cotton textile exports in meters. To obtain the value figures, I assumed a price of 1 *yuan* per meter, which was the approximate national average price at this time.

of the foreign trade of China over the past century. The relevant data are present in Tables VI.6 and VI.7.

In the first decades that followed the Opium Wars, China's trade with the outside world was extremely small when expressed as a percentage of national or agricultural product. In the years 1880–1889, for example, Chinese exports amounted to only about 1 per cent of the gross value of agricultural output.[42] Between 1870–1879 and 1900–1909, China's export trade grew rather slowly considering its small beginning. Furthermore, the export of agricultural and processed agricultural products (including textiles) grew even more slowly than the total. By 1900–1909, farm and processed farm product exports had risen to just under 2 per cent of the gross value of farm output.[43]

Comparisons such as this have led some to assume that China's foreign trade in the late nineteenth century played only a small role in China's economy. As a percentage of China's interprovince and long-distance trade, however, foreign trade appears quite large. In 1870–1879, foreign trade was about one-fourth of China's long-distance domestic trade, and this figure rose to more than 40 per cent in 1900–1909.[44]

Another key feature of China's foreign trade prior to 1900 was that the commodities traded were much the same as those involved in purely domestic trade. On the export side, tea and silk dominated trade in its early stages, while on the import side, cotton textiles were the most important item.

Given that the size and composition of China's foreign trade were similar to her domestic trade, it follows that the impact of foreign trade on agriculture was similar as well. But as already indicated, the impact of long-distance domestic trade on overall agricultural output was not great. The size of that trade was small and it was dominated by luxury products for the landlord and gentry classes.

For certain individual commodities, however, the role of foreign trade was significant. Tea exports throughout most of this period constituted 30 to 40 per cent of all tea produced and sold. The percentage share of the export trade in silk production in the late nineteenth century was about the same.[45]

The other interesting commodity is cotton. Prior to the 1920's, imports of raw cotton were not themselves significant since they represented only about 1 per cent of domestic production.[46] But foreign yarn and cloth imports, if con-

42. The gross domestic product of China in the 1880's (in 1933 prices) could not have been more than 70 or 80 per cent of the level of 1933 (which was according to Liu-Yeh, 1965, p. 66, 29.9 billion *yuan*). The gross value of agricultural output in the 1880's could not have been more than 90 per cent of the 1931–1937 level of 15.7 billion *yuan* (see Table D.32).

43. See previous footnote. The gross domestic product and gross value of agricultural output in 1900–1909 must have been about the same as in 1880–1889.

44. As indicated above, China's purely domestic long-distance trade must have been about 700–800 million *yuan* in 1900–1909, perhaps 20 per cent less than this in 1870–1879 (in value terms).

45. Silk and tea foreign trade figures can be found in, National Research Institute of Social Sciences, Academia Sinica, 1931, pp. 35 and 41. Production figures are given in Tables D. 27 and D.28.

46. See same source as in previous footnote together with Table D.23.

verted into a raw cotton equivalent, amounted to one-quarter or one-third of domestic cotton production.[47] To the extent to which yarn and cloth imports reduced domestic handicraft production prior to 1900 or 1910, these imports also must have cut into domestic raw cotton output, but it is unclear just what happened to handicraft yarn and cloth production.

Although the exact influence of pre-1910 cotton yarn and cloth imports cannot be easily traced, it should be pointed out that the net impact of all foreign trade on Chinese agriculture was more likely positive than negative, although the magnitude of the impact was not great in this period whatever its direction. Either Chinese farmers in effect shifted from the raising of cotton over to tea and silk, which they then exported to obtain textiles,[48] or it is possible that tea and silk production were increased and used to import textiles without cutting into domestic cotton production at all.[49] One can, of course, construct explanations where the net effect is negative, but these seem less plausible. For example, exports of tea and silk may have been taken out of existing domestic consumption, not from an increase in production. But this would imply that China's wealthy classes had presumably decided to buy cotton cloth instead of silk. The only aspect of Chinese trade which had a clear negative impact was the import of opium, but it is customary for economists to eschew moral judgments, so I shall leave the issue without further discussion.

In the two decades before the great depression in 1929, Chinese farm exports and Chinese trade in general began to grow more rapidly. Silk exports continued to grow in absolute terms, although they lost ground relative to other commodities. Tea exports, on the other hand, fell back both relatively and absolutely under the impact of Indian competition. Both trends are reflected in Chinese production figures. Chinese silk production gradually rose in this period, while tea output declined.[50]

The commodities whose share in exports gained most in this period were soybeans and other oil-producing seeds. The appearance of Japanese and Russian demand for beans and beancake more or less coincided with the heavy Chinese settlement of Manchuria. Nearly 75 per cent of Manchurian soybean production was exported abroad.[51]

Because the rise of foreign trade in the 1910's and 1920's was limited to a few

47. In 1955, it took 133.7 kilograms of yarn to make 1,000 meters of cotton cloth and 192.6 kilograms of cotton per bale of yarn (181.4 kilograms of yarn per bale) (*Wo-kuo kang-t'ieh, tien-li, mei-tan, chi-chieh, fang-chih, tsao-chih kung-yeh-te chin hsi*, p. 170). Foreign trade figures are from the same source as in the previous two footnotes.

48. The farmers who increased silk production probably were not the same ones who reduced cotton output if cotton output was in fact reduced. Cotton farmers could, for example, have shifted to grain which they then sold to those raising silk, to name one of many possibilities.

49. Such a development would imply that there was surplus labor in the silk-producing areas. If there were not surplus labor, the production of some other commodity would have had to be reduced when silk output was raised.

50. See Tables D.28 and D.29. The data in these tables are subject to a wide margin of error.

51. This is an estimate made by the South Manchurian Railway Company for 1915 and appears in *Economic History of Manchuria* (Seoul: 1920), p. 140.

commodities and was rather selective in its regional impact, it probably had less of an influence on agricultural output—and grain production in particular— than did the rise in domestic trade, except in Manchuria. Furthermore, domestic trade grew more rapidly than that with foreign countries. Thus, if as argued above, the impact of domestic trade on agriculture in this period was not very great, this conclusion applies even more to foreign commerce.

This conclusion is not greatly altered if one looks at imports as well as exports. Raw cotton imports rose sharply in the 1920's but this rise was matched by a decline in yarn imports. Imports of grain also increased, but not in a way that affected domestic grain output.[52] A rise in tobacco imports reflected the increasing popularity of cigarettes and was matched by a rise in domestic tobacco production.[53] The only other major agricultural import was sugar. Imports of sugar rose sharply after 1900 and surpassed domestic output in the 1920's.[54] Accompanying this rise in imports was a drop in domestic sugar production.[55]

In the 1950's, the Chinese government brought about several important changes in the size and structure of China's foreign trade. These changes put increasing pressure on the agricultural sector throughout the 1950's, a kind of pressure that must have had an adverse effect on farm output.

First, by 1956 agricultural and processed agricultural exports had in real terms risen to nearly three times the level of 1920–1928. Where before these exports had constituted about 3 per cent of the gross value of farm output, by 1956 they had risen to about 7 per cent.[56] Second, imports of farm products were virtually eliminated. From 1953 to 1959, imports of consumer goods of all kinds made up only 5.5 to 7.6 per cent of all imports (*TGY*, p. 176). The remaining 90-plus per cent went to the support of China's heavy industrialization drive.

The only farm products that continued to be imported in any quantity were cotton and sugar. Cotton imports, however, were reduced from a 1920–1928 annual average of 90 thousand (metric) tons to a 1955–1959 average of 60 thousand tons.[57] More important, textile yarn and cloth imports, which had fallen to negligible levels in the 1930's, were not allowed to recover.[58] Instead, the government expanded domestic cotton production.[59] Sugar imports fell

52. See discussion in Chapter VII.

53. See Table D.25.

54. The pre-war peak production of sugar was 414,000 metric tons according to *TGY*, p. 103. Sugar imports in the years 1925–1928 ranged between 500 and 700,000 tons.

55. In ten localities, the percentage of the land devoted to sugar cane fell from 7 per cent in 1904–1909 to 5 per cent in 1924–1929 (Buck, 1937, p. 217).

56. This figure somewhat exaggerates the share of exports in farm output because the value of processed agricultural products includes the wages of processors together with a variety of taxes. If these components were eliminated, the percentage might fall to 6 rather than 7.

57. See Dernberger, 1967, p. 174 and National Research Institute of Social Sciences, Academia Sinica, 1931, p. 45.

58. Figures for the 1950's can be found in Dernberger, 1967, p. 465. For the 1930's, data are in the Maritime Customs Reports.

59. See Table D.23 and the discussion in Perkins, 1966, pp. 33–38.

from a 1920–1928 level of 470 thousand tons to less than 100 thousand tons in the years 1955–1958.[60]

The decline in imports of farm and processed farm products meant that Chinese agriculture had to make up the difference.[61] In 1920–1928, 60 per cent of all imports had been agricultural and processed agricultural products (including textiles), an amount that was 20 per cent greater than exports of these same kinds of products.[62] Thus the share of the increase in farm exports when combined with the reduction in farm imports was equivalent to nearly 10 per cent of gross agricultural output. China's farmers not only had to pay for the foreign-exchange component of the industrialization program, they had to supply all domestic consumption requirements as well. The increased burden was only 10 per cent of farm output, but 10 per cent is a large figure in a country as poor as China.

Furthermore, the impact on peasant incomes and incentives in the 1950's was even greater than this 10 per cent figure would indicate. After collectivization in the winter of 1955–56, Chinese rural management cadres were encouraged to concentrate on grain and cotton production, with the result that most other crops were neglected and their output stagnated or declined (see Perkins, 1966, pp. 68–69). Many of these neglected crops were big export earners and, hence, to maintain exports domestic consumption had to be tightly controlled. Since these same commodities were rationed and their prices fixed, it is likely that the real value to the Chinese peasant of exported farm products is understated by using official prices.

With the sharp drop in agricultural production in the years 1959–1961, exports had to be cut back. Output of edible oils fell so far that exports of these items were virtually eliminated. The only commodity that could be expanded was cotton textiles and by 1961–62, one-third of all production was sold abroad in spite of a substantial reduction in domestic output.[63]

The pressures on the agricultural sector from exports were primarily a result of the government's attempt to concentrate investment almost exclusively on heavy industry, a policy that had to be abandoned in the early 1960's. Secondarily, these pressures were a result of mistakes in planning. Abolition of the free marketing of farm products was followed by decisions that took inadequate account of the value placed on alternative commodities by Chinese consumers.[64]

60. The sugar import figure for the 1950's was derived from percentages given in Eckstein, 1966, p. 126. The 1920–1928 data are from the same source as all other 1920–1928 trade data.

61. It is also possible that the agricultural sector did not make up the entire difference and, instead, domestic consumption declined.

62. Overall, imports were significantly larger than exports, hence a smaller share of imports (60 per cent) was in absolute terms larger than a higher percentage of exports. The 60 per cent figure was derived from data in National Research Institute of Social Sciences, Academia Sinica, 1931, pp. 15–25.

63. According to estimates by Dernberger (1967), cotton yarn and fabric exports in 1961 and 1962 came to about 1.1 billion meters per year. According to R. M. Field (1967, p. 294), cotton textile output in 1961–1962 was 3 billion meters.

64. The government, of course, rejected the concept of consumers' sovereignty in favor of planners' sovereignty. But for the commodities produced by agriculture, planners' and consumers' preferences should have been roughly the same.

CONCLUSION

The analysis in this chapter has dealt with three kinds of Chinese trade: rural trade taking place entirely within a limited region, long-distance domestic trade, and foreign trade. The line of demarcation between the first and second type of trade is imprecise, but nevertheless meaningful.

Before 1910, trade within a market town or between neighboring market towns dominated China's rural commerce. Perhaps 20 to 30 per cent of all agricultural output was marketed in this limited region. Only 5 to 7 per cent was shipped out to areas a hundred or more miles distant and another 1 to 2 per cent was sent abroad.

By the 1920's and 1930's this structure had begun to change significantly. Foreign trade still took only 3 per cent of China's farm produce but long-distance domestic trade reached 10 per cent of agricultural output or more. In the 1950's, the major change was the rise in exports to 7 per cent of farm output. Domestic shipments out of rural to urban areas amounted to about 15 per cent of total agricultural produce, that sold within rural areas another 15 per cent. Some of the output shipped to urban areas in the 1950's was not sent more than a few miles, whereas a certain amount of the trade within rural areas was transferred to points hundreds of miles distant, but the amounts so involved were not very large. Thus the percentages for the 1950's are for categories roughly comparable to those for earlier periods.

The effects of this trade on farm output can only be discussed in rather general terms. Rural commerce which involved the exchange of goods between farmers and handicraftsmen located only a short distance from each other probably had only a limited effect on grain production both before and after 1910. This trade, however, did allow specialization by handicraftsmen and farmers raising cash crops that would not otherwise have been possible. This specialization presumably raised the productivity of land and labor devoted to such activities.

Long-distance foreign and domestic trade prior to 1910, in contrast, had only a minor influence on farm productivity except for a few individual commodities, principally tea, silk, and to a lesser extent cotton. Half of this trade was devoted to supplying the luxury demand of the gentry and other wealthy classes. Almost all of the trade, luxury or not, was confined to commodities which could only be produced in a few regions of China.

In the 1920's and the 1930's, the greater efficiency of modern processing industries and the cheapness of rail and steamship transport led an increasing number of farmers to send their produce to cities for processing, particularly to Shanghai and Tientsin. The development of modern industry also led to an expansion of foreign trade and an increasing urban population, both of which depended upon deliveries from the agricultural sector.

The rise in modern processing industries probably had little impact on the yields of major crops. The labor time freed by this shift was in the off seasons. To the degree the shift did have an impact therefore, it was to cause a change in the nature of some rural subsidiary occupations. The increasing demands on agriculture for the cities and for export were still modest enough not to put much of a burden on the farmer.

In the 1950's, however, the pace of industrialization and urban development was stepped up. The increase in deliveries required from the rural sector became a serious burden on peasant farmers, particularly by the latter half of the 1950's. The strain was enhanced by the government's concentration on heavy industry. Thus agriculture was expected to supply more and more to feed and clothe the urban population and for export without getting much in return except for a portion of the products it had sent to the cities for processing.

The sharp decline in farm output in the years 1959–1961 made it impossible to pursue this trend further. Instead the government clamped a tight lid on the rise in urban population, supplied more goods to the rural sector principally in the form of chemical fertilizer, and imported grain so as to make possible a reduction in rural deliveries.

The strain of increased deliveries in the 1950's was felt throughout the agricultural sector. The greatest impact, however, was on the production and marketing of grain. The next chapter, therefore, contains a more detailed analysis of the China grain market.

CHAPTER SEVEN

Urbanization, Famine, and the Market for Grain

During the past several years, China's dependence on the grain stores of Canada, Australia, and France has focused attention on an age-old problem, that of feeding China's grain-deficit areas, particularly her cities. In this chapter, China's grain market has been singled out for more detailed analysis for two reasons. First, because grain has been by far the most important crop and source of nourishment and hence has throughout been the central concern of this study. Second, because grain more than any other single commodity directly or indirectly determined many of the key features of Chinese commerce, even though it was not itself the largest single commodity in long-distance trade.

In a fundamental sense, for example, it was grain marketing problems that influenced the size and location of Chinese cities, and these cities in turn set the amount and direction of long-distance internal commerce. In the previous chapter, the determinants of internal commerce were said to be transport costs, differences in regional geographic conditions, and the size and location of the upper classes. The statement that the grain market was also a determinant does not contradict the analysis of the previous chapter. It is rather an elaboration of that analysis. The emphasis in this chapter is on the long-distance trade in grain. Local grain marketing occasionally enters into the discussion, but is less important to an understanding of the pressures that industrialization places on agriculture, a key theme of this chapter.

In the first part of this chapter, an attempt is made to explain the reasons for the high degree of interdependence between urbanization and the grain market. This discussion is followed by a description of changes in the size and direction of the grain trade over time and the effect of those changes on farm output. The final section looks at the relationship between harvest fluctuations, grain marketing, and agricultural productivity. Particular emphasis in this section is placed on the impact of the railroad on famine conditions in China and, in turn, the impact of famine on farm productivity.

The period covered by the analysis in this chapter extends from the early eighteenth century into the 1960's. The discussion could probably be extended back to the Ming dynasty, but data for the eighteenth century appear to be the best available (for an early period) and it is not likely that the essential features of the system changed much between early Ming and the 1720's.

URBANIZATION AND THE GRAIN TRADE

There were many reasons why wealthy Chinese preferred in the past to congregate together in cities of varying sizes. Most such reasons had little to do with economics. But supplying the basic needs of these urban concentrations of wealth and political power was nevertheless a major economic problem. Cities had to be located in such a way as to minimize these problems, and the overall size of China's urban centers could not exceed a limit set by the amount of the surplus extracted from agriculture. Industrialization and the railroad altered the pattern of Chinese urbanization in the twentieth century, but only partially changed the city-farm relationship.

Prior to the advent of the railroad and for sometime thereafter, the principal urban supply problem was how to cheaply import enough grain to feed those living in the cities. There are several reasons why the urban grain supply problem was so difficult to solve. First, grain consumption by city residents was large, particularly relative to the amounts of other goods consumed. Second, as mentioned in the previous chapter, transport costs were high prior to the twentieth century, and, third, grain output and marketings were subject to wide fluctuations over time.

Commodities other than grain were not comparably difficult to handle. Supplying urban residents with meat when it was available was not a major problem because the quantities involved were never very large. In Shanghai and Peking in the 1950's, for example, the average per capita consumption of meat (mainly pork) fluctuated between 20 and 30 catties (Sun Kuang, 1957, p. 63). In contrast, grain consumption has generally averaged around 500 catties (unhusked) per year.[1]

The only other food consumed in large quantities was and is vegetables. In 1955 urban residents in China on the average ate 230 catties of vegetables, nearly half their grain intake. The vegetable supply problem was further complicated by the fact that vegetables spoil rapidly without refrigeration. Hence in China they have usually been grown in the immediate neighborhood of large cities where they could be harvested and sold in the same day. This situation would

1. Derived from data in *Jen-min jih-pao* editorial, "Basically Settle the Vegetable Supply Question," *Hsin-hua pan-yueh-k'an*, July 10, 1957, p. 149.

complicate urban food delivery problems enormously if it weren't for one fact—
that vegetable yields per acre are much higher than for grain.

To take an extreme example, the New Territories of Hong Kong in 1961 were
able to supply over 90 per cent of the colony's vegetable needs on only 6,172
acres (37,000 *mou*) due to the attainment of yields of around 25,000 catties per
acre[2] (average rice yields in China are one-tenth that level). More than twice that
amount of land was needed to supply only 5 per cent of the colony's cereal
requirements. According to estimates of Kenneth Walker, private plots in 1956
which represented only 5 per cent of China's cultivated land area could supply
peasants with all or most of the vegetable and pork requirements and still leave
something over for sale on the market (Walker, 1965, p. 31).

The only time that the supply of vegetables in China appears to have placed a
burden on long-distance transport facilities was during winter when the cities
of the north are unable to grow their own.[3] During the first three months of 1957,
for example, railroads carried 150,000 metric tons of vegetables to the north, an
amount that, as we soon shall see, was dwarfed by the size of grain shipments.
Hence the problem of feeding a city of one million was principally one of
supplying it with 250,000 tons of grain every year. Other food supply requirements could be met more easily.

As pointed out in the previous chapter, where water transport was available,
this grain could be shipped by junk at relatively low cost. Where no navigable
rivers or canals were nearby, goods had to travel over land. For long-distance
travel over land, animals were on the average approximately three times as
expensive as a junk in the 1930's according to Buck. Buck's national averages,
however, obscure the much wider differential (six times as expensive and more)
between the junk rates on the Yangtze and animal carriage in the north.[4] Data
from missionary and other foreign sources for the 1890's suggest that land
carriage of goods may often have been twenty to thirty times as expensive as a
large junk on the Yangtze. Where rivers were shallow, full of rapids, or simply
flowed in the wrong direction, costs of water transport were also high. Land
transport costs, of course, also varied with the terrain or, as was the case in an
area of Kwangsi (SE), when there were "dangers to be met along the road from
tigers and pirates." [5]

The supply of cities in north China where land transport was used[6] was at an

2. Hong Kong is an extreme case because vegetable yields are probably significantly
higher than in China proper and the city's per capita consumption of vegetables is less than one-
third that prevailing in China. All these figures are from *Hong Kong, Report for the Year 1961*,
pp. 94–95, 420.

3. Sun Kuang, 1957, p. 64. There is some vegetable production in greenhouses in the
north in the winter.

4. Buck, 1937 (Statistical Volume), p. 347. Buck's national averages are unweighted
averages of the various estimates for each area in the sample. An area with little commerce is
given equal weight in the average with a major commercial district.

5. These 1890's data (and quotation) are from Royal Asiatic Society, 1890. This is a
collection of replies to a questionnaire sent out by the China Branch of the Royal Asiatic
Society to various foreign residents of China.

6. There were, of course, some navigable rivers in north China. This statement is only
applicable to cities not serviced by such rivers.

even greater disadvantage relative to cities on the Yangtze than even these cost figures would suggest. Because grain yields in north China were only half those of the south and the percentage of grain marketed was lower than in provinces along the Yangtze, the area required to feed a city of any given size was probably two to four times greater in the north.[7] Hence grain had to travel a greater distance in the north, perhaps as much as twice as far as along the Yangtze. All told, the transport cost of supplying a city with grain by land must have been nearly ten times the cost of provisioning a city of the same size by water. Under the circumstances, it is not surprising that the Manchus preferred to feed Peking with rice from the provinces of the lower Yangtze shipped via the Grand Canal than to attempt to extract a surplus from Hopei (N) Province.

This transport cost structure prevailed until the latter part of the nineteenth century when it was radically altered by the advent of the steamship and the railroad. The railroad, in particular, brought costs of shipment over land down to the level of the most efficient junk transport.

Prior to the arrival of the railroad, the difficulties involved in supplying northern cities were not solely problems of high land transport costs. Also important was the great instability of the northern grain harvest. South China, to be sure, was also subject to flood and drought, but not to the same degree as in the north. In a severe drought, even one limited to a relatively small area, a northern city might see its entire source of supply wiped out. Under such circumstances, the city's population would be faced with the alternatives of either abandoning the city or paying exhorbitant prices for grain shipped from a great distance.

GRAIN MARKETING IN THE EIGHTEENTH AND NINETEENTH CENTURIES

The influence of these factors on the location on China's major urban centers and the way in which these urban centers in turn determined the nature of the grain marketing system can be seen most clearly in the eighteenth and nineteenth centuries. In analyzing the impact of urbanization on grain marketing and output, therefore, it is desirable to start with a full description of the system as it existed before 1900. This discussion is then followed by an analysis of changes in the system during the late nineteenth and twentieth centuries and the impact of those changes on grain marketing and output.

The relationship between grain marketing and urban location prior to 1900 can be seen from the pattern present in Map VII.1. Of the 46 cities with more than 100,000 persons, 24 or over half are on or capable of being supplied by Yangtze river traffic and another 8 are on the southeast coast. In fact, excluding Manchuria's four main cities, the only cities not on a major water route were the provincial capitals of Kweichow (Kweiyang) (SW), Shansi (T'aiyuan) (N) and Suiyuan (Kueisui, now called Huhehot) (NW) and Peking (N), the national

---

7. The percentage of land cultivated is also relevant, but the North China Plain was at no disadvantage on this score (the rate of land utilization in Shantung was only surpassed by such areas as southern Kiangsu).

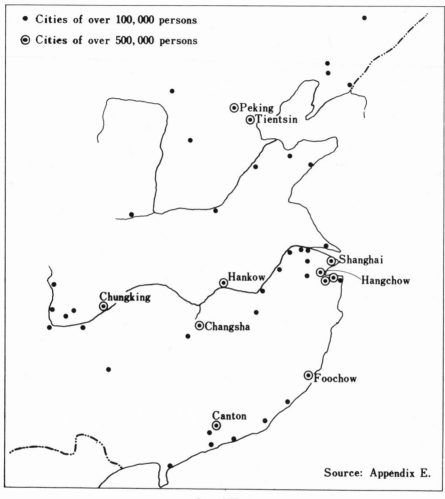

• Cities of over 100,000 persons

◉ Cities of over 500,000 persons

◉Peking
◉Tientsin

◉Shanghai
◉Hankow
◉—Hangchow

Chungking

◉Changsha

◉Foochow

Canton

Source: Appendix E.

Map VII. 1
Cities of China
(Circa 1900)

capital. Of these, the only really large city was Peking, the supply of which occupied the attention of a high proportion of the government's personnel.

Before we go on to discuss the grain-supply system for these cities in more detail, a brief word is in order regarding the quality of Chinese urban population data. (The subject is taken up in greater detail in Appendix E.) The principal problem arises from the fact that, although Chinese governments often made considerable efforts to collect general population data, the unit for which data were collected was the *hsien* or prefecture and few attempts were made to differentiate between urban and rural areas. Thus, one is forced to rely on estimates of various observers.

For the early part of the twentieth century there are usually a number of estimates that can be checked against each other and against other kinds of data, qualitative as well as quantitative. When one attempts to move back in history, however, it is impossible to arrive at any reasonably reliable figures, except occasionally for the national capital. To Marco Polo, for example; China was full of grand cities, but his standard of comparison was presumably Europe where only rarely did a city at that time have more than 100,000 inhabitants (Pirenne, 1936, pp. 170–71). Even in more recent times one can find figures that must be wildly unrealistic (e.g., 16 million for Peking and 8 million people in Hankow). Nevertheless, there is enough evidence to suggest that the largest cities in 1900 (those over 500,000 persons) were, with the exception of Shanghai and Tientsin, of roughly the same size at least as far back as the 1840's.[8]

Although there is not as much quantitative material on grain shipments to these cities in the eighteenth and early nineteenth centuries as one would like, the basic grain-marketing pattern is clear. There were three major chronic deficit areas, the southeast coast, principally Canton, but also Swatow and various Fukien (SE) cities; Peking–Tientsin (N); and southern Kiangsu (E)-northern Chekiang (E) at the mouth of the Yangtze river. This last area not only contained the largest concentration of major cities in the Chinese empire, but was also the principal mulberry- (for silkworms) and cotton-producing area. In the 1920's for example, over half the cultivable land in several *hsien* in this area was sown to cotton (see Map VII.2). Nor was this situation in any sense a recent phenomenon. Data for 1581 suggest that the mulberry area in many of the *hsien* marked on Map VII.2 was already quite large, although perhaps smaller than in the twentieth century.[9]

Therefore, although land at the mouth of the Yangtze and around Hangchow (E) was rich, the area still had to import large quantities of grain. This grain not only went to feed urban residents, but also to supply those farmers who devoted their land to the production of raw materials for the cities' industries.

In spite of this concentration on non-grain crops, the richness of the area enabled it to supply much of its rice and wheat needs from nearby *hsien*, particularly those in Kiangsu (E) to the west and north of the cotton-producing area. But not all the region's food needs could be supplied so easily. This area had also to rely heavily on grain shipments from Kiangsi (C) and Anhwei (E) provinces, and particularly from Hukwang (C) (present-day Hunan-Hupei), nearly 900 miles away by water.

8. Comparatively reasonable estimates for a number of major cities appear in an official report to the British government (Martin, 1847, vol. 1, pp. 11–14, 17; vol. 2, pp. 28, 266, 287, 293, 306, and 311). The only major city not dealt with by Martin is Chungking, but from the descriptions of Huc (1855, vol. 1, pp. 195 and 217), it is clear it was certainly a city of considerable size.

9. Ch'en Heng-li, 1958, pp. 120–23. The data presented in this study were collected from various *hsien* and *fu* gazetteers.

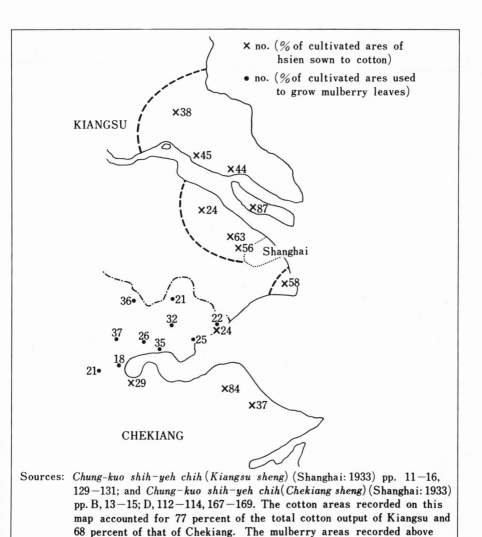

× no. (% of cultivated ares of
    hsien sown to cotton)

• no. (% of cultivated ares used
    to grow mulberry leaves)

KIANGSU

×38

×45

×44

×24   ×87

×63
×56   Shanghai

×58

36•   •21

32

22
×24

37   26   •25
•   • 35
      •

18
21•   •

×29

×84

×37

CHEKIANG

Sources: *Chung-kuo shih-yeh chih* (*Kiangsu sheng*) (Shanghai: 1933) pp. 11—16,
129—131; and *Chung-kuo shih-yeh chih* (*Chekiang sheng*) (Shanghai: 1933)
pp. B, 13—15; D, 112—114, 167—169. The cotton areas recorded on this
map accounted for 77 percent of the total cotton output of Kiangsu and
68 percent of that of Chekiang. The mulberry areas recorded above
accounted for 75 percent of the total mulberry area in Chekiang.

Map VII. 2
Major Cotton and Mulberry Areas (Kiangsu—Chekiang)
(1928)

There is substantial evidence that this basic pattern of trade goes back at least
to the early eighteenth century and probably as far back as the twelfth century.[10]
This evidence is principally in the form of memorials submitted by officials,
mainly in the 1720's, which discuss the major sources of supply of the coast

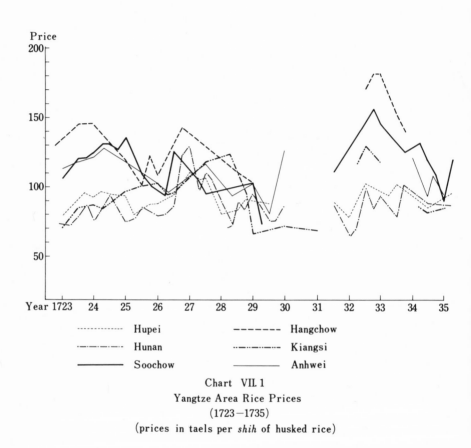

Chart VII 1
Yangtze Area Rice Prices
(1723—1735)
(prices in taels per *shih* of husked rice)

SOURCE: The data and chart (slightly rearranged) are from Ch'uan Han-sheng and Wang
Yeh-chien, 1959, pp. 161–68. Because of gaps in the data, this chart represents seasonal (as
against year-to-year) fluctuations only imperfectly. A *tael* of silver differed from one region to
the next, but not enough in this period to upset conclusions drawn from this chart.

10. For a discussion of rice marketing in the Sung period and its similarity to the present,
see Ch'uan Han-sheng, 1956, pp. 222–33.

deficit areas.[11] That the Yangtze valley was to some degree an integrated market is also suggested by the similarity in price movements in Soochow (E), Hangchow (E), Anhwei (E), to some extent Kiangsu (E), and to a lesser extent Hunan (C) and Hupei (C) (see Chart VII.1). Further some of the discrepancies in price movements can also be used to indicate the integrated nature of the Yangtze grain market. For example, it is known that in the first half of 1734, merchants shipped 5 million *shih* from Hukwang (C) to Kiangsu (E) and Chekiang (E).[12] This amount, which equals or surpasses the quantities shipped from Hunan in the 1930's, was probably atypically large due to the big price differential then prevailing between Soochow-Hangchow (E) on the one hand and Hunan-Hupei (C) on the other (see Chart VII.1).

To some extent the Szechwan (SW) grain market was also tied in with the other Yangtze river provinces. By the early twentieth century, little grain was shipped either in or out of Szechwan (SW) (see discussion below), but in the eighteenth century and earlier there are a number of references that suggest a fairly steady flow of grain to Hupei (C) and, during poor harvests in the deficit areas, all the way to Chekiang (E) and even Kwangtung (SE). The quantities involved appear frequently to have reached several hundred thousand *shih*, (several 10,000's of tons), a significant figure but one well below the probable normal export levels of Hunan (C) and Kiangsi (C).[13]

That grain could be shipped from as far away as Hunan (C) and even Szechwan (SW) on a commercial basis was, of course, a result of the cheapness of Yangtze junk transport. The increase in price from Changsha (C) to Soochow (E) was probably not much over 30 per cent of the original price.[14] This price, although relatively low, was, one suspects, still high enough to keep Hunan (C) from ever replacing less distant sources of supply. During poor years in Hunan (C) or good harvests in Kiangsu (E), it is likely that little grain made the long journey east. Even the high 5 million *shih* figure for 1734 probably represented only from 10 to 20 per cent of total consumption (of the area delineated by the cotton and mulberry areas in Map VII.2).[15]

Thus the role of the areas upriver from Soochow (E) and Hangchow (E) was essentially that of a safety valve that prevented the price of rice in the deficit

11. See, for example, the memorials of Ho T'ien-p'ei (1726) Wei Wang-chen (1723), and Li Wei (1726) in *Chu p'i-yü che* (1738 preface), Box 3/Book 3/p. 63b, 17/1/59, 13/1/69a. The volume was compiled by Ngo Erh-t'ai and Chang Wang-yu.

12. One *shih* = 1.5 *piculs* (approx.) (see Table G.1). This figure is given in the memorial of Man Chu, 1734, Box 17, Book 2, p. 117b. As Ch'uan Han-sheng points out, total shipments for the whole year may have been 10 million *shih* (p. 17).

13. *Pa hsien chih* (1820), 3.38, 3.43, and *K'uei-chou fu chih* (compiled 1827, reprinted in 1891), 13.2, are the most useful references. There are also a number of memorials dealing with various aspects of the Szechwan grain trade. The largest shipments referred to are 400,000 *shih* to Kiangsu-Chekiang in 1753 and 400,000 *shih* to Shantung in 1758. For the nature of Szechwan's rice trade in an earlier period, see Ch'uan Han-sheng, p. 224.

14. This figure is derived using the junk freight rates on the Yangtze prevailing in the 1890's. See footnote 5 for the source.

15. Except for the city of Shanghai, the population of this area doesn't seem to have changed much during the past few centuries. If the total population was 7 million and average consumption was 4 *shih*, then Hunan imports would represent 18 per cent of total consumption.

areas from climbing very high. The area from which these supplies could come was so large that only very unusual circumstances could combine to deprive the lower Yangtze of needed shipments.

The upper Yangtze, Hunan (C), Anhwei (E), and Kiangsi (C), together with Taiwan, played a generally similar role with respect to such cities as Amoy and Foochow on the Fukien (SE) coast. Even in good years, the mountainous terrain of Fukien (SE) was incapable of supporting such large cities. The amounts involved, however, appear to have been much smaller than those involved in the supply of Kiangsu (E) and Chekiang (E). In 1729, for example, Taiwan was ordered to send 83,000 *shih* to various areas in the southern part of Fukien (SE), while in 1730 a memorial speaks of the shipment of 30,000 *shih* from Soochow (E).[16]

The province of Kwangtung (SE) occasionally received grain from surplus areas on the Yangtze, but basically the province (particularly the city of Canton) was dependent on its own resources and those of neighboring Kwangsi (SE) province.[17] Even when there was a good harvest in Kwantung (SE), Canton and the other large cities on the Pearl River delta received one to two million *shih* annually from Kwangsi (SE).[18]

GRAIN TRIBUTE TO THE NORTH (BEFORE 1900)

The principal commercial grain shipped north from the Yangtze area went via the Han river to Shensi (NW) province (see Map VII.3).[19] Honan (N) and Shantung (N) provinces and even southern Manchuria (NE) also produced small surpluses, but in none of these cases does it appear that more than several hundred thousand *shih* were involved.[20] The shipments upriver on the Han and part of the Honan (N) surplus were presumably used to supply Sian in Shensi (NW), the only really large city in the northwest.

The only other large city in all of north China was Peking, the national capital, whose population was about one million. China's national capitals have always presented peculiar supply problems. First, they have had to be largely supported by tax revenue. Unlike the large cities on the lower Yangtze that sent silk, textiles, and pottery west in exchange for their grain, Peking produced little or nothing for export except the services of government. Peking, of course, was not

16. Memorials of Shih I-chih (1729) and Ch'en Shih-hsia (1727) in Ngo Erh-t'ai and Chang Wang-yü, 16/3/27b and 2/3/39b.

17. In 1726, large shipments came overland from Kan hsien in southern Kiangsi (memorial of P'ei Shuai-tu [1726], 2/6/49b), but 1726 was, as is shown below, a year of severe famine.

18. Memorial of Ngo Erh-t'ai (1737), 9/7/57b. See also Abe Takeo, 1957, p. 193.

19. Memorials of the Hukwang Governor General in 1731 and 1733 in Ngo Erh-t'ai and Chang Wang-yü, 17/2/42–32 and 17/21/79a. The former mentions the shipment of 100,000 *shih* and the latter speaks of 1,500 rice boats of unknown capacity (perhaps 100 *shih*) going north.

20. This statement refers to grain over and above the grain tribute from these two provinces. See memorial of Hung Ch'ao-en (1734), 18/1/118b. One can find statements that suggest that Manchurian exports were quite large, but according to T. Hoshino (1920, pp. 138 and 152), no wheat and only small amounts of soybeans were exported from Manchuria until the latter half of the nineteenth century.

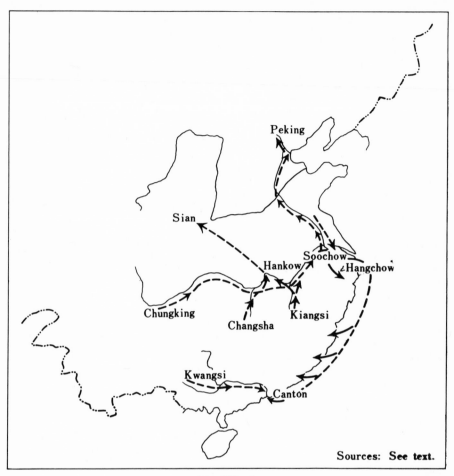

Map VII. 3
Major Inter-Province Grain Shipments
(18th Century)

SOURCES: See text.

alone in receiving tax support. Provincial capitals and lower-level seats of government also depended in part on taxes, but these cities seldom grew very large (above 100,000 persons) unless they were also commercial and industrial centers.

Second, ease of obtaining food has been only one of several considerations in deciding on the location of the national capital. At times, lack of an adequate grain supply has forced the abandonment of a particular site. Thus the Chin emperors in the thirteenth century had to abandon Peking and move south of the Yellow river to K'aifeng after the Mongols had laid waste most of the area north of the river. But generally military-political criteria have dominated and this was certainly the case with Peking during the Ch'ing period.

When the Mongols built their capital at Peking, they solved the grain problem by building a canal (the Grand Canal) with massive applications of corvee labor, although they also made use of sea transport. The Grand Canal remained the main supply route to Peking for the next six centuries, until first the advent of safe and efficient ocean transport and then the railroad.

The distance on this canal from its junction with the Yangtze to Peking was about 1,000 miles. In the first few decades of the nineteenth century about 3 or 4 million *shih* were sent north annually, three-quarters of which came from northern Chekiang (E), Kiangsu (E), Anhwei (E), and Kiangsi (C), with the remainder from Hunan (C), Hupei (C), Chekiang (E), Shantung (N), and Honan (N) (Parker, 1901, vol. 1, pp. 95–96, 107, 112, 114–15, 119, 120, 123, 132). Even if one ignores the cost of maintaining the canal, the transport expenses alone must have been a third or more of the original price of the grain and perhaps triple that amount for junks returning empty of cargo. When one takes into account the fact that Kiangsu (E) was an area where grain prices were high [because Kiangsu (E) in turn depended on Kiangsi (C) and Hunan (C)], the difference in real cost to the empire between feeding a city of one million at Peking (N) and at say Hankow (C) must have been on the order of twice or three times. And this doesn't include the great expense of maintaining the Grand Canal itself.

Thus, although the amount of grain going north to Peking was trivial in comparison to total national output (0.2–0.3 per cent),[21] it represented a substantial portion of total interprovince or long-distance grain shipments measured in terms of ton-miles (perhaps 25 to 35 per cent).[22] Put another way, the real value of grain tribute (the value of the grain at its origin plus the cost of getting it to Peking) was about 15 per cent of the total revenues of the central government in the early nineteenth century.[23] Under these circumstances, it is little wonder that tribute shipments occupied as much of the government's attention as they did. It is also no surprise that the North China Plain was not sprinkled with large cities.

But if grain tribute was a heavy burden to the government, it is clear that it could not have been a serious drain on the resources of the average peasant

21. This percentage is based on a total grain output of 1.6 billion *shih* (4 *shih* per person, 400 million people), but obviously would not be changed much whatever assumptions one cares to make regarding population and per capita consumption.

22. This figure is based on estimated total shipments of grain of 26–27 million *shih* and an average distance traveled for non-tribute grain of 400 miles. These figures were in turn obtained from guesses about the size and distance traveled of grain transport from each of the major exporting provinces. The margin of possible error is, of course, quite large. The estimate, however, is more likely to be too high than too low.

23. I assumed normal revenues to be 60 to 70 million *taels*, of which 4 million *taels* represents grain tribute (valued at price sold in most of the empire). If we revalue the grain at 8 or 10 million *taels*, one arrives at something like 25 per cent. Yeh-chien Wang estimates that total revenue in 1753 was about 59 million *taels* ("China's Land Taxation in the Late Ch'ing").

farmer. The amount of grain was small in relation to output even if food consumed by boatmen, officials, and workers involved in maintaining the Grand Canal were included in the total. The quantities of grain moving in regular commercial channels along the Yangtze and elsewhere were much greater and yet even these quantities could not have been a sufficient drain on rural surplus areas to have much affected productivity.

CHANGES IN THE PATTERN (1890–1936)

The arrival of Western technology after the opening of China to free trade in the 1830's upset the grain-trade pattern prevailing in the eighteenth and early nineteenth centuries, but at first only slowly.

Perhaps the first change was in the supply of Peking. Beginning in the 1870's, the coastal steamer rapidly replaced grain-tribute junks on the Grand Canal. By the 1890's, the only substantial amounts of grain carried by canal junk were the shipments of millet from Shantung (N). The cost of shipping by steamer was probably about 20 per cent of the original value of the cargo, higher than present-day rates (which are about 5 per cent of the original value of the cargo), but well below the previous real cost of grain tribute.[24]

The principal economic significance of this change was that large northern cities, at least those near the coast, had a cheap and reliable source of food. In the late nineteenth and early twentieth century the principal beneficiary was Tientsin (N) which rapidly grew into a major industrial center rivaling Shanghai. The change also meant that Peking maintained its size and even grew after the fall of the Manchus in 1911 and the shift of the national capital to Nanking (E) in 1928 instead of withering away to insignificance as had several other capitals. There were also a number of significant linkage effects of the new system. Most conspicuous was the development of the K'aip'ing coal mines north of Tientsin in part in order to provide steamers with a return cargo to Shanghai (Carlson, 1957, p. 7). But none of these changes could have had much influence on agricultural productivity.

The effect of the steamship on the Yangtze river grain market was less dramatic. In fact, the cause of the principal changes that did occur was more the rapid rise of Shanghai and, to a lesser degree, of Hankow. Shanghai's population grew from a few hundred thousand in the 1860's and 1870's to over 3 million by the 1930's (Murphey, 1953, p. 22). The case of Hankow is less clear. Apparently most of its growth prior to 1949 occurred before 1900. An estimate by the governor of Hupei (C) in 1745 puts the population of Hankow at 200,000.[25] Although such estimates are none too reliable, this together with other evidence

24. The real cost of grain tribute (including the value of the grain, but excluding the cost of canal upkeep) must have been about halved. The first steamer-cost figure is based on data in Feuerwerker, 1958, p. 106, and an assumed grain rice per *shih* of 2 *taels*. The figure for the present (actually 1956) is based on rates given in *Shui-yun-chia hui-pien* (Peking, 1956) and an assumed price of grain per metric ton of 200 *yuan*.

25. For data to support the belief that Hankow did not grow much between 1900 and 1938, see Appendix E. The 1745 figure is in, Ho Chang-ling, 1963, p. 1,031.

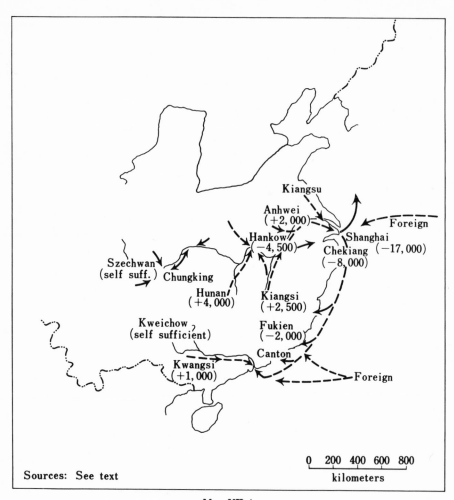

Map VII.4
South China Inter–Province Grain
Shipments (1930's)

(numbers in parentheses are net grain imports (−)
or exports (+) of province in 1,000's of piculs)

20 piculs=1metric ton

SOURCES:

Szechwan: Chang Hsiao-mei, ed., *Szechwan ching-chi tsan-k'ao tzu-liao* (Shanghai: 1939), pp. U-3 and U-7. This source gives domestic trade figures (including grain) for 1934–1937. *Shina nenkan* (Tokyo: 1920, p. 989) states that the grain trade around Chengtu and Chungking was local in nature.

Kweichow: Chang Hsiao-mei, ed., *Kweichow ching-chi* (Shanghai: 1939), pp. G7–9, 12–14. This source gives a *hsien*-by-*hsien* account of the grain trade as of 1937.

Hunan: Chung-kuo shih-yeh chih (Hunan sheng) (Shanghai: 1935, pp. D-18–21, B-121–154) also gives a *hsien*-by-*hsien* account of the Hunan grain trade about 1933.

Hupei: Hupei sheng nien-chien (No. 1), (1937), pp. 176–79, 361–64.

Kiangsi: Kosei beikoku unsho chosa (Tokyo: 1940), pp. 162–65, 174–75. The figure is for 1932 (includes railroad shipments as well as water transport).

Anhwei: The *Wuhu hsien chih* (1919) gives a figure for Wuhu about 1910 of 3,400,000 *piculs.* In the 1930's, according to Sun Ching-chih, 1959a, p. 132, this had dropped off to about 1 million *shih.*

Kiangsu: The Shanghai deficit is simply the population of Shanghai times 5 *piculs* per capita. *Chung-kuo shih-yeh chih (Kiangsu sheng),* pp. 102–118 gives a detailed, *hsien-by-hsien* account of the Kiangsu grain trade, but it is too complex to put on the map.

Chekiang: Cheng Pei-kang and Chang Chih-i, *Chekiang sheng shih-liang chih yun-hsiao* (Changsha: 1940), pp. 37, 41, 42–45.

Fukien: Ou Pao-san and Chang Chih-i, *Fukien sheng shih-liang chih yun-hsiao* (Changsha: 1938), pp. 9, 16–17, 21, gives figures for 1931–1935 for four ports in Fukien.

Kwangsi: This figure for the 1930's is from Sun Ching-chih, 1959b, pp. 252–53.

lends support to the belief that the population of Hankow was much smaller in the eighteenth century.[26]

Another major factor in the changing pattern of the Yangtze grain trade was the Taiping rebellion (1850–1864). This rebellion, which resulted directly or indirectly in the deaths of several tens of millions of persons primarily in such major grain surplus areas as the districts around Poyang lake in Kiangsi (C) and a number of *hsien* in southern Kiangsu (E).[27] Initially this slaughter appears to have virtually ended Kiangsi's (C) role as a grain exporter in the late nineteenth century, but this change was temporary and Kiangsi (C) was a major exporter again after 1915.[28] Although it is impossible to prove, the general reduction in population on the lower Yangtze probably also raised the income of those who remained (because of less pressure on the land), and hence raised the portion of grain that they were willing to market. It is unlikely, however, that there was any significant increase in per acre productivity in the area.[29]

Whatever the reasons, there is considerable evidence in support of the belief that the pattern of grain shipments did change. The principal change was that the upper Yangtze provinces [Hunan (C) and Szechwan (SW)] ceased being major suppliers of the lower Yangtze deficit areas. Hunan (C) still had a surplus, but it was shipped to Hankow (C), where it was consumed.[30] Szechwan (SW) actually imported more grain than it exported, but the amounts in either case were very small. Northern Chekiang (E) remained a major deficit area and, of course, the needs of Shanghai grew rapidly, but their domestic sources of

26. For example, the number of trade guilds and associations of fellow-provincials increased substantially throughout the eighteenth and nineteenth centuries, with particularly rapid growth between 1862 and 1907 (49 of the 96 associations whose founding date is known) (*Hsia-k'ou hsien chih* [1920], 5/22–34).

27. For a discussion of the effects of the Taiping rebellion on population in Kiangsu, see Yeh-chien Wang, 1965, pp. 120–58; and Appendix A of this study.

28. Kiukiang customs recorded only 72,000 *piculs* of rice exports in 1915 and less in the years prior to that (e.g., an average of 7,000 *piculs* in the 1870's). In 1916 the amount jumped to 440,000 and hit a temporary peak 2,500,000 in 1920. The sharp drop in the 1930's reflects primarily a shift to the railroad (principal source: *Kosei beikoku unsho chosa* [Tokyo: 1940], pp. 162–65, 174–75).

29. See Chapter II.

30. This is clear from the sources for Hunan and Hupei referred to in the notes to Map VII.4.

supply were limited to Kiangsu (E), Kiangsi (C), and Anhwei (E) (see Map VII.4).

The real dynamic force for change in the grain market in the first few decades of the twentieth century, however, was not the steamship or recovery from the Taiping rebellion. It was rather the dramatic rise of China's northern cities that was made possible by the construction of railroads and the new requirements of industrialization.[31]

If the high cost of supplying northern cities with food was the principal deterrent to the rise of large commercial and handicraft centers in the north prior to 1900, this factor was certainly not as crucial once the much greater gains from modern industry (than from commerce and handicrafts) became available. In fact, if a commodity were to be singled out as a key bottleneck, it would be coal. The vast quantities of coal required by modern industry[32] probably could only have been efficiently supplied by railroads.[33] If grain was not the major bottleneck, however, it was still an important one. More important for our discussion, the rise of northern cities significantly increased the impact of urbanization on agriculture.

The problem created for the grain market by the rapid industrialization of the north plus Shanghai had three parts. First, the movement of people from farms to cities required farmers to increase their marketing of grain. Second, the burden of feeding these cities fell unevenly, principally on Hunan (C), Hupei (C), Kiangsi (C), and Szechwan (SW). Finally, the major industrial areas and the main grain surplus areas were a long distance apart, placing a heavy load on a badly overburdened transport system.

The rapid development of the modern industrial sector can be seen from the data in Table VI.4 in the previous chapter. The effect of this and other developments on the rise of large urban centers can be seen from the figures in Table VII.1. Although the urban population of the Yangtze area and the southeast coast grew little if at all, that of north China plus Shanghai rose from 4.6 million in 1900–1910 to 13 million in 1938, nearly a three-fold increase.

In spite of this rapid rise, the burden of increased deliveries on Chinese farmers does not appear to have been very great in this period. There were several reasons why this was so. First, although the percentage increase in population in cities over 100,000 was large, the absolute number of people involved only rose by 10 million. Supplying these new urban residents probably required about 50 million *piculs* of grain (2.5 million tons) or under 10 per cent of the total amount of grain marketed in the 1930's.[34]

31. See sources referred to in notes to Map VII.4.
32. Nearly 40 per cent of the tonnage (tons originated) carried by Chinese railways (in 1958) was coal (Hunter, 1965, p. 81).
33. Unlike in the U.S., in north China there was nothing comparable to the Mississippi–Missouri–Ohio River complex nor is coal conveniently located at one end of a connected series of major lakes with iron ore at the other end (as are Pennsylvania coal and Mesabi iron ore). Even the Yellow River is poorly suited for navigation.
34. Total grain marketings came to 18 per cent of 153 million tons (see Tables VII.2 and D.14) or about 27.5 million tons. This figure, of course, is only a rough estimate.

Second, much of the increase took place in Manchuria (NE). But industry was not all that was growing in Manchuria (NE). Large numbers of immigrants into Manchuria went into farming. Thus agricultural output and the marketed grain surplus in Manchuria (NE) rose along with industrialization and there was no need to turn to the grain surplus regions to the south.

TABLE VII.I. URBAN GROWTH BY REGION (1900–1958)
(Cities over 100,000)

	MANCHURIA, HOPEI, AND SHANGHAI		OTHER NORTH[1]		YANGTZE VALLEY AND SOUTHEAST COAST[2]		SW[3]		TOTAL
	(1,000's)	%	*(1,000's)*	%	*(1,000's)*	%	*(1,000's)*	%	
1900–1910	3,230	22	1,350	9	9,960	68	100	1	14,640
1938	10,460	43	2,570	10	10,890	44	640	3	24,560
1953	22,890	48	7,491	16	15,301	32	1,850	4	47,532
1958	30,263	46	14,021	21	19,378	29	2,550	4	66,212

Sources: This table was derived from data in Table E.1, Appendix E.

1. Includes Shantung, Honan, Shansi, Shensi, I.M.A.R., Kansu, Tsinghai, Sinkiang, Anhwei (except Wuhu and Anch'ing), and Süchow in Kiangsu.

2. Includes Szechwan, Hupei, Hunan, Kiangsi, Wuhu and Anch'ing in Anhwei, Kiangsu (except Shanghai and Süchow), Chekiang, Fukien, and Kwangtung.

3. Includes Kwangsi, Kweichow, and Yunnan.

Finally, much of the increased urban population was supplied not by domestic resources, but by foreign imports. Prior to 1910, grain imports amounted to about 7 million *piculs* (0.35 million tons) per year, but by 1919–1921, the average had risen to 38 million *piculs* (1.9 million tons) and by 1929–1931 to 51 million *piculs* (2.1 million tons), or an amount equivalent to the entire increase in urban consumption (Yen Chung-p'ing, 1955, p. 75). This averaging of the figures for several years obscures many large year-to-year fluctuations, but clearly the underlying trend in grain imports in this period was upward. During the 1930's imports dropped off somewhat, but for reasons having to do with the world trade situation and hence not of concern to us here. Not all imported grain was consumed in cities of over 100,000, but most of it probably was. Further, even that consumed elsewhere presumably freed domestic grain for the urban population. Thus the strain placed on agriculture after 1910 by urbanization was not severe.

URBANIZATION AND INDUSTRIALIZATION (POST-1949)

The rapid pace of industrlialization in China in the 1950's is well known. By 1958, China's urban population in cities over 100,000 had risen from 24.6 million in the 1930's to 66.2 million (see Table VII.1). All major cities increased in size, but those in the north much more rapidly than the older cities along the Yangtze river and southeast coast. The impact of this development on the changing

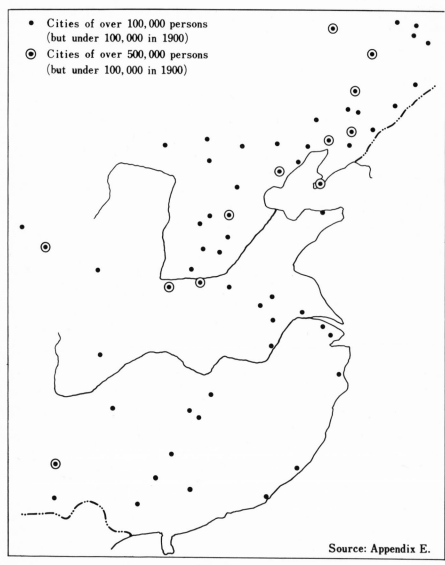

Map VII. 5
New Large Urban Centers
(1958)

location of China's major urban centers is brought out dramatically if one compares Map VII.5 with Map VII.1.

The resulting increase in urban grain demand of over 200 million *piculs* (10 million tons) was four times the increase in urban demand in the three decades prior to the war with Japan. Since many aspects of this enhanced demand for marketed grain have been dealt with at length elsewhere by myself (1966, chaps. III–IV) and others, I shall only describe those features that are of most significance to this study or which have not been fully treated in previous studies.

Basically the problem for the Chinese government was whether one could raise the marketed portion of grain without major increases in farm productivity and without substantially increasing the amount of industrial consumer goods in exchange (because of the concentration of investment in heavy industry).

The changes in the percentage of grain marketed are presented in Table VII.2.

TABLE VII.2. MARKETED GRAIN
(As Percentage of Output)

Crop	*1931–1937*[a]	*1952*	*1957*
Barley	18	—	—
Corn	19	—	—
Kaoliang	25	—	—
Millet	10	—	—
Rice	15	—	—
Wheat	29	—	—
Potatoes	24	—	—
Other	[18]	—	—
All Grains	18.0[b]	24.5[c]	29.5[c]

— Indicates data not available.

[a] All the percentages for individual crops were derived from Buck, 1937, p. 234, except "other," which was assumed to be 18 per cent.

[b] This figure was obtained by applying the individual crop percentages to output in husked grain. Unhusked grain figures appear in Appendix D. The processing rates from unhusked to husked grain were taken from Liu and Yeh, 1965, p. 29.

[c] These figures were obtained by dividing official husked grain marketing figures (see my, *Market Control and Planning in Communist China*, Appendix D) for the grain years 1952–1953 and 1957–1958 by husked grain output. Official unhusked grain data for 1957 are in Appendix D and these were converted to husked grain using the processing rates in T. C. Liu and K. C. Yeh, 1965. The 1952 unhusked grain figure can be found in Chen, 1967, p. 338. This figure was converted to husked grain by assuming that the ratio of husked to unhusked was the same as in 1957. There are two official Chinese figures for the percentage of marketings in 1952, one of 18.1 per cent, a second of 23.4, but their coverage and reasons for their inconsistency are unclear (see S. Ishikawa, 1967, p. 42).

Prior to 1949, China's marketed surplus was made possible in substantial part because of the unequal distribution of income. In particular, landlords, who made up less than 4 per cent of the population controlled perhaps 20 per cent of grain output.[35] Any substantial reduction of the marketed portion of grain after 1949 because of the elimination of the landlords was prevented by the introduction of an agricultural tax in kind. Then in November 1953, under pressure from the industrialization drive, Peking introduced compulsory grain quotas which raised marketed grain by a little more than 200 million *piculs*. Although this figure was surpassed during the good harvest of 1958,[36] essentially the government had reached the limit of what could be taken without either severely damaging farmer incentives or raising grain output.

With the crop disasters of 1959–1961, the marketed portion had to be cut back sharply, although no one outside of China knows precisely by how much. These bad harvests also brought a realization in Peking that great care had to be taken with peasant incentives if a future steady rise in output were to be achieved. Initially, China's import of 5–6 million tons of grain annually beginning in 1961 may have simply reflected a desperate food shortage together with a lack of alternative uses for available foreign exchange (because of the total disorganization of industry following the "great leap").

The continuation of this level of imports in spite of an increase in per capita food consumption since 1960–1961 of between 10 and 20 per cent (imports represent only 3 per cent of total output)[37] can best be understood in relation to compulsory grain deliveries. These imports are equivalent in size to about half of the rise in marketed grain following the 1953 introduction of quotas.

It might have been possible to increase marketings further in the 1950's if it had not been for a second problem, the unequal allocation of the burden of supplying the northern cities. In effect, the provinces of Szechwan (SW), Hunan (C), Hupei (C), and Kiangsi (C) not only had to supply their own considerable urban populations, but had to feed two-thirds of the population of the large cities of north China as well (see Tables VII.3 and VII.4).[38] The amount taken out of these four provinces as of 1957 already represented 12–14 per cent of their output as compared to only 1 per cent or less in the 1930's.[39] A doubling of the populations of the large cities of the north (they increased by 50 per cent between 1953 and 1958 alone) would have caused a major drain on the resources of the upper Yangtze provinces. Yet to take the required surpluses equally from all areas would have required, among other things, a much improved transport network. The opening of the railroad from Shensi (NW) to

35. For lack of a better source, I have used the results of a survey of 14,334 peasant households in 21 provinces made in 1954. The Communists also state that they transferred ownership of 282 million *mou* of land away from landlords, thus eliminating rent of 30 million tons of grain. These are all, of course, only crude estimates (Tung Ta-lin, 1958, pp. 7 and 9).

36. This statement is based on figures published by Peking (Perkins, 1966, p. 248).

37. Ration levels reported by refugees and other observers would seem to indicate an improvement within these limits.

38. As indicated in Table VII.4, the amount shipped out of these provinces in 1957 was around 120–130 million *piculs*. The population of cities of over 100,000 in north China was about 37 million. At 5 *piculs* per capita, these cities consumed 185 million *piculs* of grain annually.

39. Grain output figures for these provinces were obtained from Table F.2. Some may be skeptical that the rise could be so great, but it must be remembered that Szechwan in the 1930's did not export any grain to speak of and Hupei was a deficit area.

TABLE VII.3. THE GRAIN MARKET (1955–56)
(Millions of *Piculs* of Husked Grain)
20 *Piculs* = 1 Metric Ton

	Amount
Total Marketed Grain	834
Consumed in rural areas	460
Supplied to Cities and Armies	391
Shipped out of Province of Origin	175

SOURCES: For the sources of the first three figures (which are official figures published by Peking) see Perkins, 1966, pp. 248–49. The amount supplied to the cities and armies in 1955–1956 was greater than that taken out of the rural areas. The difference was presumably accounted for by a reduction in stocks on hand, not by imports (China was a net exporter of grain in 1955–1956). The figure for grain shipped out of the province of origin is based on data in Table VII.4.

TABLE VII.4. GRAIN SURPLUS PROVINCES

		GRAIN SHIPPED OUT OF PROVINCE (NET)		
		PRE-1949		POST-1949
Province	*Year*	*(1,000's of* Piculs)	*Year*	*(1,000's of* Piculs)
N				
Shansi	1930's	2–3,000[a]	1953	7–9,000[a]
Shantung	—	1,500[b]	1953	5–7,800[a]
Honan	—	—	1954	11,000
C				
Hupei	1936	– 4–5,000[c] (deficit)	1956	15,000[d]
Hunan	1930's	4,000[e]	1957	25,000 + [f]
Kiangsi	1930's	2,500[e]	1957	20,000[g]
E				
Anhwei	1930's	2,000[e]	—	—
SE				
Kwangsi	1930's	1,000[e]	1957	1,000[h]
SW				
Szechwan	1930's	0[e]	1956	33,500[i]
Szechwan	—	— (plan)	1957	67,000[i]
NE				
Kirin	—	—	1957	12,000[j]
Total*	—	—	1957	approx. 175,000[k] (=8–9 million tons)

— Indicates data not available.

* No total is given for the 1930's since it would not be meaningful without the inclusion of the surpluses of Kiangsu[l] and Manchuria[m] (not just Kirin). If these provinces were included, the total would be about 25–30 million *piculs* (1–1.5 million tons).

[a] These figures are given in or derived from data in Sun Ching-chih, 1957, pp. 89, 103, 126–27, 158, together with acreage data in my study of agricultural productivity.

ᵇ Based on the *hsien*-by-*hsien* trade figures in *Chung-kuo shih-yeh chih* (*Shantung sheng*) (Shanghai: 1934), pp. B 151–202.

ᶜ *Hupei sheng nien-chien*, pp. 176–79.

ᵈ Chin Ch'ao, 1957, pp. 99–100.

ᵉ See Map VII.4.

ᶠ Sun Ching-chih, 1959a, p. 265, states that Hunan ranks only behind Szechwan in exports of grain, but gives no precise figure. The figure in the table is a guess and may be on the low side.

ᵍ Sun Ching-chih, 1959a, pp. 405–406, states that Kiangsi exported more than Hupei, but less than Hunan. One can also arrive at roughly the same figure, by estimating total marketed grain in Kiangsi (from data in the same source) and subtracting an estimate of urban grain consumptioni n Kiangsi.

ʰ One source says that exports from Kwangsi have been basically stopped, but then goes on to say some grain is still shipped to Canton (Sun Ching-chih, 1959a, pp. 252–53).

ⁱ See Table VII.5.

ʲ Sun Ching-chih, 1959a, p. 219. This figure is not net of imports of wheat into this province, but it is not likely the net figure would be very different.

ᵏ This figure was obtained by addition of the data in the table plus about 10 million *piculs* which represents a guess at the surplus of Anhwei and any other provinces with minor surpluses.

ˡ The *hsien*-by-*hsien* trade records in *Chung-kuo shih-yeh chih* (*Kiangsu Sheng*), pp. 102–118, indicate exports out of the *hsiens* of origin of about 24 million *piculs* and imports into the *hsiens* of 6 million *piculs*. The net figure, however, does not appear to include the consumption of Nanking and Shanghai, which net, after subtracting foreign imports, would reduce the 18 million *picul* surplus to 6–8 million *piculs*.

ᵐ In 1930, Manchuria exported almost 10 million *piculs* of grain and imported almost 6 million *piculs* (*The Manchuria Year Book, 1932–1933* [Tokyo: 1932], pp. 342–44 and 364–66).

Chengtu (SW) in 1956[40] was such an improvement in that it made it possible to tap the surpluses of Szechwan (SW). But further improvements in marketing through transport development would have been much more expensive.

The long distances between the major grain surplus areas and the principal centers of urban development (see Map VII.6) also put an increasingly heavy strain on China's railways. Not only did the amount of grain carried rise (see Table VII.5), but it is likely that the increasing dependence on the upper Yangtze provinces raised the average distance traveled. This enhanced burden was placed on a railroad system that was, even without any grain shipments, the most heavily used system of any major nation.[41] Coal and various industrial products were primarily responsible for this overburdening, but grain made a significant contribution.

Foreign grain imports since 1961 thus have also been a means of reducing this demand on railroad freight capacity. Imports of 5–6 million tons a year are large enough to feed two-thirds of the population of the large cities (over 100,000) of Manchuria (NE), Hopei (N) plus Shanghai (E) and Canton (SE). Put another way, grain imports can (and apparently do) feed the entire post-1938 increase in population in these cities, thus virtually eliminating any need to import grain to these areas from other Chinese provinces. For China's cities located near the coast, ocean-going vessels have replaced the railroad, at least for a time.

40. This is the completion date given in *TG Y*, p. 70.

41. The Chinese rate of railroad utilization was much greater than that of the Soviet Union, a country renowned for its high rates of railroad use (see Hunter, 1965).

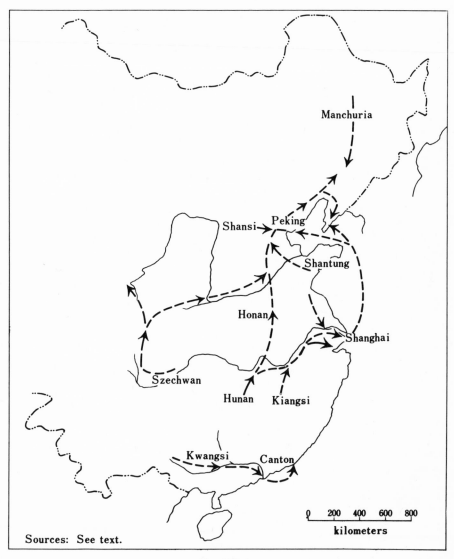

Map VII. 6
Major Inter-Province Grain Shipments (1957)

SOURCES: Based largely on the regional geographies edited by Sun Ching-chih.

TABLE VII.5. GRAIN TRANSPORTED BY RAIL
(Total Tons Originated)

| Year | Length of track[a] (Kilometers) | GRAIN TRANSPORTED BY RAIL | |
		Whole Country (1,000's of Metric Tons)	Szechwan[c]
1938–1948	24,946	—	0
1950	22,512	9,484	—
1952	24,518	—	—
1953	25,072	—	—
1954	25,873	6,590	1,000 average
1955	27,171	14,980	—
1956	29,237	17,280	1,675
1957	29,862	—	3,350 (plan)
1958	31,193	19,055	—

[a] For the 1938–1948 figure, see Yen Chung-p'ing, 1955, p. 180. The remaining figures are from *TGY*, p. 144.

[b] The 1950 and 1958 figures are derived from data in Il'in and Voronichev, *Zhelezno-dorozhnyi Transport Kitaishoi nar. res.* (1959), pp. 110–11, quoted in Hunter, 1965, p. 81. The 1956 figure is derived from data in, "State Economic Committee Extends the Method of Balancing Grain Distribution," *Hsin-hua pan-yueh-k'an*, March 25, 1959, p. 73. The figure is for grain transported on "main communications routes," so that the figure may be inflated by the inclusion of some steamship carriage. The 1954–1955 figures are derived from data in, *Jen-min jih-pao* editorial, "A Great Effort to Organize Transport Properly," 1959, pp. 72–73. These data must be for transport on main communications routes as well, but are not explicitly stated to be such.

[c] Ting Fan, Jao Hsueh-ch'eng, and Chi Hsi-ch'en, "Szechwan's Cultivated Area is Small, Why is its Surplus Grain Large," *Hsin-hua pan-yueh-k'an*, May 25, 1957, pp. 67–69. The figure is that for grain shipments out of the province. The assumption made is that all grain out of the province went by rail, whereas all within-province transport used other means.

Thus the development of modern industry in north China placed new requirements on China's grain marketing system. For nearly six decades, the pressures created by change were alleviated by a variety of measures. First, the coming of the steamship and the railroad made it possible to transport already existing Yangtze surpluses north at low cost. Then, as the Japanese began their investment in Manchurian industry, continued migration into these northeastern provinces provided, for a time, more than sufficient supplies of food.

Beginning in 1953, the Communist industrialization drive accelerated the growth of northern cities. Increased surpluses were provided through 1958 by two "one-shot" solutions, the raising of the level of the marketed surplus by means of compulsory quotas, and the building of the Shensi–Chengtu (NW)–(SW) railroad, thus efficiently tapping the surpluses of the rich province of Szechwan (SW).

Perhaps the development of more rail lines together with an increased number of trucks (and roads to drive them on) could have provided another "one-shot" boost to grain marketings. But the return on investment in such lines, at least that part of the return that was from grain shipments, would not have begun to match that on the Shensi–Chengtu line.

Whatever the potential, the extraordinary pace of industrial development and urban population growth between 1958 and 1960 had outstripped the capacity of the grain marketing system, and, in addition, was placing a severe strain on the railroads. The bad harvest of 1959 and those of the following two years turned a difficult situation into a crisis. The short-run solution was to import a substantial proportion of these cities' grain supply and to make a concerted effort to reduce urban population by sending people back to the villages.[42]

Although China could import 5–6 million tons of grain indefinitely and, in time, could perhaps even double that figure without halting her industrialization drive,[43] this would be just another temporary alleviation of the problem. In the end, China would still have to fall back on the only possible long-run solution, the raising of farm output fast enough to feed a growing rural population and to provide a more or less voluntary surplus for her burgeoning cities. Any other step would be self-defeating in that pressure for increased involuntary deliveries would reduce the rate of growth in output and make it impossible to obtain the required deliveries.

FAMINE RELIEF AND FARM PRODUCTIVITY

The increasing pressure of urban demand on the grain market was by the late 1950's probably interfering with rising farm productivity. But not all changes in the grain market in the twentieth century were negative in their impact. The construction of railroads and the creation of a strong central government fundamentally altered the nature of famine relief in China and by so doing affected not only peasant welfare but farm productivity as well.

The nature of the traditional relationship between famine and the grain market can be seen from an analysis of grain prices during two severe famine periods in Kwangtung (SE) province in the eighteenth century. Kwangtung (SE) was picked partly because of the availability of much price data for the eighteenth century, and partly because of its middle position on a scale of commercial development (particularly vis-à-vis grain). Unlike the commercial areas of the lower Yangtze, Kwangtung (SE) could not rely on the great rice bowl of the Upper Yangtze during a poor harvest, but had instead to rely on the surpluses, if any, of the single underpopulated province of Kwangsi (SE). On the other hand, unlike the north, much of Kwangtung (SE) was close to the sea or other water transport and was one of the few areas of China where two crops of rice a year could be raised.

42. This statement refers to individuals sent back to the villages on a more or less permanent basis, not those sent down to the farm for a few weeks or months in order to improve their ideological outlook.

43. As of 1965, grain imports used up about one-sixth of China's annual foreign exchange earnings. How serious a handicap an increase in this figure would place on the industrialization drive would, of course, depend in part on how much exports could be expanded over the years.

In spite of these advantages, during famine years the grain market in Kwangtung (SE) was so thin that grain prices skyrocketed. In the famine years of 1726–1727, for example, the price of rice in the city of Canton reached double or more of its normal level (see Map VII.7). Canton, however, was comparatively well off. Other areas of Kwangtung where transport was difficult or where the marketing system was less developed saw the price of rice reach seven times and more its normal level. With such prices, savings if any were quickly wiped out. If a peasant did not have land to put up as security for a loan (and less than half the farmers of Kwangtung did), he either grew sweet potatoes (if possible) or fled to the city on the slim hope of finding work there, or he stayed and died. In the provincewide famines of 1726–1727 and 1786–1787[44] there was no sanctuary to flee to and one suspects that enormous numbers of people starved. Nor were these by any means the only famine years for Kwangtung in the eighteenth century, they were only the most general and severe.

The consequences of such wide fluctuations in price were not confined to the health of the peasants. Even in comparatively good years, wide fluctuations in price made dependence on the market for food a risky business. A farmer who planted all of his land to cash crops might physically survive a 50 per cent increase in the price of rice, but his losses might well be sufficient to deprive him of his savings, his land, or both.

For many centuries the Chinese government has been charged with the duty of preventing the causes of famine and of alleviating its results when it occurred. To this end, the government has often authorized the diversion of tribute grain or allowed provincial governors to prohibit the export of rice from a province suffering severe deprivation. Perhaps most important were the public granaries which were maintained for just such occasions.

During the eighteenth and first half of the nineteenth century the total amount in these granaries fluctuated between 25 and 40 million *shih*.[45] Even in the early eighteenth century, when the population of China was not much more than half of its 1840 (or 1930) level, this amount probably represented little more than 3 or 4 per cent of the nation's grain output. Only a small fraction of this amount, of course, was available to any single famine-stricken province, enough for minor, but not major and widespread disasters.

Even if these stores had been in peak condition, they could not have prevented more than a part of the mass starvation during the great northern drought of 1876–1879. As it was, the stores had been allowed to dwindle after 1840 to less than 10 million *shih*.[46] In the three years of this great drought, it is estimated that

44. In 1786, at least, the famine was more than provincewide. Various *hsien* gazetteers for Shantung, for example indicate that prices rose to a comparable level there.

45. These figures and the figures used in the subsequent discussion of the granaries are all from *Ch'ing shih-lu* (Kao-tsung, Jen-tsung, Hsuan-tsung, Wen-tsung, and Mu-tsung editions). The data cover the years 1741 to 1873. For the Yung-cheng period (1723–1735), Abe Takeo estimates that the granaries held some 33.8 million *shih* (1957, p. 144).

46. The precise figures are difficult to arrive at because the data after 1845 in the *Ch'ing shih-lu* are incomplete (the stores of several major provinces are not included in the total). There is enough information, however, to support the belief that the totals dropped sharply to at least as low as 10 million *shih*.

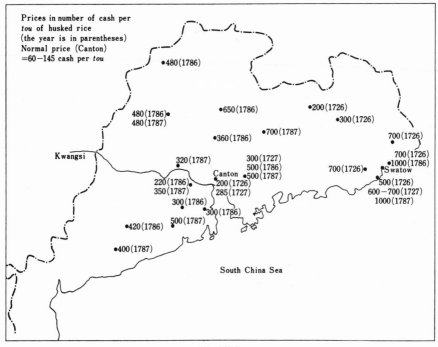

Prices in number of cash per
tou of husked rice
(the year is in parentheses)
Normal price (Canton)
=60−145 cash per *tou*

•480(1786)

•650(1786)   •200(1726)
480(1786)•   •300(1726)
480(1787)
                                          700(1726)
         •360(1786) •700(1787)   •

Kwangsi   700(1726)
              320(1787)   300(1727)   •1000(1786)
                           500(1786)   700(1726)• Swatow
          Canton •500(1787)   500(1726)
      220(1786)• •200(1726)   600−700(1727)
      350(1787) 285(1727)   1000(1787)
        300(1786)
           •300(1786)
  •420(1786) 500(1787)

  •400(1787)

                  South China Sea

Map VII. 7
Famine Rice Prices (Kwangtung −− 18th Century)

SOURCES:

   (1) For Canton, Ch'üan Han-sheng and Wang Yeh-chien, 1959, p. 164.
   (2) *Shun-te hsien hsü chih* (1929), 23.3b.
   (3) *Lien chou chih* (1870), 8.4b.
   (4) *Cheng-hai hsien chih* (1815), 5.11b and 16a.
   (5) *Ch'ing-yuan hsien chih* (1880), 12.19a.
   (6) *Ying-te hsien chih* (1843), 15.19a.
   (7) *Tung-kuan hsien chung-hsiu chih* (1911), 33.4a and 15b.
   (8) *K'ai-p'ing hsien chih* (1823), 8.36b.
   (9) *Yang-shan hsien chih* (1823), 13.10a.
  (10) *Yang-chiang hsien chih* (1822), 8.18b.
  (11) *Yang-chun hsien chih* (1820), 13.18b.
  (12) *Hsing-ning hsien chih* (1929), 12.79a.
  (13) *Chao-chou fu chih* (1762), 11.10a, 18b, and 53b.
  (14) *Lung-ch'uan hsien chih* (1818), 5.5b.
  (15) *Lung-men hsien chih* (1851), 16.9a.
  (16) *Kao-ming hsien chih* (1894), 15.13b.
  (17) *San-shui hsien chih* (1819), 13.29b.

   Note: 10 *tou* equal 1 *shih* (one *shih* today (see Table G.1) is equivalent in weight to 150
          catties).
          Roughly 1,000 *cash* equal 1 *tael*.

13 million persons died in Shensi (NW), Shansi (N), Hopei (N), Honan (N), and Shantung (N) provinces. Because of the poor system of communications then prevailing, it was months after people were in severe straits before the capital and coast even heard of the distress.[47]

In 1920–1921 virtually the same conditions prevailed in north China, but less than half a million people died. The major difference was the arrival of the railroad providing a cheap and rapid means of transport. Prior to this, north China had depended on men or animals carrying the grain into the stricken areas. A substantial portion of the grain had to be consumed by the carriers themselves before it ever got to the distressed villages.

What had not changed in 1920–1921 were the severe limitations on the resources which a government was willing to commit to famine relief. According to one estimate (Mallory, 1926, p. 3), the total spent on famine relief in 1920–1921 was 37 million Chinese dollars (or the equivalent of only about 2 million *shih*), half of which was from international sources.

It was not until the Communists came to power and centralized control over the entire national grain market that there were adequate resources available to deal with a major agricultural disaster. As early as the grain year 1951–1952, the total grain tax in kind was over 400 million *piculs* (20 million metric tons), ten times the average level of grain stores (30 million *shih*) during the better days of the Ch'ing dynasty. By 1954, the total marketing of grain, all of which by then was under central government control, was over 800 million *piculs* (40 million metric tons) or more than 20 per cent of total output. The point is not that total marketings of grain had increased over previous levels. They had, but only to a limited degree (see Table VII.2). But the government's ability to direct the allocation of this "surplus" had been fundamentally altered.

The impact of this change was clearly demonstrated in the poor harvests of 1959 through 1961. The 15 or 20 per cent drop in grain production which probably occurred in the entire country[48] in years past would have meant many millions of deaths in the areas most severely affected. Tight control, particularly an effective system of rationing, together with the past development of the railroads, meant that few if any starved outright. Instead the nutritional levels of the whole country were maintained, perhaps not with precise equality, but with a close approximation to it. As a result, the regime averted a major disaster.

CONCLUSION

Clearly the nature of the Chinese grain market has influenced agricultural productivity in general and the yields of major crops in particular even if there is no way of measuring that influence. For a region to specialize in cash crops or

47. This discussion of the 1876–1879 and 1920–1921 famines is based on Mallory, 1926, pp. 29–32.

48. Peking has not published grain output figures since 1959 and the 1959 official figure is admittedly worthless. The 15–20 per cent figure represents the judgment of outsiders based on refugee rations and other indirect evidence.

handicraft manufactures it had to be reasonably certain that a cheap source of food would always be available. During large-scale famines in the centuries prior to 1900, the most commercially developed regions could be caught short and starvation would ensue. But in areas where the grain trade was limited or non-existent, even comparatively minor fluctuations in output could cause great hardship for those dependent on external sources of food.

Hence the regions that could benefit most from specialization prior to 1900 were those along the Yangtze River and the southeast coast. It is unlikely, however, that the rise in grain yields that occurred in these provinces after the fourteenth century was caused by any changes in the pattern of specialization. There simply weren't many changes of this type. It can be said, on the other hand, that if this area had not been so highly developed commercially, yields would have been lower.

Industrialization and the coming of the railroad in the twentieth century may have stimulated productivity in the south and brought some of the benefits of specialization to the north. The railroad, for example, opened up a larger and more regular market for the grain surpluses of the provinces of central China and Szechwan (SW), which may in turn have increased these areas' incentives to raise output. Whether increased specialization in the north stimulated an increase in grain yields in that area is difficult to say. The major forms of specialization in the north in the twentieth century involved the rise of modern industry dependent on such raw materials as iron ore and coal. Further, if there was a shift in cropping patterns, it may simply have been away from grain to cash crops. Both forms of specialization (industry and cash crops) may, therefore, simply have made the north more dependent on southern grain surpluses. Still it would appear likely that northern grain farmers would have benefited as well.[49]

Even if northern grain farmers were stimulated to raise yields, still the major impact of urban and industrial development on grain output in the twentieth century was felt in the major grain-surplus provinces. Initially this impact may have been beneficial, but by the late 1950's the pressure on these surplus areas was severe and the incentive to increase output must have been adversely affected. This pressure did not cause the harvest failures of 1959 through 1961 although it was a contributing factor. These harvest failures, however, did make it clear that China's industrialization could not be pushed without reference to what was happening to agriculture. The only long-run solution was to ensure that grain output rose fast enough to provide food for the increasing non-farm population on a more or less voluntary basis. The less voluntary the surplus, the harder it would be to provide farmers with the incentive to raise their production. With this incentive problem presumably in mind, the Chinese government continued importing 5 to 6 million tons of grain a year long after recovery from the 1959–1961 harvest failures had been assured.

49. It would seem probable, for example, that as a result of an improved commercial network there was some shift of cash-crop land to grain crops because the land was more suitable to the latter (and vice versa). Farmers with grain surpluses in the north may also have been stimulated by higher prices to raise grain yields.

Finally, one cannot end this discussion without again mentioning the twentieth-century changes in grain distribution that have greatly reduced the likelihood of starvation in China. Increased peasant health and welfare from this source must have had some positive impact on productivity. Improved grain distribution has also, of course, contributed to the rise in the rate of increase in population which has, in turn, made a rise in grain output all the more necessary.

CHAPTER EIGHT

Centralized Government
and the Traditional Economy

Throughout the six centuries covered in this study, China was unified and ruled from the national capital in all but a few decades. During the 1630's and 1640's, several independent warlords controlled the various regions of China, but they were quickly destroyed or brought under control by the Manchu invaders. Again in the 1910's and 1920's regional military figures dominated the scene. In the remaining five and one-half centuries there were numerous rebellions, some of considerable size and strength, and occasionally rebel leaders briefly ruled large parts of the empire (as in the Taiping Rebellion). But throughout these five and one-half centuries, a single emperor was generally recognized as the ruler of all or most of the people.

But was a single emperor ruling over all of China really necessary or even desirable from the point of view of a prosperous agriculture? Would grain yields have risen more or less as they did even if China had been twenty states instead of one? The central government, of course, did not itself grow grain, but many of its actions could have influenced agricultural production either positively or negatively. An appraisal of the actual performance of the Ming and Ch'ing governments and the effect of that performance on farm output is the subject of the first half of this chapter. The principal theme in this discussion is that Chinese farmers did sometimes benefit from official activities, but that the actions that benefited them most tended to be those carried out by local authorities. Only rarely did the rural Chinese economy require much that the central government in Peking was able to give.

If China's economy, or at least its one paramount sector, agriculture, did not depend heavily on a centralized government for its basic prosperity, were there still elements in that economy that made a centralized form of government the most likely or suitable choice for China? This question is not of central importance to an analysis of the rise in grain yields, but much of what has been said in previous chapters is of relevance to it. The latter part of this chapter, therefore, deals with whether or not there were economic forces in China that tended to promote either centralization or decentralization of governmental control and the degree to which these forces were altered by industrialization and other economic influences in the twentieth century.

AGRICULTURE'S INDEPENDENCE OF GOVERNMENT AID

Most agricultural activities required no coordination from higher authorities. A peasant farmer hoed his own plot, collected fertilizer from his hogs, and carried his produce to a nearby market. At the time of transplanting or the harvest, neighbors and relatives might join together to speed the work. In addition the rich often rented labor animals to the poor and the poor sold their own labor to the rich. But this interdependence seldom reached beyond the individual village or market town.

Most farming activities that involved the actual growing of crops not only *were* not coordinated by higher authorities but in most cases *could* not be efficiently handled in a centralized manner. At no time was this fact brought home more clearly than during the cooperative and commune movements of the late 1950's. Although in principle the communes in their initial form (in 1958–1959) were not supposed to centralize labor-allocation decisions related to raising crops beyond the level of the village, in practice the production activities of ten or twenty villages were often directed from a single source (see Perkins, 1966, chap. IV). The result was a considerable amount of crop mismanagement and a retreat by the government back to a group controlling such decisions that was on the average small enough so that there could be two or three such units within a single village.

In Tokugawa Japan (pre-1868) economic pressures apparently encouraged the breakup of much more modest forms of communal farming and their replacement by single-family farms. The increasing skill and specialized knowledge connected with a changing technology demanded a "tight, disciplined, and socially homogeneous" labor force and the nuclear family was such a force, whereas a farming unit based on an extended family plus hereditary servants was not.[1] The technology that Thomas Smith is referring to in his discussion of these developments in Japan is one that had prevailed in China for most of the post-1400 period.[2]

1. See Smith, 1959, p. 105. Much of the book, in fact, deals with the trend toward individual farming.

2. By this statement I mean that China had an individualistic labor-intensive technology, used commercial fertilizers (e.g., beancake), and had a highly developed traditional commerce long before the nineteenth century.

Still there were some activities that could benefit from coordination at levels higher than the village and hence where governmental action could conceivably have played a role. Included in this category were water control, marketing, and the maintenance of peace and security. K. A. Wittfogel (1957, pp. 22–29) has used the need for high-level coordination in water-control activities to explain the origins of "oriental despotism" in China and elsewhere. Whatever was the case in Han times or earlier, from the fourteenth century on, water-control activities generally could be and were managed by the villages themselves or by regional government bodies such as *hsien* or *fu* magistrates. Irrigation water in much of central and south China, for example, was supplied from locally built reservoirs or ponds. According to data in Tables H.4 and H.5, the average-size project in most areas involved only a few miles of dikes and several thousand acres of irrigated land. There were numerous arguments in any particular project over the share of water to go to one village versus another or to one field rather than another, but these were local arguments which could be settled locally. Construction of the reservoirs in the first place was generally accomplished with a region's own labor either privately organized or conscripted by a local magistrate.[3]

Around major lakes, a tendency to dike and farm land along the shoreline might raise the water level and flood the crops of other farmers, so that eventually a magistrate from higher levels might have to intervene. A similar problem involved the planting of corn in highland areas for a number of consecutive years until the topsoil was so far gone that it wouldn't support any plantlife and erosion and flooding became serious. In the early nineteenth century, for example, gentry in Anhwei (E) and Chekiang (E) petitioned the provincial authorities to prohibit the intensive farming of corn on mountainsides, apparently with some success (Ho, 1959, p. 148). If the barren hills of northwest China are appropriate testimony, however, the more common occurrence was for the erosion to take place without much effort by government authorities to stop it. Certainly more vigorous government action could have contributed to raising or maintaining grain output in many regions, but there is no reason why the central government in particular had to become involved except perhaps where the number of farmers on the hillsides was so numerous that substantial military force would have had to have been used to remove them.

In some areas, of course, water-control systems were much more complex than those described that involved comparatively small ponds and reservoirs. The canal network of an area such as southern Kiangsu (E) and northern Chekiang (E) was quite extensive and complex and hence required more elaborate regulation,[4] but not necessarily by the central government.[5]

Flood control along the Yellow River was and is a different story. To maintain

3. For a further discussion of water control, refer to Chapter IV and Appendix H.
4. For an idea of the complexity of the canal systems in the Chekiang-Kiangsu area, see King, 1912, pp. 932–33.
5. It is possible to argue that water-control activities required authoritarian control at, say, the prefecture level.

the dikes along this unruly river, the Ch'ing government created an independent authority for that purpose. When this authority was at its peak efficiency, it together with vigorous local officials were able to prevent major flooding of the North China Plain. But, when corruption became rampant in that administration, the dikes were neglected and the silt-laden river broke out of its confining walls and inundated large areas of farmland.[6] Thus without a strong regional government, the grain crop in areas affected by the Yellow River would have fluctuated more from year to year and the long-run average yield would have been lower.

But one should not exaggerate the importance of control of the Yellow River to Chinese farmers as a whole. The three provinces on the North China Plain affected in a major way by the river contained only about 20 per cent of China's total population and perhaps only a quarter of these were in much danger from Yellow River floods.[7] Other rivers in China also on occasion inundated large areas of farmland, but these rivers were not so long and hence required less high-level coordination.

Even the degree of coordination exercised by the Yellow River administration can be overstated. Proper control of this river in modern terms, as indicated in Chapter IV, requires an elaborate and expensive system of dams on the upper reaches of the river to go with the dams and dikes on the lower reaches. Prior to the twentieth century, however, all that was done was to build dikes on the lower reaches and, when silting raised the level of the river, the dikes were simply built higher until the river actually flowed above the surrounding plain.

A second activity that required a degree of centralized control was commerce. Goods will not be shipped far if they are heavily taxed every few miles or in constant danger of being stolen by brigands. Excessive taxation and theft, however, were principally problems peculiar to long-distance trade. It was more trouble than it was worth to attempt to extract any substantial sum from exchange between farmers at the local market town. In addition the degree of security required was of a much lower order than that necessary to guarantee the safety of, say, a load of silk over a distance of 500 or 1000 miles through uninhabited regions.

But, as pointed out in Chapter VI, it was local commerce that most influenced the lives of China's rural population. Long-distance trade mainly carried luxury goods to China's gentry class or necessities to China's cities. China's cities in turn were either centers of political administration or of commerce and luxury handicrafts such as the silk industry. Hence if this trade across provincial boundaries had been sharply reduced, its direct effect would have been to raise slightly the cost of living of the gentry class[8] and to make more difficult the

6. This discussion is based on that in Ramon Myers.
7. A precise figure of the percentage of population directly affected by the Yellow River is difficult to come by. Does one, for example, include all people affected by the Hwai River as well, since the Yellow River for long periods flowed to the sea in the bed of the Hwai? The figures presented in the text are rough guesses only.
8. The elimination of long-distance commerce would presumably have forced handicraft producers of luxury goods to disperse around the country rather than to concentrate in those areas where they could produce most efficiently. See discussion in Chapter VI.

creation of large cities such as Peking.[9] Centralized government and long-distance commerce were necessary each to the other, but the rural population was not very dependent on either.

On the other hand, if China's long-distance trade had been severely circumscribed by internal boundaries between small nation states set up within the area inhabited by the Han people, there might have been a number of indirect barriers to agricultural progress and a rise in grain yields. China might have been more like Japan prior to the Meiji restoration, where contact between the country's different regions was restricted and where new techniques tended to remain bottled up in advanced regions. The existence of such internal barriers in China would probably also have impeded the flow of migrants from one region to the next and certainly would have restricted the movement of officials.[10] Both migration and the frequent transfer of magistrates from one district to another widely separated from the first contributed to the flow of technology and knowledge in general.

Famine relief was also somewhat more effective when the region struck by disaster could draw on a surplus in another area. Even with centralized government, however, the high degree of independence of individual viceroys often inhibited transfers. As indicated in Chapter VII, it was a common practice for viceroys to prohibit sales of grain outside of the area under their jurisdiction when times were hard within that area. Further, the amount of grain transferred from one region to another in times of famine was never large enough to be more than a temporary palliative for the average farmer. Most famine relief depended on local granaries, and even they weren't very large.

Finally, agriculture could not prosper if constantly subjected to pillaging, destruction and arbitrary taxation from roving armies and bandits. But there was nothing inherent in the agricultural system that required that security from such actions be maintained on a China-wide basis. If security could not be maintained regionally, it was because it was not militarily or politically possible to do so and not because there was some fundamental economic difficulty. For example, regional ties were probably not strong enough for a "Kingdom of Szechwan" or a "Kingdom of Kwangtung" to acquire legitimacy as an ongoing political entity. Nor could a kingdom of that size hope to defend against the unified Mongol tribes. But if legitimacy and defense had been possible on a regional basis, this would have been adequate for the needs of agriculture.

If this analysis is essentially correct, then the existence of a centralized government in China did contribute to the six-century rise in grain yields that is the central theme of this study by preventing or alleviating some of the effects of flood and famine and by accelerating the diffusion of better seeds and improved techniques of farming. But if China could have been broken up into several independent kingdoms without them being constantly at war with each

9. See discussion of the relationship of commerce and urbanization in Chapter VII.

10. See, for example, Mary Wright's discussion of government efforts to resettle people on land devastated by the Taiping rebellion and elsewhere (1957, pp. 157–61). These efforts presumably would have ended if China had not been unified.

other, one suspects that grain yields would still have risen between 1400 and the nineteenth or twentieth centuries, although perhaps a little more slowly.

THE ECONOMIC BASIS FOR REGIONALISM

The story of the rise of China's authoritarian tradition and the struggle of various emperors with regional feudal alternative sources of power has been told elsewhere.[11] The victory of the forces of centralization has been attributed to the need to coordinate water-control activities on a large scale, to authoritarian aspects of the Chinese family system, to the need to present a unified defense against the barbarian hordes on China's borders, and many other elements of the Chinese tradition.

To assess the relative importance of these alternative explanations would require a profound knowledge of conditions in China in the two millenia that preceded the beginning point of this study. By the end of the fourteenth century, many if not most aspects of Chinese political behavior and systems of political control had become deeply imbedded in the tradition. Actual and potential rulers of China had a successful model of how to rule the country to draw upon for guidance and, in a broad sense, only one such model. The possibilities for discovering different methods for dealing with problems, new or old, was further inhibited by a tradition that glorified precedent.

There is little in this study of agricultural productivity that is of clear and obvious relevance to an understanding of the origins of the Chinese bureaucratic state. In any case I do not have sufficient knowledge of the two millenia prior to the fourteenth century to know what is relevant and what is not. But there are parts of the analysis in this and previous chapters that shed light on whether or not economic conditions in China in the six centuries after the founding of the Ming dynasty reinforced centralization or tended instead to pull it apart.

The principal thesis of the remaining part of this chapter is that pre-modern economic forces favored regional rather than centralized power in China and that only conditions outside economics prevented a breakup of China. Further, the economic forces favoring regionalism tended to increase over time and hence were much stronger by middle or late Ch'ing than during the early Ming period. These economic forces contributed to the increasing strength of regional bases of power in the late Ch'ing, although economic forces were by no means solely responsible for that development.

By the 1960's, however, industrialization had completely altered the regional distribution of economic power. The financial-economic resources of a few areas such as Manchuria (NE), Hopei (N), and Shanghai (E) were overwhelming relative to those of the rest of the nation. In addition, a revolution in military technology had greatly altered the relationship between economic and political-military power.

11. See, e.g., Reischauer and Fairbank, 1958.

The thesis that China's traditional economy of the Ming and Ch'ing periods tended to favor regionalism is based on two broad propositions. First, there is the negative proposition that China's agricultural economy did not depend for its prosperity on a centralized government and hence breakaway regions did not have to worry that the mere act of dividing the country would bring about major economic dislocation with all the dangers that that would imply. The analysis upon which this proposition is based was made in the first half of this chapter.

Second, economic power, particularly in the Ch'ing period was dispersed widely and fairly evenly over the whole country. Further, the central government's tax revenues, the principal source of its economic power, were limited and vulnerable to usurpation by regional authorities. Before going on to an analysis of the decentralized nature of China's economy and the dispersion of control over economic resources, however, it is useful to begin with a discussion of the relationship between economic and other forms of power in the pre-modern era.

It is a well-known Maoist saying that "power grows out of the barrel of a gun." Power also, of course, grows out of many other conditions as well. Most successful governments obtain at least a degree of "popular support" by acquiring an aura of "legitimacy," by convincing people that the government works in their interest, and by other means that do not necessarily involve a large standing army. Still, a large standing army was an important component of political power in China in the past and it remains so to this day.

Prior to the Republican era, Chinese armies were generally of three types. They were either made up of conscripted peasants, of mercenaries, or of members of a ruling "racial" minority (e.g., the Mongols and Manchus). Whichever the case, military power was highly labor-intensive. Capital investment involved the acquisition of horses and a stock of fairly simple weaponry, together with food and transport. There was also the construction of walls around cities or in the case of the Great Wall, along the country's effective borders. Wall construction was itself a labor-intensive operation.

Thus military power in China required control over a reasonably large population and a surplus food supply to feed the troops, the animals, and those people making weapons and constructing walls. Given this level of military technology, it was possible for a small area to mobilize a large army. A hypothetical province of 20 million persons or 4 million families, for example, could readily mobilize an army of several hundred thousand men if some way could be found to feed or pay them.

If economics alone had determined military power in pre-modern China, then China would have been dominated militarily by its richest agricultural regions, since it was these regions that could feed the largest number of troops, animals, and men in support activities. In practice, the country was ruled after the fourteenth century from one of the poorer agricultural regions [Peking in northern Hopei (N)]. During half this period, a few million men (the Manchus) from a poor and primitive frontier area (Manchuria) imposed themselves on 400 million Chinese and ruled without a major challenge for two centuries (1644 to the Taiping Rebellion in the 1850's). In the military strength of a particular region, therefore, such things as tactics, organization, leadership, and discipline all played roles that sometimes dwarfed economic resources in significance.

Still, economic resources clearly were not irrelevant to military strength, particularly when the opposing forces were made up only of Chinese and hence where differences in organization and leadership were less likely to be pronounced. The issue that concerns us is whether or not the central government in China was able to command such a large share of the country's agricultural surplus that it was able to overwhelm regional forces with much smaller surpluses at their disposal.

In practice, something like the opposite situation prevailed. The single most striking fact concerning the financial power of China's central government in pre-Republican times was that government's small share in the total wealth of the country as a whole. Prior to the late nineteenth century, the principal source of government revenue was the land tax. In the Ming period this source provided the government with 26 to 28 million *shih* of grain, or perhaps around 10 per cent of total grain output and a much smaller share of national income.[12] By the mid-eighteenth century, total land tax revenue had risen absolutely and was according to the estimates of Yeh-chien Wang, 50 million *taels* of silver (see Table VIII.1) or about 50 million *shih* of husked grain, but this sum was perhaps only 5 to 6 per cent of total grain output at that time.[13] And much of this 50 million *taels* was siphoned off before it reached the central treasury. Other sources of central government revenue, before the latter half of the nineteenth

TABLE VIII.1. GOVERNMENT REVENUES
IN THE CH'ING PERIOD
(1,000 *Taels*)

	YEAR	
Tax	*1753*	*1908*
Land tax	48,057	102,480
Salt tax	5,561	30,000
Native customs	4,325	3,900
Maritime customs	—	32,902
Likin	—	21,408
Miscellaneous	1,053	45,000
Total	58,996	235,690

SOURCE: Yeh-chien Wang, "China's Land Taxation in the Late Ch'ing." These are preliminary estimates. The land tax figure for 1908 was recalculated from a wide variety of local records and is much higher than that normally quoted for this period.

12. Ming taxes are given in *shih* of husked grain. If one assumes that the Ming population around 1400 was 80 million and that per capita output (not consumption) of husked grain was 3 to 4 *shih* (450 to 600 catties of husked grain, perhaps 550–700 catties of unhusked grain), then total output was about 240 to 320 million *shih*.

13. The 5 to 6 per cent figure is based on a population figure of 250 million and a per capita grain output figure of 3 or 4 *shih*.

century, supplied only one-quarter the amount of funds obtained from the land tax. The *likin* tax and the maritime customs tariffs did not exist until after the Opium Wars and the Taiping Rebellion in the middle of the nineteenth century. Even by 1908, the land tax, which had increased in value but not in real terms over its mid-eighteenth–century level, still constituted over 40 per cent of the income of the central government.

In absolute terms, land tax revenue alone in 1908 was about 100 million *taels* (see Table VIII.1), less if measured in the prices of the 1880's.

By way of contrast, Chang Chung-li (1962, p. 327) estimates that the personal income of the gentry class in the 1880's amounted to 675 million *taels* annually. It is also interesting to contrast landlord resources (all landlords, not just "gentry") for a single large province with those of the central government. In Szechwan (SW), for example, 65 to 70 per cent of all land was rented out, so that landlords presumably received about 30 to 35 per cent of the main crops (one half of 65–70 per cent of the total output of these crops).[14] In the early part of the twentieth century, Szechwan (SW) may have produced as much as 15 million tons of grain (unhusked).[15] The landlord share would thus come to about 5 million tons of unhusked grain, or something under 50 million *shih* of husked grain, a figure about the same as that of the land-tax revenue of the central government.[16] Szechwan (SW), of course, was the largest single province, but one could arrive at similar figures by combining Kwangtung (SE) and Kwangsi (SE), or Chekiang (E) and Fukien (SE).

Thus if local gentry-landlord economic power could be mobilized and placed under unified control, it could meet the economic power of the central government on nearly even terms. If several major provinces combined, the authorities in Peking were powerless to prevent it unless they could mobilize similar gentry resources in areas loyal to the central government. The more remote the rebelling province and the greater its natural defenses, the more difficult was the task of Peking. Further as more provinces broke away from central control the power of the center declined, since it was a simple matter for the rebelling province to end the remittance of local land-tax revenue to Peking.

Areas where gentry-landlord power was more limited, as in much of north China, probably could not so readily mobilize independent financial power. The potential surplus in the north would appear to have been smaller and was, in any case, spread over too many people to be easily brought under unified control. Per capita grain output in 1957 in the three provinces of Shansi (N), Hopei (N), and Shantung (N), for example, was only 447 catties (224 kilograms) as against

14. This method of estimation is, of course, very crude. Substantial differences between the quality of land held by landlords as against that held by farmers, variations in the proportion of the crop going to rent, and many other things could change the total. The estimate presented here, therefore, is meant only to indicate roughly the general magnitude of landlords' share of income.

15. For grain crop output in Szechwan, see acreage and yield data in the tables in Appendixes C and D.

16. Five million tons of unhusked grain is about 4 million tons of husked grain (depending on the mix of rice, wheat, etc.) which at about 75 kilograms per *shih* is 43 million *shih*. Like all others in this chapter, this calculation is extremely rough.

638 catties (319 kilograms) in Szechwan (SW).[17] But if financing an army was more difficult in the north, it was not necessarily impossible. The Communists in the late 1930's and 1940's were able to maintain substantial forces from an economic base that was at times confined to the relatively inaccessible mountainous areas (i.e., the poorest) of such provinces as Shensi (NW) and Shansi (N). The Communists, of course, did not obtain their financing from gentry-landlord resources. Revenue instead came directly from the peasants.

The relative economic power of local and central authorities during the six centuries covered by this study was far from static. In broad terms there was a relative decline of centralized economic power from Ming times until the middle of the nineteenth century, a slight rise from then until 1949, and a dramatic increase after 1949.

During the first five decades of the Ming dynasty, about half of the total population of the empire was within 200 to 300 miles of the capital (see Map VIII.1) which was then at Nanking (E).[18] Four prefectures in southern Kiangsu (E) alone contributed just under 20 per cent of the central government's land-tax revenue.[19] These prefectures were the ones where the government had confiscated a high proportion of landlord holdings. Thus in an area containing half the country's people, the central government was clearly the dominant force. The resources of Nanking (E) probably matched those of the entire gentry-landlord class within the area. Further many of these gentry were key figures in the central government and those who were not could not easily have combined against Nanking (E). It would have been comparatively easy for Nanking (E) to discover and crush them before they got far.

Even the financial predominance of the early Ming government did not guarantee it security when that government was weak in other respects, however. Chu Ti, although a member of the royal family, rebelled against the 16-year-old successor to the Hung-wu emperor from his base in north China and succeeded in making himself emperor (1403–1424). But splits within the central government are fundamentally different phenomena from regional rebellion. This point is also relevant to an understanding of the long-run significance of the divisions in the Chinese government in 1966–1967.

By 1800, central government revenues in real terms had risen little if any over the levels of the late fourteenth century, but China's population had risen five or six times and had spread over an area of more than one million square miles. Areas that had been remote and lightly populated remained fairly remote, but now were filled with Chinese (see Map VIII.1).

The central government's financial position was further weakened by the location of the capital at Peking (N) after 1421. There were, of course, compensating features. Peking (N) was located in the Yung-lo emperor's original base

17. See data in Table F.2.
18. These mileages are in terms of air distances. In terms of waterway or road mileage—which is, of course, more relevant but also very difficult to estimate—the distances are greater.
19. Liang Fang-chung, 1935, p. 105. The prefectures referred to in order of importance for revenue purposes were Soochow, Sung-chiang, Ch'ang-chou, and Ying-t'ien.

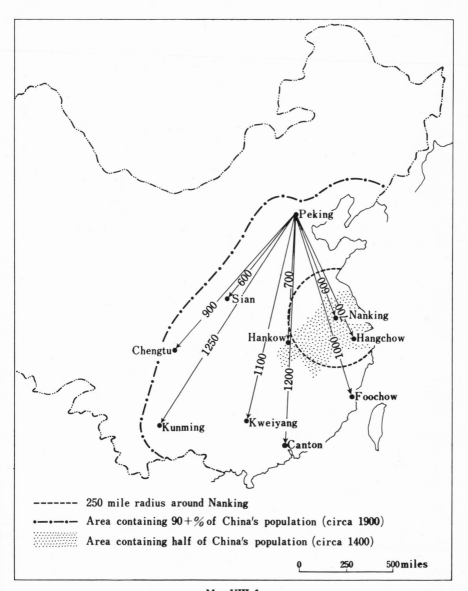

250 mile radius around Nanking

Area containing 90+% of China's population (circa 1900)

Area containing half of China's population (circa 1400)

0   250   500 miles

Map VIII. 1
Air Distances from Peking and Nanking
(in miles)

area and later, under the Ch'ing, Peking was close to the Manchu homeland. But by no stretch of the imagination was Peking (N) in the center of a rich agricultural area. Not only was per capita grain output in Hopei (N), Shansi (N), and Shantung (N) 20 per cent below the national average (see above), but even if the individual peasant farmer had been much better off than he was, there still was no easy or cheap way of getting whatever surplus existed to the capital. As pointed out in the previous chapter, for all the great expense involved in maintaining the Grand Canal, it was still easier to obtain grain from the south via this canal than to attempt to extract it from the north. Prior to the advent of the steamship, however, dependence on the Grand Canal made the capital vulnerable to blockade by any regional force strong enough to sit astride of some portion of that thousand-mile waterway.

Given this economic balance of power, it comes as no surprise that such provinces as Kwangtung (SE) and Szechwan (SW) had a high degree of autonomy, or that in the nineteenth century viceroys in many parts of China would often ignore the wishes of Peking. Nor was it unusual for a major rebellion, the Taiping, to arise in a single province, Kwangsi (SE) and have or acquire the force to sweep across much of south China.

The surprising fact is that China held together at all. Many scholars have attributed this unity to the strength of the hold of Confucian ideology on the ruling elite, to the great administrative talents of that elite and of the system itself, and to a sense among most Chinese that China and Chinese culture were properly a single entity and that Szechwan culture, for example, could never acquire comparable status. The discussion above tends, if anything, to reinforce these arguments by indicating that these forces held China together in spite of the ease with which regionalism could have found economic support.

The regional distribution of economic power slowly began to shift in the latter part of the nineteenth century and the first decades of the twentieth century. The rise of foreign trade and the preeminent position of Shanghai in that trade created two new sources of concentrated economic power, the Shanghai Chinese business community, and the revenues of the imperial maritime customs. The latter source, however, was under foreign control. Because the foreign powers recognized Peking as the proper recipient of customs revenues, these funds enhanced the economic position of whoever controlled Peking, not Shanghai. Before 1911 the customs revenue may have strengthened the declining Manchu fortunes, but that government used the funds so ineptly that there was no major gain in power from this source. After 1911, and particularly after the fall of Yuan Shih-k'ai several years later, Peking became a prize much sought after by warlord armies, in part because customs revenues continued to be paid to whomever held the city.[20] But these revenues alone or in combination with other local resources were not large enough to tip the balance of power in favor of the northern warlords.

In 1927 the Nationalist forces under Chiang Kai-shek were able to restore at least a degree of unity over most of the nation. Again this unity was a victory

20. Peking also had considerable symbolic significance. On both points see Wilbur, 1968.

not of relative economic power, but a victory of ideology, principally the ideology or idea of Chinese nationalism. Prior to the arrangement with the Shanghai business community which came after the Nationalist armies had control of much of China south of the Yangtze, the Nationalists had one of the weaker, not one of the stronger, economic bases.

The Communist victory in 1949 was also achieved from a weak economic base and reflected the disintegration of Nationalist political and administrative capacities, among other conditions. Events since 1949, however, have radically altered the economic basis of regional power. The central government in China today is less dependent on a unifying ideology than its predecessors, although such an ideology clearly continues to exist.

The changes since 1949 have involved both military technology and the underlying economic and financial basis of that technology. China's army no longer travels only on its stomach. Even in the Korean War in the early 1950's only about 20 per cent of the supplies required at the front were food (Futrell, 1961, p. 289). The remainder were ammunition and fuel. Since Korea, the firepower and to a lesser degree the mechanization of the People's Liberation Army has risen markedly. In addition, there are more than 2,000 aircraft in the Chinese airforce (Institute for Strategic Studies, 1964, p. 10). If a Chinese division in combat in Korea in 1951–1952 used fifty tons of supplies a day (ten of which were food), then today that same division would probably use several times that amount and most of the increase would be in munitions, parts, and fuel, not food.

Such a military establishment requires a substantial industrial base and is expensive. The published military budget for China averaged 6 billion *yuan* per year in 1955–1957 (Chen, 1967, p. 447). Total revenue (in comparable prices) in 1908 was one-fifth that amount or less. In the warlord period, a figure of several hundred million *yuan* (in 1952 prices) was considered a large sum by those in the business of raising armies.[21] Furthermore, the 6 billion *yuan* figure for the 1950's probably excludes most investment in the construction of military support industries.

When the main economic component of a Chinese military organization was grain, economic power was diffuse. Certain regions had higher grain output per person or per unit of area or, because of widespread tenancy or better transport, may have been able to mobilize surplus grain more readily. But these advantages were never sufficient to allow one region to dominate all others because of its preponderance of wealth. In contrast, in the early 1960's Chinese industrial and financial power was heavily concentrated in Manchuria (NE), Hopei (N), and Shanghai (E). If the above analysis is correct in stating that Chinese military technology is today dependent on an industrial base, then a determined group in political and economic control of Hopei (N) (including Peking and Tientsin) and Manchuria (NE) would have overwhelming power vis-à-vis a group in control of, say, Szechwan (SW) or Kwangsi (SE)–Kwangtung (SE).[22] Independent regions

21. During the northern expedition, for example, the Kuomintang army required $1.6 million every five days (about 5 million *yuan* in 1952 prices: Wilbur, 1968).

22. In the short run, a regional force possessed of substantial stores of weapons, spare parts, and ammunition might be able to put up considerable resistance until the stores ran out.

within China, therefore, are likely to arise for only so long as a government in Peking is divided within or unwilling to use its potential power.[23] In this fundamental respect, the Chinese political and economic system has taken a step away from a structure that revolved in part at least around the production and marketing of grain. But, as the poor harvests of 1959 through 1961 demonstrated, it was only a first step.

23. I have left nuclear weapons out of this discussion on the assumption that no one would use such weapons in a civil war or even threaten their use. I have also left aside the whole problem of dealing with guerilla warfare.

CHAPTER NINE

Conclusion

During the millenia prior to the founding of the Ming dynasty in A.D. 1368, China's population spread into the rice-growing regions surrounding the Yangtze River and from there further southward into present day Kwangtung (SE). This great migration required a whole new technology fundamentally different from that used on the dry millet and wheat lands of the North China Plain.

THE INSTITUTIONAL FRAMEWORK

At the same time that rice farming was being developed, Chinese institutious that affected agriculture were also undergoing basic changes. Because much of the southern half of China was serviced by major waterways and good harbors, commerce in the T'ang and Sung periods (A.D. 618–1278) expanded significantly. Even more important, the central government during these centuries finally won its struggle with a semi-feudal landed aristocracy and the Chinese bureaucratic state attained a form that it was to retain until the twentieth century. Great landed estates were broken up, land could be bought and sold freely, and peasants could migrate more or less at will to new lands and opportunities. If these peasant farmers rented land, their principal obligation to the owner was only to pay rent.

By the fourteenth century this evolution of institutions had largely been completed. The pattern of a highly developed traditional commercial network in the south and a lower level of trade in the north was well established and not to change fundamentally until the coming of the railroad in the twentieth century.

There may have been some increase in the exchange of commodities among farmers living within the same market town or in nearby market towns. We simply do not know enough as yet about rural marketing to tell. But it is unlikely that there was a major rise in long-distance commerce in per capita terms, or any basic change in the nature of that trade. The exchange of goods between urban and rural areas and across provincial boundaries was too small between 1400 and 1900 and too devoted to the luxury trade to have much of an impact on agricultural productivity except as a vehicle for bringing in new seeds and other new techniques. This commerce was small, not because it was oppressed by government action, but because it was cheaper for farmers to depend on themselves or other nearby sources of supply.

Nor does China's land tenure system appear to have changed much after the fourteenth century. The amount of tenancy was high in the rice regions of the south and low elsewhere. Because the rate of return on land was low, most landlords made their fortunes outside of agriculture and held land as an easily marketable asset and a source of prestige. Generally, the owners of the land lived away from the village and took little interest in efforts to raise the yield of their property. Where large capital investments were necessary to maintain or increase yields, however, the rental contract was commonly made for a long period of time and the rent was a fixed amount so that farmers would have an incentive to invest their own resources. In the north, tenancy contracts were often only for a year and rents were set at a percentage of the harvest, but tenancy was low in the north and capital requirements less, so that this system was not a major bar to improvements.

The evidence is sketchy, but land tenancy was high in most rice regions in all periods for which data are available. Occasionally new settled areas in the south would have low tenancy, but usually not for long. In the north landlords never seem to have controlled a large share of the land. Nor did the pattern of long-term–fixed-amount contracts in the south and short-term–percentage-share contracts in the north change much, at least after the eighteenth century.

In a general way, therefore, the institutions of greatest relevance to agriculture did not evolve significantly after the fourteenth century. On the other hand, there was no real need for them to do so. These institutions were not themselves vehicles of progress, but neither were they major barriers to rising agricultural output.

POPULATION GROWTH, MIGRATION, AND THE DEMAND FOR FOOD

There was one major difference between the centuries prior to the fourteenth and those that followed it, however. From the Later Han dynasty (which ended in A.D. 220) to the founding of the Ming (in A.D. 1368) there were only a few centuries when there was anything like a sustained growth in population. And the increase that did occur was wiped out by the ferocity of the Mongol invasions. After the fourteenth century, in contrast, population crept upward at an average pace of 0.4 per cent per year. Only twice was this rise interrupted, first by the warfare connected with the downfall of Ming and the entry of the Manchus in the seventeenth century, and then by the Taiping Rebellion in the middle of the nineteenth century. As a result, by the middle of the twentieth century the number of people had risen seven to nine times, from 65 to 80 million around 1400 to 583 million in 1953.

The combination of a rising population together with an institutional framework that did not discourage improvements brought about an expansion of grain output that more or less matched the increase in the number of people. Per capita grain consumption, on a secular basis, either remained constant or may even have risen slightly. From one year's harvest to the next, of course, there was considerable fluctuation.

The core chapters and appendixes of this book are devoted to explaining how this increase in grain production (in absolute terms) was made possible. Perhaps half of the rise can be accounted for by Chinese migration onto previously uncultivated land. By the fourteenth century, China's population was highly concentrated along the lower reaches of the Yangtze River. Previously heavily settled areas in north China and on the central and upper reaches of the Yangtze [Hunan (C), Hupei (C), and Szechwan (SW)] had been laid waste by the Mongols. The provinces in the southernmost regions of China [Kwangtung (SE), Kwei-chow (SW), and Yunnan (SW)] began to receive migrants in large numbers only in the late Sung period and in some cases not until after the fourteenth century.

In the early part of the Ming period, most of the migration out of the heavily populated areas was still toward the south [to Kwangtung (SE)] or into central China [Hunan (C) and Hupei (C)]. Gradually, however, people began to move back onto the North China Plain and into the northwest in large numbers. Szechwan (SW) also received migrants in the Ming, but its gains were wiped out by the rebellion of Chang Hsien-chung in the seventeenth century. These trends continued right through the eighteenth century. Increasingly in the Ch'ing period, however, the major recipients of migrants were the provinces to the west, particularly the southwest, rather than the southeast and the North China Plain.

None of these population movements was great enough to reduce effectively the pressure of people along the lower reaches of the Yangtze. The population in this area continued to rise until the middle of the nineteenth century when the Taiping Rebellion succeeded where migration had failed. These provinces had become so overcrowded prior to the arrival of the Taipings that after the rebellion had ended they only partially recovered their pre-rebellion levels of population in the century that followed. People continued to prefer to migrate to the west.

In the twentieth century there was still some virgin land left. The Manchus had partially succeeded in keeping Chinese out of their homeland in the north-east and there were also regions in the northwest that could be brought under cultivation. The land in these areas, however, was not as rich as that in the southwest and hence what there was was quickly filled up.

By the middle of the twentieth century, the amount of cultivated land in China was four times the level of the late fourteenth century. As indicated, this increase accounted for only about half of the rise in grain output. The remaining half was the result of a rise in grain yields per acre.

RISING YIELDS WITHIN A STAGNANT TECHNOLOGY

In Japan in the late nineteenth century, a fairly rapid rise in grain yields was achieved through the spread of the "best" traditional technology from advanced to backward regions. This spread had not occurred earlier because of institutional barriers erected or maintained by the Tokugawa Shogunate in the centuries prior to the Meiji restoration in 1868. Superficially China presents a similar picture. Grain yields in 1400 in the provinces of the lower Yangtze and the southeast coast were nearly twice as high as those of more recently settled rice-producing provinces and yields in these "advanced" provinces reached the levels of the 1950's at an earlier date than elsewhere.

But there the similarity ends. In China there were few improvements in "best" technique in the six-century period covered in this book and little apparent spread of that "best" technique from "advanced" to "backward" regions. The major innovations that did appear in the post-fourteenth–century period had to do with improved seeds and new crops from the Americas. Improved seed varieties were being discovered in China and brought in from abroad throughout these six centuries and in previous centuries as well. These seeds raised yields, reduced crop fluctuations, and contributed to the increase in double cropping. But there was no general movement of improved varieties from "advanced" to "backward" regions. If anything, the trend was in the opposite direction. Corn and potatoes from the Americas did enter China through an advanced province [Fukien (SE)], but their impact was small relative to that of other changes prior to the twentieth century. The great increase in corn acreage in the twentieth century did not result from farmers suddenly becoming aware of its uses. Instead there were highland areas in the southwest and northwest that were particularly suitable for corn, but these areas were not heavily farmed until migration and natural population growth had filled up the richer lowlands.

Population increases in earlier periods, together with water-control construction activities, also played a major role in the expansion of the double-cropped area, particularly the double cropping of rice and wheat, but, in addition, that involving two crops of rice in a single year. The technology required for double cropping was known in China long before the fourteenth century. But in most parts of China there were only a few weeks within which the first crop had to be harvested, the land prepared, and a second crop planted (or transplanted). Each of these activities consumed large amounts of labor. Where rice was involved, there also had to be an assured source of water. In some areas rainfall or relatively simple methods of diverting water from nearby rivers was adequate. In others, however, elaborate water-control works had to be constructed and pumps powered by men or animals manned. Double cropping, therefore, was a highly labor-intensive operation and one where labor requirements were heavily concentrated in a few short periods during the year. Hence, although early ripening seeds played some part in the extension of winter wheat acreage and in the planting of a second crop of rice, the key to increased grain output from this source was population growth and the increasing density of people in any given area.

The construction of water-control works by corvees of labor did much more than simply make possible more double cropping. On the North China Plain the dikes containing the Yellow River were all that separated farmers from disaster, even when the level of the river was normal. In the south, ponds, ditches, and canals made rice growing in some areas feasible where otherwise dry-land crops would have had to have been planted. Because rice yields on the average were double or more those of dry-land crops such as millet and corn, water-control construction that made it possible to grow wet rice had a major impact on the productivity of land in any given area. Most of this construction seems to have gone hand in hand with migration onto new lands, particularly in the south. Instead of first planting dry-land crops and then switching over to rice, most farmers instead settled on land where rice could be grown without much prior investment in water control and then they gradually spread onto other nearby areas as the water supply situation was gradually improved. Surprisingly, however, there was little extension of rice land to the north. There just was not enough water in most of the north to allow rice to be grown. Artesian wells could be dug in a few places, but the water table in most areas of the north was far below the surface. Surface wells could only be used on a limited basis. Because of the vast quantities of silt carried by the Yellow River, even its water could not be used without first bringing the upper reaches of the river under control, a task not within the technical competence of pre-modern Chinese engineers.

Pre-modern Chinese water-control technology, on the other hand, was in many respects quite sophisticated. The Grand Canal, in particular, was something of an engineering achievement. But there is little evidence of any improvement in this technology after the fourteenth century or any spread of advanced methods to backward areas. The key to increases in water-control construction activities was labor. When a region had sufficient numbers of people to move the necessary amounts of rock and dirt, it did so. After several centuries of activity, most of the irrigation and drainage facilities that could be built by such labor-intensive methods were completed. At that point there was pressure on farmers to find new ways of improving the systems already built. Some improvements were, of course, made, but it is unlikely that many of these could be labeled technological change as contrasted to further investment in the existing technology. Whatever the case, the pace of water-control construction slowed markedly once the major systems were finished. This slowdown occurred first in the heavily populated areas of the east and southeast and was followed by central and north China. Only the newly settled and resettled provinces of the northwest and southwest continued major activity right through to the end of the Ch'ing dynasty.

Water-control construction and seeds were not the only forms of capital invested in pre-modern China. There were also many different kinds of farm implements, draft animals, and fertilizer. Both the number of implements and of draft animals appear to have increased along with population. There was little capital-deepening of the kind that occurs in modern agriculture when a farmer substitutes a tractor for a horse or a mechanized reaper for more labor-using methods. Implements were neither so complicated or so expensive that peasants had to scrimp and save for many years to afford them. Oxen and water buffaloes were expensive and poorer farmers often did not own them. But they could rent their services or accomplish many of the same results by substituting their own labor on their small parcels of land.

Perhaps the most important capital input outside of water was fertilizer. The increasing number of people per unit of cultivated land increased the available supply of nightsoil. More important, the rise in the number of hogs and draft animals made it possible to more or less double the application of fertilizer per *mou* between the fourteenth and twentieth centuries. The number of hogs, however, also does not appear to have increased any faster than population. Pork was an expensive way to produce calories once a farmer had exhausted his supplies of garbage and chaff and had to feed his hogs grain. Any substantial increase in the number of hogs, therefore, depended on first expanding the production of grain, and not the reverse.

It is the central theme of this study that by the nineteenth and twentieth centuries, changing cropping patterns and rising "traditional" capital inputs per unit of land had succeeded in doubling the national average yield per *mou* of all grains taken together. Because most of these changes were closely tied to population growth and an expanding labor force, there was no easy way in which output per capita could be increased much by such methods. A rapid improvement in the "traditional" technology could have changed this situation and caused per capita grain output to rise as it did in Meiji Japan. But most of the more significant improvements in Chinese agricultural technology had occurred long before the fourteenth century when the analysis in this study begins. From the early Ming period on, the one really important change was the introduction of corn and potatoes, but these two crops explain only a small portion of the increase in grain output. Beancake may also have been introduced after 1400 and there were a few minor alterations of farm implements. Finally, there was continuing experimentation with and adoption of new seeds.

If any of these or other techniques had remained bottled up in a few areas for long periods of time and suddenly burst forth over, say, several decades and spread rapidly across the country, they might have succeeded in raising per capita output for a time. But, in practice, most new ideas for growing grain did not remain for long in a single region. Migrants, traders, and officials all carried the improved methods to distant provinces, and farmers, although conservative, were quick to seize new opportunities once it was clear they wouldn't risk a major crop failure by doing so. Most new seeds or new crops, for example, were known and used across all of China within a century or two after they had gained a foothold on the coast or wherever else they first appeared.

While China's traditional methods of producing grain were not able to raise

China's per capita consumption of food, the system was capable of preventing a decline in food intake as long as there were new lands to open up. By the middle of the twentieth century, however, there was little new land left. Manchuria was heavily settled and further expansion to the northwest could only be accomplished in combination with a solution to the area's lack of water.

POST-1949 IN HISTORICAL PERSPECTIVE

Just as China was running out of new land, her population growth began to accelerate. It is probable that this acceleration began early in the twentieth century with the coming of the railroad and the consequent improvement in transport and famine relief. But the biggest push came after 1949 with the systematic application of modern public health measures. The rate of increase in the number of people jumped from under 1 per cent a year in the decades prior to 1949 to over 2 per cent after that date.

There is nothing in the analysis of China's "traditional" agriculture that would lead one to believe that it could by itself respond adequately to such a challenge once there were no more new lands for people to migrate to. More people meant more labor and more fertilizer and hence some increase in yields per unit of land, but these measures alone could never have raised grain output by 2 per cent per year and more. Water control construction was most effective when carried out in combination with virgin land development and hence had long since reached a point of sharply diminishing returns. The impact of new seeds may also have been declining. In any case, there were no ways within the "traditional" system for the pace of discovery and adoption of new seeds to be raised to meet the accelerated growth of population.

If the "traditional" system could not maintain existing levels of food consumption on its own, the Chinese government after 1949 apparently believed it could do so with the help of a number of institutional reforms. To the degree that cooperatives and later communes were set up for economic purposes, it was to enable peasants to accelerate the pace of water-control construction, to expand the areas on which two crops of rice per year were grown, and to speed the introduction of such techniques as deep plowing and close planting. There were, to be sure, increases in the number of modern farm implements (the double-wheeled double-bladed plow, for example) and a little chemical fertilizer, but the measures of central importance were ones that had been used in China for centuries. Only the methods of organizing labor to carry them out had changed.

Altering the way in which labor was organized was not unimportant. Any positive gain from such a change taken by itself, however, depended to a substantial degree on whether there was much room for increases in productivity left in the "traditional" technology. There was a rapid expansion of the irrigated area in southwest China in the 1950's and also an extension of the area sown to two crops of rice. But these appear to have been one-shot gains whose potential had largely been exhausted.

Up through 1957 or 1958, grain output probably rose at least as fast as population growth and perhaps somewhat faster. Some of the increase in output in the 1950's was probably in essence only a recovery from the damage and disruption caused by more than a decade of war and civil war. The rest was presumably a result of extension of traditional methods described above and some improvement in incentives as a result of land reform in the late 1940's and early 1950's.[1] Part of the officially reported annual rate of growth of 3.6 per cent between 1952 and 1957 may have been due to improvements in the statistical reporting system.

By the late 1950's and early 1960's the rate of growth of grain output using traditional methods had begun to slow down,[2] but the demands on that output from the rise of modern industry had begun to accelerate. The industrialization of China did not begin in the 1950's. The textile industry had gotten its start around the turn of the century, along with a number of other consumer-oriented industries. Steel and machinery had begun to surge forward under Japanese impetus in Manchuria during the late 1930's and early 1940's. Industrialization in turn contributed to urbanization and the population of China's large cities (of over 100,000 people) tripled between 1900 and the early 1950's.

Initially this rise in urban population did not put a heavy burden on the producers of grain. Cities in Manchuria could be fed from the region's own expanding surplus. Elsewhere, the railroad increased the ability of the system to tap existing surpluses and get them to previously inaccessible (at reasonable cost) cities, mainly in the north. Nor had the rise of Shanghai progressed far enough to be a heavy drain on the surpluses of the Yangtze River. Further, Shanghai, Tientsin, and other large cities could pay for their food requirements with the products of their own rapidly expanding consumer goods industries. Hence this food was obtained voluntarily through the market. What could not be so obtained, was imported from abroad.

After 1949, the negative effects of land reform on the marketed grain surplus were offset by the introduction of a fixed agricultural tax. The government was also able to buy time by opening up the Shensi (NW)–Chengtu (SW) railroad, effectively tapping the large surplus of Szechwan (SW) Province.

But by the middle and late 1950's the strain of feeding China's burgeoning industries was beginning to be felt by agriculture. This strain was increased by two decisions of the government—first, to end all imports of grain from abroad, and, second, to concentrate almost exclusively on the development of heavy industry. The pressure of these moves was felt as early as the first year of the first five year plan. In November of 1953, the state introduced compulsory delivery quotas (at fixed prices) for grain, a step that raised marketings by one-third (in absolute terms) and put off the day of reckoning for another 5 or 6 years. By 1959, however, China's stagnating grain output was unable to keep up

1. Perhaps the most thorough and interesting attempt to analyze the sources of productivity increase in Chinese agriculture in the 1950's is that by Tang, 1968.
2. In 1956 official grain statistics indicate that grain output rose by 4.4 per cent over 1955. In the ten years subsequent to 1956, the rate of growth of grain output has been only about 1 per cent per year, even if one accepts an output figure for the 1965–1967 period of a little over 200 million tons (1956 output was 182.5 million tons).

with the pace of urbanization which had been accelerated during the "Great Leap Forward" of 1958–1959. The point was brought home to the government by the failure of the 1959, 1960, and 1961 harvests, which resulted from bad weather and commune mismanagement. But, even without these harvest failures, China would have had to face the basic contradiction in her industrial and agricultural policies.

The first long-term steps taken by the government were to reorganize the communes so as to minimize management and incentive problems, and to begin importing 5 to 6 million tons of grain a year from Australia, Canada, and France. The latter move allowed the government to feed the recent increases in urban population without further damaging rural incentives.

The second major shift in Chinese agricultural policy was toward large-scale investment in modern capital inputs. The effort to get the most out of the "traditional" technology was not abandoned, but it was given only a secondary role to play. In the first half of the 1960's, there was an extension of rural electrification, and increased sales of modern farm implements, motors, power pumps and other machinery.

But the central concern was with the development of a modern chemical fertilizer industry. By 1966, imports of chemical fertilizer had more than doubled over the 1957 level and domestic production had risen by seven or eight times. These increases brought about in less than a decade what traditional methods had only been able to accomplish over a period of several centuries. As long as population continued to grow at a rate of 2 per cent or more a year, however, even such a rapid expansion of modern capital inputs was barely adequate to meet China's needs.

Chinese Population Data

For the purposes of this book, it is important to have some notion of the size of China's population in certain key periods. A principal objective of the analysis in this study is to explain how Chinese agriculture managed to feed a large increase in the number of people. Is it possible that the reported rise in population is a statistical illusion?

No attempt will be made to argue that Chinese population statistics are accurate in some absolute sense. No census is without error, and Chinese methods of registration were undoubtedly subject to a much greater margin of error than censuses in present-day industrialized countries. The only issue that concerns us here is whether population totals, nationwide and by province, for certain key years are sufficiently close to the truth to be used in the analysis. The word "sufficiently" refers to a maximum allowable percentage error, a percentage that varies depending on the question asked.

The figures most important for this study are the population totals by province for the late fourteenth century and for 1953. It is also desirable to have some idea of the number of people in each province in the early or mid-nineteenth century and in the late seventeenth and eighteenth centuries. Some effort is also made in this appendix to deal with population change between 1850 and 1953.

In looking at the data for each of the relevant periods, several considerations must be taken into account in judging reliability. These are:

1. How difficult was it to count the number of people in China?
2. Were the institutions set up to register the population suitable for the task?

3. Are the published data consistent with known historical events and plausible demographic trends?

The process of simply counting the number of people in China was not inherently difficult, at least as far as non-institutional aspects of the problem are concerned. Most Chinese lived within a family and village. A *hsien* magistrate normally had a reasonably accurate list of the number of villages in his *hsien*. His only problem, therefore, was in estimating the number of people in each of these villages. This in turn required a knowledge of the number of families in the village and the average number of people per family. Since the average size of a family does not appear to have varied much over time or among regions in China,[1] the only real difficulty for a *hsien* magistrate was in estimating the number of families per village. The average size of a village (*ts'un*) did, of course, vary, but this variation must have been fairly systematically related to the region's geography. In any case, a reasonably reliable estimate of the number of families in a village could be obtained by counting the number of houses.

Estimating the number of people in large towns and cities probably presented greater difficulties, but this component made up less than 20 to 25 per cent of the total.[2] There were also several provinces [e.g., Szechwan (SW) and Taiwan] where rural homes were not clustered in villages and hence where estimation must have been more difficult. A similar situation may have prevailed in North China after the Mongol devastation.

When all qualifications are made, it is still difficult to see how a serious effort by a *hsien* magistrate could have missed the mark by more than, say, 25 per cent, even under unfavorable conditions. If households kept the door placards listing all members living there up to date, and if these were conscientiously totalled by local personnel, errors due to double-counting or simply poor counting could hardly have amounted to more than a few per cent.

The issues to be dealt with in this appendix, therefore, concern whether Chinese officials made a serious effort to estimate total Chinese population, and the degree to which various institutional barriers and biases may have hampered their effectiveness in this regard. Since it is impossible to establish a conclusive case for either accepting or rejecting the data on institutional grounds alone, the published data must also be tested for consistency with known historical events and other relevant considerations.

On the institutional side, it will be obvious to the informed reader that I owe a heavy debt to the works of Ping-ti Ho (1959) and John S. Aird (1968). In fact, I shall add little to their institutional analysis. For the purposes of this study, however, neither Ho nor Aird gives sufficient attention to the problem of the

1. This statement applies only to the size of the nuclear family. The extended family could vary greatly in size. But all evidence for the most recent century indicates that, as a rule, only very rich extended families actually lived together for long under a single roof. Less wealthy rural families tended to live apart after a few years of trying to live together. There was also some regional variation in the average family size, but local magistrates would presumably have become aware of this where the differences were significant.

2. See Appendix E on urban population data.

plausibility of the actual data or provide estimates of the possible margin of error. Aird does make some effort in this direction as do such writers as Irene B. Taeuber and Nai-chi Wang (1960), and John D. Durand (1960). For the data of particular concern to this study, however, more can be done. I shall deal first with the early Ming data, next with the 1953 census, then the Ch'ing data, and finally the various estimates and censuses for the years between 1850 and the 1930's.

POPULATION IN THE FOURTEENTH CENTURY

It is not possible here to improve on Ping-ti Ho's analysis of the institutional aspects of population registration during the reign of the Ming emperor T'ai-tsu (1368–1398). His discussion indicates that a serious effort was made to count the entire population including women and children. Ho also presents some evidence of under-registration, but except for the non-Han populations in the provinces of Yunnan (SW) and Kweichow (SW), the degree of under-registration appears to be small. The failure to register non-Han peoples in southwest China hardly affects the analysis in this study, since the land cultivated by such people was presumably not registered either. The problem of explaining how yields were increased on the land of Han people remains.

Ho does not deal with the plausibility of the figures themselves, except to point out that data from A.D. 1400 to 1600 clearly do not reflect true demographic trends. A discussion of the plausibility of the 1390's figure and an estimate of the degree of underreporting are not attempted by him. Such an attempt must now be made.

The consistency of the late fourteenth-century figures cannot be tested by working back from eighteenth- or nineteenth-century data; the time span is much too great. One can, however, use pre-fourteenth–century data. In Table A.1, population data from the T'ang, Sung, and Yuan dynasties are presented alongside the fourteenth-century figures. We know from Ping-ti Ho that the 1390's data represent a major independent attempt to estimate China's true population.

From Franz Schurmann's work on the Yuan dynasty we know that the Mongols also made a sincere effort to register population and land. The population of north China, in particular, was apparently carefully surveyed in the census of 1235–36 (Schurmann, 1956, p. 67). The case for south China is less clear, but it would appear that some systematic effort to register population was made partly for tax purposes and in part to form organizations through which to promote improved farm techniques. There is also some evidence that suggests the existence of under-registration.[3] Perhaps more important, it is not clear from the *Yuan shih* whether the population data recorded therein for south China are

3. Durand (1960, p. 229) quotes Sacharoff to the effect that the Yuan totals were incomplete in that for some areas no figures were given. In the *Szechwan t'ung chih* (1816), the 1290 population figures for the province are said to exclude Chia-ting, T'ung-ch'uan, and Yung-ning *lu's*.

TABLE A.I. CHINESE POPULATION DATA BY PROVINCE (742–1393)
(Number of Households)

Province	T'ang 742	Sung 1080	Sung-Chin 1173	Yuan 1270 or 1290	Ming 1393
Hopei (N)	1,151,000	984,195	2,277,131[a]	*593,852	*334,792
Shensi-Kansu (NW)	969,000	962,318	—	*92,651	294,526
Shansi (N)	658,000	450,869	—	*241,969	595,444
Shantung (N)	1,054,000	1,370,800	—	*363,611	753,894
Honan (N)	1,298,000	823,066	—	*162,962	*315,617
Subtotal:	5,130,000	4,591,248	6,987,000[b]	1,455,045	2,294,273
Hupei (C)	246,000	589,302	267,000	*527,518	775,851
Hunan (C)	221,000	811,057	1,005,134	*1,819,145	
Anhwei (E)	467,000	2,152,814	1,161,339	676,115	537,614
Kiangsu (E)	515,000			1,602,281	1,375,320
Chekiang (E)	729,000	1,830,096	2,295,863	2,384,274	2,138,225
Kiangsi (C)	259,000	1,365,533	1,862,614	2,648,299	1,553,923
Fukien (SE)	91,000	992,087	1,424,296	1,364,467	815,527
Subtotal:	2,528,000	7,740,889	8,016,246	11,022,099	7,196,460
Kwangtung (SE)	211,000	565,534	526,913	681,477	675,599
Kwangsi (SE)	109,000	242,110	505,883	*386,239	211,263
Subtotal:	320,000	807,644	1,032,796	1,067,716	886,862
Szechwan (SW)[c]	1,168,000	1,403,484	2,721,911	*99,538	215,719
Total:	9,146,000	14,543,265	18,757,953	13,644,388	10,593,314

SOURCES:

T'ang: These figures are those of H. Bielenstein as reported in Durand, 1960, p. 253.

Sung: The 1080 data are from Ma Tuan-lin, *Wen-hsien t'ung-k'ao* (Yuan), vol. 10, p. 114. Except where otherwise noted, the 1173 figures are from the *Sung hui yao chi kao*, vol. 7, p. 6368. The principal problem with Sung is matching Sung districts (*lu*) with present-day provinces. The matching areas are listed in Table A.2.

Yuan: These data are from the *Yuan shih*, vol. 58, p. 3b to vol. 63, p. 15b. The regional breakdown of the Yuan data that I used was much more detailed than that of the Sung and hence matching Yuan districts (*lu*) with modern provinces could be accomplished with greater precision. The precise date of many of the figures, however, is not clear.

Ming: These data are from Liang Fang-chung, "Ming population, land, and land tax statistics," *Chung-kuo chin-tai ching-chi shih yen-chiu chi-kan*, vol. 3, No. 1, pp. 75–129.

* Provinces in which major warfare occurred during the period of dynastic transition.

[a] *Chi-fu t'ung chih*, (1884) vol. 96, pp. 3907–3908. This figure is for the Chin period, probably the late twelfth century.

[b] Durand, 1960, p. 228 gives a figure for the total population of Chin. For purposes of consistency, I have added to this the population of one Sung *lu* in the present-day area of Honan.

[c] Szechwan includes Yunnan and Kweichow.

the figures obtained in Yuan censuses or instead are simply late Sung data carried over into the early part of the Yuan. The Hunan (C)–Hupei (C) estimates are particularly suspicious. Analysis of these figures will be made in terms of their historical plausibility.

Finally, one has the Sung population figures. The key problem with these data is that the average number of persons per household is far too low. The issue thus becomes a question of whether the household figures are too high or the population data too low.

There is a substantial literature, particularly in Japanese, on various aspects of the Sung population figures. To my knowledge, however, there is no comprehensive work (in English) on Sung census institutions comparable to that of Ping-ti Ho for Ming and Ch'ing. I shall not undertake such a work here.

Instead I present the Sung population totals in families in Table A.1 for what they are worth. The family totals for provinces not devastated by the Mongols are more consistent with later data than the totals of persons (mouths). Practices in other dynasties suggest that women and children were often not recorded and this may have been the case during the Sung as well.[4] There is direct evidence that women and children were not always registered during the Sung,[5] but then there is apparently also evidence that families sometimes were divided so as to receive greater allocations of land.

The Sung data in Table A.1 are also subject to error because of major boundary changes between Sung and Ming. I have made rough adjustments in the Sung figures to make them comparable to Ming (see Table A.2). It is possible to obtain Sung data on a more detailed basis and hence construct more reliable totals, but I did not feel that the effort was justified here.

Although further research might change the conclusion, it is my belief that a greater effort was made in the early Ming period to register the population than in either of the other two periods. Nevertheless, in at least the Yuan and Ming, and probably the Sung as well, some not inconsiderable effort to arrive at correct population figures was made. Equally important from the point of view of this analysis, the estimates in the three periods were made substantially independently of each other. Hence we have three more or less independent estimates of population for the comparatively short period of two centuries (three centuries if one uses the A.D. 1080 figures). These estimates can, therefore, be usefully tested for consistency with each other and with relevant historical events.

The value of this check is greatly enhanced by the conspicuous historical events of demographic significance that occurred during this period. Foremost among these events was the Mongol invasion. The great relevance of the Mongol conquest of China for the purposes of this study is that, first, it was almost

4. In early Ch'ing, for example, the counting of persons was largely confined to males between the ages of 16 and 60 (*ting*). In all periods a greater effort was generally made to record adult males because only they served in labor corvees and like projects organized by the government.

5. For example, one Kiangsi official made a special point of saying everyone in his district, both men and women, should be registered. As a result, the population total in that district rose 23 per cent (*Sung hui yao chi kao*, vol. 7, pp. 6367 and 6370).

TABLE A.2. COMPARABILITY OF SUNG AND
CONTEMPORARY REGIONS

Province (As of 1957)		*Roughly Comparable Sung Area* (lu)
Fukien (SE)	(1)	Fu-chien
Kwangtung (SE)	(2)	Kuang-nan-tung
Kwangsi (SE)	(3)	Kuang-nan-hsi
Chekiang (E)	(4)	Liang-che
Kiangsu-Anhwei (E)	(5)	Huai-nan-tung
		Huai-nan-hsi
		Chiang-nan-tung
Kiangsi (C)	(6)	Chiang-nan-hsi
Hunan (C)	(7)	Ching-hu-nan
Hupei (C)	(8)	Ching-hu-pei
Szechwan (SW)	(9)	Ch'eng-tu
		T'ung-ch'uan
		Li-chou
		Tzu-chou
		K'uei-chou
Shansi (N)	(10)	Ho-tung
Shantung (N)	(11)	Ching-tung
Honan (N)	(12)	Tung-ching-k'ai-feng-fu
		Ching-hsi
Shensi-Kansu (NW)	(13)	Shen-fu-hsi
Hopei (N)	(14)	Ho-pei

SOURCE: To determine the boundaries of Sung districts, I used Herrmann, 1966, pp. 42–43.

unbelievably destructive and, second, it was selective, devastating certain provinces while leaving others relatively untouched.

The issue with which we are concerned is: are the population estimates for these two centuries consistent with the pattern of the Mongol invasion? The Mongols first attacked the Chin empire, which had in turn pushed the Sung out of North China. One of the principal purposes of the first Mongol campaigns was to destroy the economic and military base of the Chin. This was done by laying waste the entire area north of the Yellow River and then doing the same to Shensi (NW) and finally the China area south of the Yellow River in Honan (N) (see Map A.1). In many instances, populations of entire cities were put to the sword. Others were made to form the initial assault waves on resisting cities. Those who escaped the sword found little to eat and a government too weak to help in any way. In addition, epidemic disease was prevalent under such conditions. For example, an epidemic in 1232 in the Chin capital of K'aifeng apparently took hundreds of thousands of lives (Hartwell, 1967). It was not until toward the end of the war against Chin that the Mongols were converted to the belief that a living population was a source of wealth and not simply a hindrance to the grazing of one's horses. Probably the only reason anyone at all survived north of the Yellow River was that the Mongol armies were too small and the local Chinese population too large. Changing Mongol policy, in con-

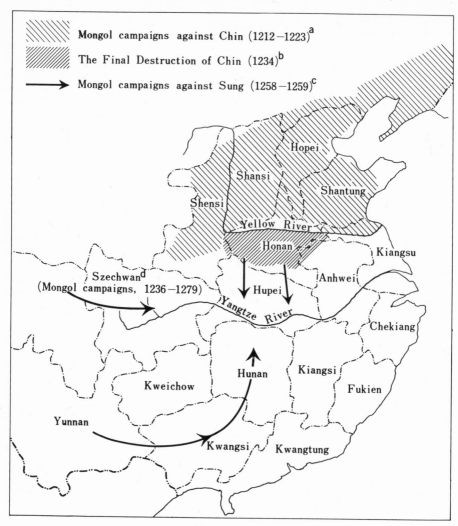

Map A. 1
Areas of Greatest Mongol Devastation

[a] Martin, 1950, pp. 155–218, 239–82.
[b] M. Prawdin, 1940, pp. 244–45.
[c] *Ibid.*, pp. 313 and 316.
[d] See discussion of Szechwan in the text.

trast, probably accounts for the comparatively high rate of survival of the population between the Yellow and Yangtze Rivers.

By the time of the attack on Sung, the policy of good treatment for those who did not resist was fairly well established. For this reason, and also because horses were not very effective in rice paddies, the later stages of the conquest of Sung involved as many intrigues as battles. Before intrigue could replace military action, however, the Mongols had first to demonstrate the inevitability of their victory over the Sung armies. This they did in a three-pronged attack, Khubilai at the head of an army moving south through Hupei (C), Mangu in Szechwan (SW), and Uriangkatai invading from the south through Kwangsi (SE) and Hunan (C). Yunnan (SW), populated largely by non-Chinese, had been laid waste some years before. Uriangkatai's armies, at least, continued the older Mongol military tradition of spreading terror by means of murder and pillage (Prawdin, 1940, p. 316).

The situation in Szechwan (SW) and Hupei (C) is less clear. Fighting between the Mongols and the Sung proceeded in Szechwan for over forty years, far longer than any other province. That fact alone must have caused an exodus from the province, however much destruction was actually perpetrated by the Mongols. There were also serious epidemics among the Mongol troops and presumably the Chinese population as well.[6] According to one source, Mangu himself was a "humanitarian," in one instance beheading a soldier for taking an onion from a peasant and in another decreeing death for members of a hunting party who had trampled a wheat field (D'Ohsson, 1834, vol. II, p. 333). Even under the best of circumstances, however, major warfare, particularly as then practiced, was highly destructive and it is likely that the invasions of Hupei (C) and Szechwan (SW) took a heavy toll.

So much for the historical events. Are they reflected in the population data? Certainly the destruction of North China is. The Yuan population in the five major provinces of the north and northwest was only one-quarter the size of the population in that area a century before (see Table A.1). By way of comparison the population in the five provinces affected by the Taiping Rebellion in the mid-nineteenth century fell to under 60 per cent of the pre-rebellion total. Uriangkatai's march through Kwangsi (SE) also led to a significant drop in population, although not so dramatic a decline as in the north, but then the campaign in Kwangsi was not as prolonged as those in the north.

The drop in population in Szechwan (SW) may be overstated. Marco Polo's descriptions of the area when he traveled through twenty years later do not jibe with a population of only 100,000 families in a province as huge as Szechwan. Nor are his descriptions of the amount of destruction consistent with what would have had to have occurred to have reduced the population by so much. The principal areas destroyed, as described by Marco Polo, were all to the west of the city of Chengtu, that is, not in an area where Szechwan's people have generally concentrated.

The population of provinces not invested by the Mongols (Anhwei through Kwangtung in Table A.1) show little change over the two centuries. The Sung figure for Anhwei (E) and Kiangsu (E) in 1173 is the principal exception and that probably only reflects the loss of much of these areas to Chin. The Yuan total for Anhwai and Kiangsu is roughly the same as the Sung figure for 1070.

6. I am indebted to Professor Robert Hartwell for pointing out the possibility that epidemics may have played a particularly important role in depopulating Szechwan.

The one major inconsistency between the recorded data and Mongol destruction is the lack of decline in the figures for Hunan (C) and Hupei (C). These areas must have suffered heavy destruction and yet their populations increased. Furthermore, the Ming data do indicate a sharp drop and yet these provinces were not the major areas of combat during the fall of Yuan and the rise of Ming. My own guess (for which I have no direct evidence) is that many of the Yuan figures for south China and particularly those for Hunan (C) and Hupei (C) were arrived at during the years immediately following the fall of Sung by simply copying the Sung records. Population data for the early fourteenth century may reflect a genuinely independent attempt to count the population of these south China provinces, but I have not been able to discover figures for those years. Thus the Ming data for Hunan (C) and Hupei (C) probably better reflect Mongol destruction than do the Yuan data.

Events at the fall of the Yuan were of far less demographic significance. The greatest area of destruction was in Hopei (N), where virtually all Mongols who could be found were killed. The fall in population in this province would probably appear even more dramatic than in Table A.1 if we had a later Yuan figure. The other areas of major fighting were in Honan (N), Anhwei (E), and perhaps Kiangsu (E), but in none of these areas were events comparable to those in Hopei.[7] The rise in population in north China outside of Hopei probably occurred as a result of both immigration and natural increase. The decline from Yuan to Ming in many southern provinces may reflect either emigration, generally poor conditions under Mongol rule, or simply the fact that the Yuan data were copied from Sung records.

The purpose of this lengthy discussion has been to demonstrate that the Ming population figures are generally consistent with Sung and Yuan data and known history. This fact together with what Ping-ti Ho has shown regarding the serious manner in which Ming T'ai-tsu set out to estimate the population of his empire suggest strongly that the 1393 figure reflects the "true" total population of China.

How large could the error plausibly be? It is difficult to see how the actual north China population could have been more than say a million families higher than the 1393 total, given the nature of the Mongol invasion and what we know about migration in the Ming and Ch'ing (see below). There may also have been significant under-reporting in Szechwan (SW), Kwangtung (SE), and Kwangsi (SE), but it is difficult to raise the total for these provinces by more than a million families or so. The greatest efforts to attain an accurate count were made in the remaining provinces. If the margin of error in these provinces was 20 per cent, then one could add another million and a half families. I consider these fairly extreme but not implausible assumptions, and yet they only succeed in raising the total population to 14–15 million families, or a total still under 80 million people. Errors due to over-reporting (or over-estimation) are also possible, but not as likely and, in any case, would only reinforce the conclusions drawn regarding agricultural productivity.

7. The principal sources of this information are Ch'en Hou (Ed.), *Ming chi*, vols. 1–3, and Fang Chueh-hui (Ed.) *Ming t'ai-tsu ko-ming wu-kung chi* (1940 preface), vols. 1–7 and 11.

The most likely population total for the late fourteenth century, therefore, is between 65 and 80 million persons. One cannot completely rule out a figure as high as 100 million, but the probability attached to such a figure must be low. Anyone who argues the total is any higher must also be prepared to state that the census total had no relation to reality whatsoever, in which case it is rather difficult to see why Ming T'ai-tsu went to all that trouble.

THE 1953 CENSUS

For the purposes of this study it is important to have a population figure for an early period (e.g., the fourteenth century) and a late period. The 1953 census is clearly the best figure available for this later period. There has, to be sure, been considerable discussion of the 1953 census and some skepticism expressed as to whether it constituted a "true modern census." It should be reiterated that what concerns us here is the total figure of 583 million. Sex ratios, birth and death rates and the like are much more difficult to estimate, but they concern us less than the total.

Fortunately, John Aird's careful study (1968) should put to rest most of the concern as to whether the Communists really made a major effort to count China's population. Aird also argues that the 1953 census probably understates the true population by from 5 to 15 per cent. Since a principal objective of my study is to verify and explain a rise in population that was significantly greater than the increase in cultivated acreage, a downward bias in the 1953 data presents no real problem. If population was in fact over 650 million rather than 583 million, then the rise in the man–land ratio was just that much greater.

My own inclination is to doubt that the margin of error could be as high as 15 per cent. Such an error would imply that the census takers missed two persons in every three families investigated, or perhaps failed to register as many as 1 in 7 families. If the remarks at the beginning of this appendix regarding the nature of the problem of counting China's population are roughly accurate, it is difficult to see how such an enormous number of mistakes could be made. For this reason, and because it is the conservative thing to do from the point of view of this study, I have decided to use the official census figure for 1953 without adjustment.

Since 1953 through 1959 there are a number of good reasons for believing that population was growing by at least the officially estimated rate of 2 per cent per year or more. Ma Yin-ch'u, a generally objective observer, argued in 1957 (p. 34) that the rate was probably even higher than this. Even highly critical visitors to and analysts of China admit that Communist public health measures have been both far-reaching and effective, and a similar case can be made for the food distribution system. Nor is there any reason to believe that political purges or resistance to the cooperatives and communes had any significant effect on the rate of population growth. Only for the bad harvests of 1959 through 1961 can one plausibly argue that economic (or political) conditions might have lowered the birth rate and raised the death rate enough to have some impact on the rate of population growth.

Further, Peking's great concern with the agricultural situation would make little sense, given the government's other goals, if population were rising slowly or not at all. Finally, these considerations remain valid whatever assumptions one makes regarding the thoroughness and accuracy of population registration since 1953.

CH'ING POPULATION STATISTICS (1644–1911)

The principal issue regarding Ch'ing population data is whether the *pao-chia* registration figures for 1776 to 1850 are reasonably reliable. There is no way yet discovered for reliably estimating population under the Ch'ing in the late seventeenth century, although I shall make a few remarks on this subject below. It is also clear that the provincial *pao-chia* data for the years 1851 through 1898 involved little more than changing the date on early nineteenth-century figures.[8]

The two sides of the argument over the quality of the 1776 to 1850 data are represented, on the one hand, by Ping-ti Ho (1959, pp. 46–47), who states they are quite reliable, and, on the other, by Irene Taeuber and Nai-chi Wang (1960, pp. 411–14, 416) who state they are not. Taeuber and Wang base their conclusion on the fact that artificial regularities and implausible irregularities exist in the data. Both sides of the argument have contributed to our understanding of the Ch'ing data, but as John Aird points out (1968), the Taeuber and Wang arguments suffer from "(1) failure to establish clearly the criteria for determining that artificial regularities are present; (2) ambiguity or inaccuracy in describing the regularities found; and (3) over-generalization." Aird himself does not reach any firm conclusions regarding the margin of error or general plausibility of the 1776–1850 data. His experiments with alternative population models for this and later periods are interesting indications of the general plausibility of the Ch'ing figures, but the models are preliminary ones and not sufficiently based in historical fact to be used here.

As indicated at the beginning of this appendix, a key question is whether the authorities made a serious effort to compile accurate registration data. Ping-ti Ho recognizes certain shortcomings in the efforts made to record the population, but the gist of his argument is that the Ch'ing government at the peak of its power in the late eighteenth and early nineteenth century had both the will and the way to obtain roughly reliable figures. Two Western observers who spent long periods in China in the 1840's and whose observations on other matters were generally careful and astute, both felt that the *pao-chia* system was an effective method of estimating China's population (Huc, 1855, p. 98; R. M. Martin, 1847, vol. 1, p. 28).

Estimating population from *pao-chia* data involved three basic steps. First, each family had to have a placard prominently displayed in its doorway listing all members of the family. Second, the *hsien* magistrates had to compile this

8. These data appear in, among other places, *CKNY*, vol. I, pp. 10–17. A five-minute glance at these figures is sufficient to establish that these statistics could not reasonably reflect population trends during these decades.

information in order to obtain a total for the area. Finally, these *hsien* totals would be sent up to higher levels where they would be added together to form the provincial and national estimates.

There is little reason to doubt that the first and third steps were reasonably systematically carried out. Foreign observers as well as local records testify to the fact that the door placards were maintained. There was some under-registration at this level, but the penalties for such behavior were severe and one doubts that such under-registration was a major source of bias. The third step involved little more than simple addition. The principal problem at this level was that Chinese documents often do not bother to note when a missing *hsien* or province was not included in the totals. Such omissions, however, are usually fairly obvious and for the 1776–1850 period, at least, are not a major source of bias.

The principal cause of bias in the totals comes from the failure of *hsien* magistrates to record the data in their area properly. In large part this failure, when it occurred, seems to have been the result of an inadequate and over-burdened magistracy staff. Unfortunately, there is not enough evidence to determine clearly for large areas when the *hsien* magistrates were conscientious and when they were not. There are a good number of documents showing that the emperor and various provincial governors ordered their subordinates to carry out the registration. There is some detailed evidence on the care with which certain magistrates carried out their duties. Such evidence can be found for individual magistrates in Hopei (N) (1764–1769), Hunan (C) (1787–1790), Shensi (NW) (1807–1817), Fukien (SE) (1813–1819), Szechwan (SW) (1825–1828), Kwangsi (SE) (1826–1828), and Kiangsu (E) (1832–1834).[9] These magistrates often drew up quite elaborate forms, although little or no effort was made to ensure consistency of forms among regions. In several of the above cases, there was also considerable effort made to cross-check the results to insure accuracy.

But there is also evidence at the magistrate level of slip-shod or nonexistent registration efforts. A magistrate in Chekiang (E) (1814–1816) states that the *pao-chia* system had been considered to be "little more than a formality." Similar references can be found for *hsien* in Kiangsu (E) (early nineteenth century), Kwangsi (SE) (1826–1828), and Kwangtung (SE) (1813–1819).[10]

Although it is difficult to judge which of these two extremes in performance best represents nationwide behavior, one thing is clear: *pao-chia* registration was carried out sporadically even by conscientious officials. There must have been few if any districts where *hsien* records were kept up to date on a year-to-year basis. Thus, provincial population figures—to the extent they reflect anything at all—represent the population of the various *hsien* in the province as recorded sometime during the previous decade and perhaps even further back. An increase in the rate of population growth in a province in a particular year might

9. These materials were compiled and published in, Hsü Tung, *Pao-chia shu* (1848) vol. 2A, pp. 1–50; vol. 2B, pp. 1–7a, 21a–21b, 26b–28a, 41–46; and vol. 3, pp. 156–66, 24–26a; and Ho Chang-ling, *Huang chao ching shih wen pien* (essays on statecraft in the Ch'ing dynasty, reprinted in 1963), pp. 1903 and 1909.

10. Hsü Tung, *op. cit.*, vol. 2A, 17a; vol. 2B, pp. 24a and 41a; and Ho Chang-ling, 1963, p. 1932.

simply be the result of more widespread registration efforts in that year (or decade). If such reasoning leads one to avoid drawing demographic conclusions from year-to-year fluctuations, it also provides an explanation for unusually large jumps in the totals in particular years, jumps that disturb Taeuber and Wang, among others.

Whether or not the 1776–1850 population figures are usable turns in part on whether *hsien* magistrates who had not had time to take a census simply copied the results of a previous census or made up figures of their own. If they did make up figures on their own, they were more careful in doing so than, say, those who estimated *hsien* population in the 1914–1918 estimates. Where *hsien* data for the 1776–1850 period are available, as they are for Kiangsi (C) and Shensi (NW) and several other provinces, there are no implausibly low figures (the smallest *hsien* generally have more than 7,000 or 8,000 families) as there are in the 1914–1918 data (where many *hsien* report only a few hundred families). Detailed data for Kiangsi (C) are presented in Table A.3 because they were the most complete figures that I was able to find for a single province. To save space, only the first thirty *hsien* are listed.

It is clear from the table that the 1869 figures were obtained by copying some earlier year, probably 1851. Among the 1782–1851 figures, in contrast, there is only one example of copying an earlier figure. Nor is there any support for the thesis that magistrates mechanically added a certain number of people per year, presumably either to please the emperor or to get a larger share of famine relief. The rates of population growth within *hsien* and between *hsien* vary considerably. Some *hsien* grew by only a few per cent, others by 100 per cent and more. For 1916, the data for several *hsien* appear to be well outside a plausible range, but there are no comparable cases for 1782 to 1821 and the two examples for 1851 appear to be recording errors.

The decline in population in many *hsien* from 1851 to 1935 is not difficult to explain. The Taiping Rebellion laid waste much of this area. Many of these *hsien* also lie along the old trade route to Canton (SE), a route which after 1851 was largely replaced by coastal shipping and the rise of Shanghai (E). More will be said about population after 1851 in Kiangsi (C) and elsewhere below. The principal point to be made here is that Kiangsi (C) provincial figures were obtained by adding up the individual *hsien* data and that these *hsien* data prior to 1869 are demographically plausible.

Hsien data are also available for Shensi province (NW), but for only one year (1823) are they complete.[11] For Shensi, as well, it is clear that the provincial total was obtained by adding up the *hsien* figures, not by arbitrarily adding an increment to the provincial total. The lack of significant change in the provincial total from 1819 through 1860 is suspicious and suggests that no new province-wide survey of population was taken after the 1810's. The lack of a new survey may also explain why most of the 1823 data were rounded to the nearest 1,000, something that it is not characteristic of data for other periods.

---

11. *Hsü hsiu Shensi t'ung chih kao* (1934) 31. 2b–19b.

TABLE A.3. KIANGSI POPULATION DATA
(Number of Families)

Hsien Name	1782		1812		1821		1851		1869	1916	1935
Nan-ch'ang	129,939		191,350		221,065		283,092	*	283,130	228,724	119,125
Hsien-chien	82,088		105,812		120,789		114,017	*	114,058	153,758	40,782
Feng-ch'eng	109,643	*	109,643		159,643		111,373	*	111,373	**225,187**	77,439
Chin-hsien	59,908		60,599		60,921		60,937	*	60,941	52,839	37,150
Feng-hsin	29,331		39,718		40,528		42,605	*	42,432	44,652	38,405
Ching-an	16,690		18,583		21,544		25,576	*	25,597	26,947	20,854
Wu-ning	33,538		34,544		36,668		38,035	*	38,050	32,796	27,987
I-ning-chou	46,727		48,976		50,683		51,075	*	43,727	—	—
Kao-an	96,050		97,674		99,118		104,677	*	104,352	87,639	69,307
Shang-kao	19,592		48,574		26,168		26,750	*	26,779	**128,497**	31,249
Hsin-chang	47,374		57,977		63,668		64,949	*	65,015	53,461	30,769
I-ch'un	46,144		52,776		55,772		64,974	*	64,966	71,700	68,483
Fen-i	24,192		26,313		28,922		32,879	*	32,920	39,228	21,225
Ping-hsiang	37,472		45,229		47,723		46,847	*	46,889	86,920	93,199
Wan-ts'ai	24,154		28,579		31,357		33,860	*	33,938	**77,686**	33,005
Ch'ing-chiang	66,108		67,923		74,772		69,866	*	69,805	51,504	35,204
Hsin-kan	56,015		57,589		58,778		60,667	*	60,695	49,706	21,319
Hsin-yu	63,696		65,337		65,792		64,718	*	64,772	31,893	38,721
Hsia-chiang	32,623		52,929		53,501		63,575	*	63,572	30,720	9,072
Chi-an	131,205		135,299		143,783		151,668	*	150,014	**324,270**	58,209
T'ai-ho	91,472		92,264		104,201		135,832	*	135,834	75,371	42,591
Chi-shui	51,743		51,945		52,286		55,538	*	55,558	54,601	31,409
Yung-feng	44,999		45,932		47,830		**82,443**	*	48,020	**94,109**	30,243
An-fu	87,012		88,713		89,110		**63,661**	*	82,452	59,823	22,264
Lung-ch'uan	44,950		46,793		47,414		63,661	*	63,531	49,817	32,478
Wan-an	62,274		63,138		64,707		103,250	*	103,250	44,045	21,156
Yung-hsin	40,438		41,479		42,665		42,870	*	42,886	65,357	32,146
Yung-ning	10,039		10,300		10,590		11,122	*	11,124	21,079	7,310
Lin-ch'uan	101,994		103,114		105,110		108,474		108,281	151,628	96,859
Lien-hua	19,589	*	19,669	*	19,703	*	19,648	*	19,654	25,567	29,385

* Indicates where the change from one period to the next was less than 100 families.
Bold face figures indicate totals which appear inconsistent with other data in the table.
SOURCE: Kiangsi Government Statistical Office, *Kiangsi nien-chien* pp. 74–97.

For *hsien* in Shensi (NW) for which population figures are recorded for the late eighteenth century, as well as 1823, it is reasonably clear that there was no policy of arbitrarily adding a small increment to the total for the *hsien* each year. Of the 21 *hsien* reporting late eighteenth-century data, the population had fallen by 1823 in four *hsien*, had not changed in one, rose by from 5 to 45 per cent in eleven, and rose by over 50 per cent in five. Some of the larger increases probably indicate greater vigor on the part of those carrying out the registration rather than a real rise in population. It is improbable, however, that changes of this nature reflect competition among *hsien* magistrates for relief supplies or attempts

to please the emperor, two explanations for deliberate falsification that are sometimes put forward. One could undoubtedly extend this analysis to other provinces, although for most the data in the provincial gazetteers are less complete
than for Shensi.

So far the discussion has concentrated on the question of whether the provincial population figures were in fact obtained by adding up data from individual *hsien*, and whether the *hsien* magistrates seem to have made a serious effort
to count the true population. There remains the question of the consistency of
the provincial totals with what we know of Chinese history in the period. The
analysis of this issue is broken down into two parts. First, we attempt to check
the 1776–1850 data with what we know of internal migrations and wars in the
period prior to 1850 (including the Ming). Second, developments from 1850
through 1953 are looked at in some detail.

To anticipate the conclusion of the first part of the analysis, it is my judgment
that the early nineteenth-century totals do reflect in a rough way the true total
population by province in that period. The major exceptions to this conclusion
are Kwangtung province (SE) and perhaps Szechwan (SW). However, for provinces into which large numbers of migrants flowed, the timing of these migrations
is rather poorly reflected in the population data, even in the 1776–1850 period.

As Ping-ti Ho points out (1959, p. 52), the population data for a number of
Kwangtung *hsien* contain many irregularities. In addition, the provincial totals
from 1771 through 1851 start from an improbably low base and rise at much too
rapid a rate. Migration into Kwangtung had been going on for several centuries
prior to 1771 and, if anything, slackened off after that date. The extraordinary
increase from 1771 to 1776 and the doubling of population from 1776 to 1851
probably reflect little more than rather arbitrary guesses by officials. It will be
argued below, however, that the 1851 figure itself is probably too high and,
hence, under-registration would not be the explanation. Kwangtung, of course,
was a province over which the central government maintained rather ineffective
control until after 1949.

According to Ping-ti Ho (1959, pp. 149–53), the major migrations within
China between 1644 and 1850 were into Szechwan (SW) and the Han river
drainage area [parts of Shensi (NW), Kansu (NW), Honan (N), and Hupei
(C)]. In addition, Hunan (C) and the other sections of Hupei were also recipients
of a net inflow of people. But these areas were also recipients of large net inflows
during the Ming.[12] Even if migration to these areas in the Ming was not large,
certainly large-scale migration began well before 1776. The population figures
(see Table A.4), however, indicate that much of the migration to these regions
took place after 1776. This is particularly true of Szechwan (SW) and also of
Hupei (C) and Shensi (NW). The most reasonable explanation would appear to
be that newcomers were often not properly recorded until they had been in an

12. Evidence of migration into these areas during the Ming can be found in a number of
fifteenth-century memorials appearing in Ch'en Tzu-lung, Hsü Fu-yuan, Sung Hui-pi (Eds.),
Huang ming ch'ing shih wen pien (reprinted by the Kuo-lien Book Company, Taipei, 1964) vol. 1,
pp. 4/540, 4/625, 4/633, 25/355–57, 5/429–30, 6/60–61, 7/143, 7/145–48, 5/382.

area for some time, perhaps as much as several decades. For Szechwan, there is the additional problem that the 1851 total is implausibly high (see discussion in next section), an indication that there is more wrong with the Szechwan figures than simply the failure to record new migrants.

TABLE A.4. UNADJUSTED POPULATION CENSUS DATA (1393–1851)
(1,000's of People)

Province	1393	1749	1771	1776	1819	1851
NE						
Kirin	—	—	—	75	330	327
Liaoning	—	407	751	764	1,674	2,582
N						
Hopei	1,927	13,933	16,770	20,567	[22,000]	23,455
Shantung	5,256	24,012	26,000	21,497	29,355	33,266
Shansi	4,072	9,509	10,626	12,503	14,325	15,693
Honan	1,913	12,848	16,679	19,858	23,561	23,928
NW						
Shensi }	2,317	6,734	7,425	8,193	11,963	12,010
Kansu }		5,710	13,216	15,068	15,320	15,440
E						
Anhwei }	10,756	21,568	23,684	27,567	34,925	37,631
Kiangsu }		20,972	24,278	28,808	39,274	44,303
Chekiang	10,488	11,877	17,092	19,365	27,313	30,107
C						
Hupei }	4,703	7,527	8,532	14,815	28,807	33,810
Hunan }		8,672	9,082	14,990	18,892	20,648
Kiangsi	8,982	8,428	11,745	16,849	23,575	24,516
SE						
Fukien	3,917	7,620	8,170	11,220	15,942	20,099
Kwangtung	3,008	6,461	7,068	14,821	21,392	28,389
Kwangsi	1,483	3,688	4,794	5,382	7,411	7,823
SW						
Kweichow	—	3,075	3,458	5,003	5,347	5,436
Yunnan	259	1,946	2,268	3,103	6,009	7,403
Szechwan	1,467	2,507	3,068	7,790	25,665	44,752
Total	60,548	177,494	214,606	268,238	373,080	431,618

Other problems with the Ch'ing statistics include some of the arithmetic regularities in the data pointed out by Taeuber and Wang. The addition of constant increments for several years in a row for Yunnan (SW) and Kweichow (SW) may indicate that the figures for these backward provinces were only estimates, not derived from actual registration data. The jump in the Kansu (NW) total from 1749 to 1771 is also difficult to explain, at least without further research.

With these principal qualifications, the population data for 1776 through 1840 or 1850 do appear to be consistent with what we know of the history of the period. Most important, this period and the decades immediately preceding it were free of major rebellions. There were, of course, a number of minor revolts, but they generally did not involve large numbers of people and they were most commonly in out-of-the-way mountainous regions, not in large population centers.

This period may also have been somewhat freer of major floods and drought. From 1743 through 1783, according to one source, no great natural calamities are recorded (Rockhill, 1922, p. 488). Whether or not one goes along with this statement depends in part on what one means by "great." Droughts and floods did occur in several provinces in this period, as numerous gazetteers indicate, but these disasters may not have been on the scale of those in the nineteenth century. A definitive answer to this question, however, requires a major research effort which I shall not attempt here.

Another factor that must have had an impact on population growth, if one accepts the rough reliability of the population figures, is the extreme over-crowding that seems to have existed in at least Kiangsu (E), Anhwei (E), Cheki-ang (E), Kiangsi (C), and Fukien (SE). According to the figures, the population of these areas in the late eighteenth or early nineteenth centuries had reached and surpassed the 1953 census estimates.

Such population pressure, combined with poor weather, would lead one to expect a slowing of the rate of population increase, and, with the exception of several provinces, the decline after 1819 is marked. If one excludes Szechwan (SW) and Kwangtung (SE) for reasons already discussed, the increase in each of the remaining eighteen provinces between 1819 and 1851 is under 10 to 13 per cent, or less than 0.2 to 0.3 per cent per year [except Hupei (C), Fukien (SE), Yunnan (SW), and Liaoning (NE)]. If the lack of much change in the totals for Shensi (NW), Kansu (NW), and Honan (N) reflects not so much stag-nation as a failure to keep the records up to date, then these figures would have to be adjusted, but in which direction it is impossible to tell without further research.

None of the historical events discussed so far have been sufficiently dramatic to permit one to say with great confidence that the data do or do not accurately reflect their impact. The real case for the belief that the early nineteenth-century provincial totals are usable for the purposes of this study rests on their con-sistency with twentieth-century data and events that occurred between 1851 and 1953.

Before turning to the period after 1851, however, it is desirable to speculate on population in the seventeenth and early eighteenth centuries. If one accepts a total of 400 million for the early nineteenth century, and further accepts the evi-dence of prosperity during the latter half of the eighteenth century, it is reason-able to assume that population was about 200 to 250 million around 1750. If one approaches the question from the other direction, by accepting the 1393 figure together with evidence that population was rising throughout much of the fifteenth century,[13] it is possible that China's population may have reached 150 million by A.D. 1500. Without further research, it is not easy to characterize conditions in the sixteenth century. That century certainly had its share of "great droughts," nearly twice as many as the previous century according to Alexander Hosie.[14] The data compiled by Yao Shan-yu on floods and droughts, however, are not quite so conclusive (Yao Shan-yu, 1943).

The sixteenth-century situation thus requires more work, but it is quite clear that in the seventeenth century times were extremely hard. The destruction wrought by Chang Hsien-chung and the Manchus in conjunction with the fall of the Ming dynasty, may not have matched the Mongols in effect, but it certainly must have caused some population decline in the middle of the seventeenth century. Depending on what assumptions one makes about population growth from 1650 to 1750, one can get a figure for the 1650's ranging from 100 to 200 million. An estimate for 1600 would have to be 20 to 50 million higher than in 1650. If one believes, as I do that population grew between 1650 and 1750, then a range of from 100 to 150 million for 1650 would appear to cover the most probable situation.

POPULATION DATA (1851–1953)

Anyone inspecting the 1851 and 1953 censuses can hardly fail to notice the broad consistency between these two sets of independently arrived at data. This statement applies not only to the totals, but to the individual province figures as well. There are, of course, differences between the two periods, but these differences form clear patterns. There is rapid growth in the more recently settled areas of Manchuria (NE), Kwangsi (SE), Kweichow (SW), and Yunnan (SW). The five provinces affected by the Taiping Rebellion record declines in population (except for Kiangsu) ranging from 18 to 35 per cent. In the northwest, including Shansi (N), population totals change little, while in the other northern provinces (Hopei, Shantung, and Honan) growth was fairly rapid. The patterns, therefore, are clear. What remains is to see whether they reflect what we know of the history of the period.

In attempting to analyze this period, one is aided by the existence of a survey undertaken by the Agricultural Economics Department of Nanking University together with the National Agricultural Research Bureau.[15] This survey, based on 1,622 reports from various provincial reporters of the agricultural situation, estimated the percentage increase in population in each of the 22 provinces (excluding Manchuria) from 1873 to 1933 (including estimates for 1893 and 1913). Unfortunately I have been able to discover little else about this survey. There is little question that the survey was not based on the late 19th-century official Ch'ing government data, because the survey and the official data are not at all consistent with each other. But little is known of how the survey per-

---

13. See memorials referred to in footnote 12 and Ping-ti Ho, 1959, p. 23.
14. Hosie's data appear in Rockhill, 1922, p. 476.
15. These figures appear in a variety of places including *CKNY* vol. III, pp. 907–908.

centages were obtained. If one can use the survey at all, it is because of the good reputations of those organizations who undertook it and because, as will be demonstrated below, it appears consistent with known historical fact.

The data for the 1851–1953 period are presented in Table A.5. Absolute figures for the 1873 to 1933 period were obtained by applying the survey percentages to census figures of 1933 as corrected by T. C. Liu and K. C. Yeh (1965, p. 178). Liu and Yeh in their reconstruction of the 1933 data have attempted to make minor adjustments in the official totals in order to account for known biases, such as those in the sex ratio. Without going back into the original census records, I see no way of improving on the Liu-Yeh estimates. What remains, therefore, is to look at the events occurring in the various provinces and check them against the 1851–1953 data, making adjustments in the data where it seems appropriate.

The Taiping Provinces

The population of the five provinces (Kiangsu, Anhwei, Chekiang, Kiangsi, and Hupei) affected in a major way by the Taiping Rebellion (1850–1864), except Kiangsu (E), declined from 1851 to 1953. Actually, if the data in Table A.5 are reliable, the decline took place between 1851 and 1873, with slow recovery since except in Kiangsi (C). The real question, therefore, is whether a decline of 75 million persons in these five provinces is believable.

Some of the decrease probably represents emigration to nearby provinces such as Honan (N) and Hunan (C), hence the rise in population in these two provinces.[16] After taking emigration into account, however, one is still left with a decline of some 60 million which requires explanation. Part of this 60 million may be accounted for by minor downward biases in the 1933 and, hence, the 1873 figures for Kiangsu (E) and Anhwei (E). The difference between the 1933 and 1953 estimates for these two provinces is rather large. There may also be minor upward biases in the 1851 figures for all five provinces. But unless one rejects the 1851 or 1873 (1933) estimates outright, these biases could not have accounted for more than 10 or 20 million of the 60 million decline.

Is the remaining 40-plus million decline plausible? The answer would appear to be yes. Conservative estimates of the number who died as a direct result of the Taiping Rebellion put the total at 20 million.[17] These estimates, however, do not include a decline in population resulting from lowered birth rates and increased death rates only indirectly related to the rebellion (such as older people dying a little sooner). The birth rate in these provinces if expressed in terms of infants that lived (or were allowed to live) to the age of one year must have been extremely low. Birth rates usually decline under such circumstances, and in

16. If one assumes that there was some decline in the existing populations of Honan and Hunan from elements not directly connected with the Taipings, immigration into these two provinces may have been 15–17 million. It is also probable that some of the other southern and western provinces absorbed Taiping refugees as well.

17. This is the estimate of several Westerners and the one accepted by Rockhill, 1922, p. 673.

China one must also take into account the effects of infanticide during periods of hardship. Even with no change in the death rate, a decline in the birth rate from 40 to 20 per thousand, with a death rate of 30 per thousand, would lower population in these five provinces by from 20 to 30 million.

The Taiping Rebellion, furthermore, was not the only disaster that hit these provinces at this time, at least not in Anhwei (E) and Kiangsu (E). After almost eight centuries of flowing to the sea through the lower course of the Huai River, the Yellow River changed course and in the process deposited so much silt that the Huai had to filter through creeks and down the Grand Canal to reach the sea. As a result, the lower basin of the Huai became a difficult-to-drain area of marsh and swamp (Lindsay, 1958, vol. II, p. 44). Ultimately, however, silt fertilizes an area and this may help account for the comparatively rapid recovery of population in these two provinces [Chekiang (E) and Kiangsi (C) hardly recovered at all], although the rise of Shanghai was also an important source of increased population in Kiangsu. Shanghai rose from a city of only a few hundred thousand in the latter half of the nineteenth century to over six million in 1953.

The continued very low population figures for Kiangsi in 1933 may relate to the Kuomintang campaign to exterminate the Communists and their sympathizers in the early 1930's. It can also be argued that Kiangsi was seriously overpopulated in 1851, with less than 2 *mou* per capita as compared to 2.6 *mou* today. The other Taiping provinces were in an even worse condition of overpopulation, however, so that perhaps the main explanation is that Kiangsi's population didn't fall as far and hence didn't have as far to recover.[18]

Kansu-Shensi-Shansi (*NW and N*)

The decline in population in the three northwestern and northern provinces of Kansu, Shensi, and Shansi between 1851 and 1873 is readily explained. This was the scene of the Moslem rebellions of the 1860's and 1870's so ruthlessly put down by Tso Tsung-t'ang. It was also an area seriously hit by the century's worst drought in 1877–1878. Although the extent of the famine and slaughter was greatest in Kansu, it is improbable that it was as great as the figures in the table indicate. The discrepancy may arise either from the fact that the Liu-Yeh estimate for Kansu in 1933 is too low, or that for 1851 too high. Ch'ing population statistics for Kansu show virtually no change from 1786 to 1851 (15 million-plus in both cases). It is possible, therefore, that this figure does not really result from a census at all, but is some official's guess. I have not altered the 1851 Kansu figure, however, on the grounds that its probable upward bias is offset by a downward bias resulting from the lack of population data for other northwestern areas such as Sinkiang, Tsinghai, and Inner Mongolia.

The decline in Shensi's and Kansu's populations from 1913 to 1933 is also easily explained. These were areas of considerable warlord activity of a parti-

18. This does not completely jibe with qualitative evidence presented by Ping-ti Ho, 1959, pp. 245–46, so that this conclusion must be considered only a very tentative one, if that.

TABLE A.5. UNADJUSTED POPULATION DATA (1819–1957) (IN MILLIONS)
(Excluding Taiwan)

Province	1819	1851	1873	1893	1913	1933	1953	1957
NE								
Manchuria	2.0	2.9	3.3	5.4	20.1	35.3	41.7	51.5
NW								
Sinkiang	—	—⎫	[3.8]	[3.8]	[3.8]	⎧ 2.7	4.9	5.6
Mongolia	—	—⎭				⎩ 1.1	6.1	9.2
Chahar	—	—	1.4	1.6	2.0	2.2	—	—
Suiyuan	—	—	1.5	2.1	2.6	2.7	—	—
Ningsia	—	—	1.1	1.6	1.1	1.0	—	1.8
Tsinghai	—	—	0.8	1.3	1.3	1.3	1.7	2.1
Kansu	15.4	15.4	5.6	6.4	7.2	6.5	12.9	12.8
Shensi	12.0	12.0	10.1	9.5	10.0	9.7	15.9	18.1
N								
Shansi	14.3	15.7	14.1	10.9	11.6	12.4	14.3	16.0
Hopei	22.0	23.5	24.3	27.2	29.6	30.6[a]	46.6[a]	48.7[a]
Shantung	29.4	33.3	31.5	37.5	38.4	40.3	48.9	54.0
Honan	23.6	23.9	34.9	36.3	38.4	36.3	44.2	48.7
E								
Kiangsu	39.3	44.3	26.3	28.4	33.7	34.9[b]	47.5[b]	52.1[b]
Anhwei	34.9	37.6	14.5	17.7	21.2	24.0	30.3	33.6
Chekiang	27.3	30.1	17.9	18.3	19.2	22.0	22.9	25.3
C								
Kiangsi	23.6	24.5	17.7	17.7	17.7	16.5	16.8	18.6
Hupei	28.8	33.8	18.8	19.7	21.8	27.3	27.8	30.8
Hunan	18.9	20.7	23.2	27.4	29.9	33.4	33.2	36.2
SE								
Kwangsi	7.4	7.8	10.1	11.0	15.0	16.6	19.6	19.4
Kwangtung	21.4	28.4	21.7	26.7	30.8	34.0	34.8	38.0
Fukien	15.9	20.1	14.9	13.7	13.9	13.1	13.1	14.7
SW								
Yunnan	6.0	7.4	6.7	9.0	12.0	15.9	17.5	19.1
Kweichow	5.3	5.4	9.8	10.4	—	12.6	15.0	16.9
Szechwan	25.7	44.8	33.3	41.7	47.7	59.2[c]	65.7[c]	72.2
Tibet	[1.4]	[1.4]	[1.4]	[1.4]	[1.4]	1.4	1.3	1.3
Special Municipalities	—	—	—	—	—	10.1	—	—
Totals	374.6	433.0	348.7	386.7	430.4	503.1	582.6	646.5

SOURCES: The 1851 data and the Manchurian statistics for 1873 and 1893 are from *CKNY*, vol. I, pp. 9–17. These are all official Ch'ing government figures. All other 1873, 1893, and 1913 data are derived from indexes calculated by Nanking University and the NARB (*CKNY*, vol. III, pp. 907–908). The 1933 data are those of Liu and Yeh. The 1953 figures are from the official Chinese Communist census of that year. The 1913 figure for Manchuria is actually the 1916 estimate of the South Manchurian Railway Company and appears in Hoshino, 1920, pp. 6–7.

[a] The 1933 figure does not include special municipalities, while the 1953 figure includes

Peking, Tientsin, and the Province of Jehol. The latter should be divided between Hopei, Liaoning, and Inner Mongolia, but I lacked the data necessary to make such a division.

ᵇ The 1953 and 1957 figures include Shanghai, but the 1933 figure does not include any special municipalities. If such municipalities had been included, the population in Kiangsu in 1933 would have been about 40 million.

ᶜ Includes the province of Sikang.

cularly brutal sort, in addition to which the two provinces were heavily hit by drought. Abandoned cultivable land in nineteen *hsien* of Shensi in 1931, for example, was 70 per cent of all formerly cultivated land. In five *hsien*, all land had been abandoned.[19] A more graphic account is given by Sigurd Eliassen:

... the villages we passed through were heaps of ruins and gave the impression of being abandoned. Men had lost faith in the soil. Now and then a few women would come tottering across the fields. ... Only one or two got to the roadside in time to stretch out a hand with cries that were engulfed by the dust and din of our passage but needed no interpreting (1957, p. 39).

One could easily produce additional examples, but these are sufficient to explain the population decline.

The North and Northeast

Manchuria (NE) was closed to legal immigration until the beginning of the twentieth century, but there was illegal migration, particularly at the end of the nineteenth century. The 1893 official Ch'ing figure, therefore, is probably an under-estimate, but not a serious one for our purposes. The basic trend in Manchuria is clear and pronounced. The figures for Chahar, Suiyuan, Ningsia, and Tsinghai (all NW) are too small to make much difference, no matter how great the degree of error.

The decline in population in Shantung (N) between 1851 and 1873 was probably due to a combination of the depressed conditions prevailing throughout China at the time, together with the Nien Rebellions (Ho, 1959, p. 247). The decline in Hopei (N) may have been for similar reasons or it may be an illusion. The 1933 estimate for Hopei is not comparable to that for 1953. The 1953 figure includes the entire province of Jehol, whereas the 1933 figure does not include such special municipalities as Peking.

Szechwan-Kwangtung-Fukien

Szechwan (SW), Kwangtung (SE), and Fukien (SE) all show substantial reductions in population between 1851 and 1873, but these declines are not corroborated by any other evidence. Kwangtung and Fukien were the principal sources of emigrants to Southeast Asia and Taiwan, but there is no evidence of a mass exodus between 1851 and 1873. One estimate places the total number of

19. Based on an investigation by the Tientsin *Ta kung pao* and Sian *Min-i jih-pao* (in *CKNY*, vol. III, p. 909).

Chinese in Southeast Asia and the Americas at only three million in 1879,[20] as compared to 11.7 million in 1953. According to these estimates the largest increases in Overseas Chinese took place between 1899 and 1903 (3.3 million) and between 1919 and 1921 (2.3 million). Although these are crude guesses at best, they jibe with the Kwangtung population figures, which show a significantly slower rate of growth from 1893 to 1933 than between 1873 and 1893.

All three of these provinces are ones in which the degree of central control has always been weak, particularly when the central government itself has been weak. Although one would expect this to lead to under-registration of population, the opposite apparently was the case. As indicated earlier in this appendix, it may be that in the case of Szechwan, the degree of immigration into the area was only guessed at and hence the rate of population increase exaggerated. The rate of population increase in Fukien and Kwangtung between 1786 and 1851 was above the national average (57 per cent and 79 per cent respectively, versus a national average of 48 per cent), a possible but unlikely situation, particularly for Fukien whose population declined steadily from 1873 on. In the absence of any more reliable basis for estimating population for these provinces, it is assumed that Kwangtung's, Szechwan's, and Fukien's populations were the same in 1851 as in 1873. These may be slight overestimates (particularly Szechwan) but this assumption should eliminate most of the bias. These various minor revisions and their effects on total population are presented in Table A.6.

TABLE A.6. REVISED POPULATION
FIGURES (1851)
(In Millions)

	Old	New
Kwangtung (SE)	28.4	21.7
Fukien (SE)	20.1	14.9
Szechwan (SW)	44.8	35.3
Total	433.0	411.6

POPULATION GROWTH (1913–1933)

Between 1913 and 1933, China's population according to the data in Table A.5, increased by over 80 million, or at a rate of just 0.8 per cent a year. In contrast, during the twenty-year periods 1873–1893 and 1893–1913, the rate of increase was about 0.5 per cent a year. To put the situation briefly, the rate of population growth increased during China's warlord period or, more likely, grew rapidly enough during the final years of Yuan Shih-k'ai (1913–1916) and the early years of the Kuomintang (1928–1933) to make up for a slowdown during the height of the warlord depredations. Even by 1933, of course, the Kuomintang had achieved only a symbolic unification of large sections of the country.

20. Li Chang-po, *Chung-kuo chih-min shih*, in *CKNY*, vol. II, p. 642.

There are several kinds of evidence that suggest that this somewhat higher rate of population growth did occur. First, although many "wars" were fought in China at this time, only rarely did these become, by Chinese standards, very bloody affairs except in the more remote areas of the northwest and in the suppression of the Communists. There was usually more maneuver and negotation than actual fighting. Where there was major fighting, it shows up in the population figures [e.g., Kiangsi (C), Shensi (NW) and Kansu (NW)].

Second, Western medicines and health measures, the main source of the post-World War II surge in population growth, may have begun to have a significant impact in large areas of China by this period; nowhere near the impact that they have had since 1949 with the rigorous application of public health activities by the Communists, but then the Communist rate of population growth has been over 2 per cent per annum, nearly three times the rate I am attempting to explain for 1913–1933.

Finally and probably most important, the coming of the railroad greatly improved the food distribution system. As argued in Chapter VI, the 1920–1921 drought had a far smaller impact on population than that of 1876–1879, largely because of the railroad. It is worth noting in regard to this point and the previous one that India's population, which increased by only 13 million between 1901 and 1921, rose by almost 67 million between 1921 and 1941.[21]

One does not have to rely solely on indirect evidence, however. A number of sample surveys of demographic data were made in this period which lend support to the basic conclusion reached here. For example, in one survey made under the direction of Professor Kuznets, the rate of population growth under "more and less favorable" conditions was estimated. The figure for "less favorable" conditions was 7.8 per thousand,[22] a rate not far below that (9 per thousand) derived from 1913–1933 estimates in Table A.5. According to Buck, during the enumeration years the Population Survey records indicated an increase of 12 per thousand.[23] As Buck pointed out, these data are not very reliable, but taken together with the available qualitative evidence, they support the proposition that population growth during the two decades after the founding of the Republic grew at something approximating the rate suggested by the data in Table A.5.

Finally, Professor Wilcox's estimate for 1912, as adjusted by T. C. Liu and K. C. Yeh (1965, p. 173) to cover all of China, is 434 million, almost exactly the same as the figure for 1913 in Table A.5. Wilcox's estimate, like that of Liu and Yeh for 1933, involved a reasonably careful reconstruction of the official population records of the time.

21. *India*, 1960, p. 16. The figures have been corrected to coincide with current Indian political boundaries.
22. Referred to by Liu-Yeh, 1965, p. 173.
23. Buck, 1937, p. 395. Buck went on to support his allegation of a belief that there was significant population growth in this period by questioning local people whether, on the basis of such things as the increased number of buildings, they believed population growth had occurred. Communities reporting an increase were 58 per cent of the total, while decreases made up 35 per cent.

CONCLUSION

The population figures used in the analysis are presented in Table A.7. All estimates are presented as ranges. These figures are meant to indicate a range in which there is perhaps an 80 per cent chance of the true figure being included.

A confidence interval of 80 per cent has no precise statistical basis in this case. Too little is known about the distribution of the error term in Chinese population estimates for this interval to represent anything more than my best judgment. I have tried to indicate the direct evidence on which my judgment is based in this appendix.

TABLE A.7. CHINA'S
POPULATION (1393–1953)

Year	Population (millions)
1393	65–80
1600	120–200
1650	100–150
1750	200–250
1850	410 ($\pm$25)
1873	350 ($\pm$25)
1893	385 ($\pm$25)
1913	430 ($\pm$25)
1933	500 ($\pm$25)
1953	583 ($\pm$15)
1957	647 ($\pm$15)

Cultivated Acreage Data

Estimating the size of an area under cultivation requires greater skill than the counting of persons, and it can be argued that China's cultivated acreage data may be subject to a wider margin of error than the population census data. On the other hand, land cannot hide so readily from the census taker. Owner-ship of a particular plot of land can be easily obscured, but complete failure to record that acreage in official documents may make it difficult to maintain one's ownership rights.

From the point of view of this study, cultivated land has a further advantage arising from the fact that, unlike population, there are limits on the degree to which it can be expanded. Thus it is possible to set maximum limits on the cultivated acreage in any period, given a knowledge of which provinces con-tained the bulk of the population. Manchuria, for example, was only sparsely settled until the late nineteenth or twentieth centuries. Hence an estimate of cultivated acreage in China for any earlier period must be below 1.4 billion *mou* (the total acreage in 1957 minus the area under cultivation in Manchuria).[1]

The analysis of the validity of Chinese land statistics will be carried out along lines similar to those pursued in the discussion of population data. First, a few general remarks are made regarding the difficulty of estimating acreage correctly. This brief section is followed by an analysis of the degree of geographic and dynastic variation in the principal Chinese land measure, the *mou*. The re-mainder of the appendix is concerned with the degree of error in land estimates

1. See Table B.14.

217

for particular years, first the early Ming and Ch'ing periods and 1957, and then the years in between. The questions asked about the data in each period will be:

1. Was a serious effort made to record all the cultivated acreage in the empire?
2. Are there known errors or biases in the data?
3. Are the estimates consistent with data in other periods and with what we know of Chinese history?

ESTIMATING LAND AREA

Land statistics have formed a basic part of the Chinese revenue system throughout most of China's history. Given the importance of such data, one would expect Chinese governments to make some effort to obtain personnel skilled in surveying land. Accurate land figures were also important to individual land owners. Without such data, purchase and sale of land would be inhibited as would be the use of land as security for debt. Hence there is a *prima facie* case for believing that reasonably reliable data on the amount of land under cultivation were available to some one, if only the landowners and their business associates.

Can it be argued that the mechanics of estimating a given area of land were so difficult that even people who took care in measurement could be grossly in error? There is no way of answering this question definitively, but some light can be shed on it.

The total land area in any given province was not used as a basis for taxes. Furthermore, there have been relatively few significant changes in provincial borders since the fourteenth century. Hence estimates for an earlier period should exactly match those for a recent date, that is if they were accurately estimated. In Table B.1, estimates of the total land area in each province in the 1790's and 1950's are presented. If estimating land area were an unusually difficult task either because it required complicated surveying equipment and technique or because of lack of any agreement on the unit of measurement, one would expect rather wide discrepancies between earlier estimates and those made by modern techniques in recent times.

In fact, the estimates for the two periods are extraordinarily close. The major discrepancies are due to provincial border changes (Hopei and Yunnan), or to the inclusion in the province of large unsettled areas (Sikang in Szechwan and parts of Kansu) where presumably no real effort was made to obtain precise data. In the remaining provinces, the difference between the two periods' figures is greater than 10 per cent in only two cases (Shantung and Fukien). Thus estimating the provincial area was either easy or, more likely, difficult, but the central authorities had both the will and the ability to accomplish this task.

THE CHINESE LAND MEASURE (*The Mou*)

Only in recent decades, since the 1930's, has there been a real effort to standardize the Chinese land measure, the *mou*. In the past, the *mou* has varied from

TABLE B.I. ESTIMATES OF TOTAL LAND AREA
(In Square Miles)

	1790's[a] (Ch'ing)	1950's[b] (Nationalist)	1950's[c] (Communist)
NW			
Shensi[d] ⎫ Kansu ⎭	154,008	226,000	374,000
N			
Hopei[e]	58,949	55,000	75,000
Shantung	65,104	57,000	54,000
Shansi	55,268	61,000	60,000
Honan	65,104	64,000	65,000
E			
Chekiang	39,150	40,000	39,000
Anhwei ⎫ Kiangsu ⎭	92,961	82,000	96,000
C			
Hupei ⎫ Hunan ⎭	144,770	152,000	151,000
Kiangsi	72,176	64,000	67,000
SE			
Fukien	53,480	47,000	46,000
Kwangtung	79,456	85,000	84,000
Kwangsi	78,250	85,000	84,000
SW			
Kweichow	64,554	66,000	66,000
Yunnan[f]	107,969	164,000	162,000
Szechwan[g]	166,800	294,000	210,000

[a] These are the figures given to the Macartney mission to China. I obtained them from Staunton, 1799, Appendix I.

[b] *China Handbook, 1955–56* (Taipei: 1955), p. 16.

[c] Shabad, 1956.

[d] The area of Shensi and Kansu under the Communists is almost exactly comparable to the Nationalist provinces of Kansu, Ningsia, and Shensi. The Ch'ing period area includes only the Nationalist provinces of Kansu and Shensi, not Ningsia. The area of Ningsia was 91,000,000 square miles. When this figure is added to the 1790's estimate, the total is still well below the estimates for the 1950's.

[e] The borders of Hopei (Chihli) Province have changed considerably from period to period. During the 1930's, the province of Jehol was created out of territory that today (and during the Ch'ing) is included in Hopei.

[f] Both Communist and Nationalist maps include in Yunnan all of Burma north of Myit-kyina. This area appears to be at least 30 or 40,000 square miles and hence accounts for most of the difference between the Ch'ing and Communist figures.

[g] The Nationalist figure includes Sikang province. After 1949, Sikang was abolished and divided more or less evenly between Szechwan and Tibet. The Ch'ing borders are roughly comparable to those after 1949, but some of the difference in the two area figures may be due to border variations.

dynasty to dynasty and among different regions. The notion of a standard *mou* applicable to the whole country, however, has also existed—in principle if not in practice. When the local *mou* size in a given region differed by a factor of, say, two or three times from the standard *mou*, it was often given a special name. Examples include the *hsün* (equivalent to 3 *mou*) in Shensi, the *fen* (equivalent to 24 *mou*) in Szechwan, the *hsiang* (equivalent to 6 or 7 *mou*) in Manchuria and numerous others.[2]

Even if the notion of a "standard" *mou* had some substance, this notion had not permeated China to such an extent that there were no differences at all over time or among regions. The problem of changes in *mou* size over time is probably the less serious of the two. The greatest changes in *mou* size appear to have occurred prior to the T'ang dynasty (see Table B.2). From T'ang to Ming there was little change, from Ming to Ch'ing a rise of 5 per cent, and from Ch'ing to the present an increase of 8 per cent.

TABLE B.2. CHANGES IN THE "STANDARD" *Mou*

Period	No. of Square Steps (Pu) per (Mou)	No. of Square Feet (Ch'ih) per Square Step	Length of Foot (in Shih Ch'ih)	One Mou Equals—Fraction of One Acre
Han	240	36	0.8295	0.1669
Later				
Han (1)	240	36	0.6912	0.1133
(2)[a]	240	36	0.7125	0.1204
T'ang	240	25	0.9330	0.1434
Sung	240	25	0.9216	0.1399
Yuan	240	25	0.9216	0.1399
Ming	240	25	0.9330	0.1434
Ch'ing	240	25	0.9600	0.1518
Present	240	25	1.0000	0.1647

SOURCE: The data in this table were taken or derived from Wu Ch'eng-lo, *Chung-kuo tu-liang-heng shih* (Shanghai: 1937), pp. 66, 67, and 76.

[a] This measure was sometimes used between A.D. 81 and 206.

Lack of much change over time in the "standard" *mou* does not constitute proof that no such changes occurred in local measures. Undoubtedly changes over time in them did occur, but it is unlikely that they were of great significance. The constancy of the "standard" *mou*, it would seem, would have tended to militate against local alterations over time. The principal direct evidence in support of this proposition is that acreage totals in areas densely settled centuries ago (e.g., Chekiang), and hence where cultivated acreage could not be expanded, did not change much over time.[3]

2. The Shensi measure is from the *Hsü hsiu Shensi t'ung chih* (1934), 196.5b; the Szechwan measure from the *Szechwan t'ung chih* (1816), 87.2a–10a; and that for Liaoning from the *Wen-hsien t'ung-k'ao* (Ch'ing dynasty), p. 4896 (also see Mathews dictionary, p. 376). Other measures include the *shuang* (in Yunnan) and the *pa* (in Kiangsi).

3. See Table B.9. Similar evidence can also be obtained for other areas as well.

It does not follow from the above discussion that regional differences were insignificant. Some idea of the regional variation can be seen in Table B.3 derived from Buck's data. This table, however, somewhat exaggerates the problem. If the half dozen extreme observations are removed, the remainder fall within 20 per cent above or below the median, and most fall within a range of 10 per cent. These figures, of course, do not include distortions from *mou* conversion (poor land to rich land equivalents). This latter difficulty did not really arise from differing measurement systems as such, but from fiscal considerations.

TABLE B.3. VARIATIONS IN *Mou* SIZE (1929–1933)
(Hectares per Local *Mou*)

Area	AVERAGE (*One* Mou = —Hectare)	(*One* Mou = —Acre)	RANGE (*One* Mou = —Hectare)
Spring Wheat	0.06136	0.152	0.05729–0.06834
Winter Wheat—Millet	0.06479	0.160	0.05056–0.07562
Winter Wheat—*Kaoliang*	0.08290	0.205	0.04977–0.25933
Yangtze Rice—Wheat	0.06703	0.166	0.05980–0.10456
Rice—Tea	0.06815	0.168	0.04538–0.07994
Szechwan Rice	0.07148	0.177	0.06534–0.07434*
Double Cropping Rice	0.07118	0.176	0.05871–0.08214
Southwestern Rice	0.06538	0.161	0.06144–0.08438

SOURCE: Calculated from data in Buck, 1937, p. 473. To convert the data in the table to acres, I have multiplied by 2.47.

* It appears that a decimal point has been misplaced in the figure 0.5766 which appears in the Buck table. To be on the safe side, this figure has been excluded from the average.

Differences of 10 and 20 per cent are not trivial. Fortunately, there is no pronounced upward or downward bias in these differences so that provincial averages should be closer than 10 per cent to the "standard," although one cannot be certain.

Not all of the acreage data used in this study suffer from this source of error. It is reasonable to assume that the *shih mou* had become pretty well accepted throughout the country by 1957. Although the standardized *shih mou* was introduced by the Kuomintang soon after coming to power, even the best of the estimates for the 1930's could hardly have succeeded in completely eliminating distortions arising from different units of measurement. However, the Liu-Yeh estimates, discussed in a later section, adjusted in light of the 1957 figures, probably remove all but relatively minor distortions. The 1873–1933 statistics, because their absolute quantities are derived from the 1933 figures, are probably also subject to no major bias from this source.

It is the Ming and Ch'ing data that are subject to significant distortions because of local *mou* differences. This problem is only one among many that concern the Ming and Ch'ing estimates, however.

MING ACREAGE DATA

If there were 1,678 million *mou* under cultivation in 1957, it is difficult to see how total cultivated acreage in the late fourteenth century could have been much over 600 million *mou*. Manchuria, the northwest (excluding Shensi), Szechwan, Yunnan, Kweichow, Kwangsi, and Kwangtung in the southwest and southeast (containing 732 million *mou* under cultivation in 1957) were empty or only sparsely settled. The seven highly populated provinces in central and east China in 1957 had a total acreage of only 401 million *mou*. There were another 543 million *mou* in the north (plus Shensi) in 1957, but it is highly unlikely that more than 100 or 200 million *mou* of these were under cultivation in the fourteenth century. And yet the official Ming estimates place total cultivated area in 1393 at 851 million *mou* (740 million *shih mou*).

Most discussions of land data stress biases from under-reporting in order to avoid taxes. Yet it would appear that the major problem with the early Ming land data was an upward, not a downward, bias. The basic argument in this study is that population grew much faster than cultivated acreage, and hence this population could only have been fed by an increase in per acre yields. If the early Ming data have a strong downward bias (i.e., the true figures were much higher than the reported figures), the conclusion that yields must have risen is reinforced. An upward bias is much more serious because if the bias were sufficiently pronounced, there might have been no increase in yields at all. In fact there is little danger that the bias could be so large, but it clearly is desirable to set limits on the possible margin of error in the Ming land data.

The first question to be answered is whether serious efforts were made in Ming times to register land. There is fairly general agreement that major land surveys were undertaken in 1368, 1398, and 1578. Ping-ti Ho (1959, pp. 107–108) argues that the 1398 survey was confined to Chekiang and parts of Kiangsu and that "the rest of the country had never been surveyed with equal care." The evidence he presents, however, is limited to the survey carried out in Chekiang and Kiangsu and only indicates that these provinces were surveyed carefully. There is little or no information available concerning what did or did not happen in the other provinces. Although more work on the institutional side of these surveys would be desirable, I cannot add anything further here, but will instead rely on a direct analysis of the plausibility and consistency of the figures themselves.

The land figures for the Ming period that are most often seen in recent professional literature are those for 1393, 1502, and 1578 appearing in the *Ming hui-tien*. Clearly the 1393 figures do not reflect the land survey of 1398. It has also been demonstrated by Professor Shimizu that the 1578 data do not include the results of the land survey begun in that year.

The figures for 1393 and 1502 are presented in Table B.4. The question that concerns us is which of these two figures, if either, best reflects the situation about 1400. If the 1502 data represent any period, it is presumably 1398 and not some later date, since no new survey was made after 1398 until

TABLE B.4. MING CULTIVATED ACREAGE DATA (1393 AND 1502)

| | 1393 | | 1502 | |
	Total (*1,000 Ming* Mou)	Per Capita[b] (*Ming* Mou)	Total[a] (*1,000 Ming* Mou)	Per Capita[b] (*Ming* Mou)
NW				
Shensi Kansu	31,525	13.6	26,066	11.2
N				
Hopei	58,250	30.2	26,971	13.8
Shantung	72,404	13.8	54,293	10.3
Shansi	41,864	10.3	39,081	9.6
Honan	144,947	76.3	41,610	21.8
E				
Chekiang	51,705	4.9	47,234	4.5
Anhwei	66,114	21.1	24,991	8.0
Kiangsu	60,515	8.0	56,026	7.4
C				
Hupei Hunan	220,218	46.9	223,613	47.6
Kiangsi	43,119	4.8	40,235	4.5
SE				
Fukien	14,626	3.7	13,517	3.5
Kwangtung	23,734	7.9	7,232	2.4
Kwangsi	10,240	6.9	10,785	7.3
SW				
Kweichow	—	—	—	—
Yunnan	—	—	—	—
Szechwan	11,203	7.6	10,787	7.3
Total	850,464	14.4	622,441	10.3

[a] These data are taken from Liang Fang-chung, 1935, pp. 98–99, 102.

[b] The per capita figures were obtained by dividing by population figures for 1393. The 1393 population figures were used because they are clearly superior to 1502 population data and because the 1502 acreage figure was probably based primarily on the 1398 survey.

1578.[4] Even a cursory glance at Table B.4, however, convinces one that there are major errors or biases in the land statistics for both periods.

Several explanations for biases and errors in the Ming land data have been put forward. Ping-ti Ho refers to the problem of "*mou* conversion," the conversion of several *mou* of poor grade land into a single *mou* for purposes of equitable taxation. As Ho points out, however, *mou* conversion was primarily a problem in the northern provinces (Hopei, Honan and Shantung), and probably much more serious at a later time, particularly during the Ch'ing dynasty. In any case,

4. It is unlikely that the 1502 data exactly reflect the results of the 1398 survey. There were undoubtedly minor tax adjustments subsequent to that date. For Fukien province, for example, the 1502 figure is slightly different from a statistic published a few years earlier (in 1491). (See Sakakida, 1967, p. 24.)

under-reporting resulting from *mou* conversion is not the principal source of bias in the Ming acreage data.

A check of the internal consistency and plausibility of the 1393 and 1502 figures leads one directly to the conclusion that the Honan (N) and Hu-kwang (Hupei-Hunan) (C) data contain a significant upward bias. The 1393 estimate for Hu-kwang is 60 million *mou* larger than the estimate for 1957 (50 million *mou* larger if the 1393 figure were converted to *shih mou*), and that for Honan is 20 million *mou* larger. Furthermore, the per capita acreage in these two provinces was four to ten times that of most other provinces. Other implausible figures include those indicating a declining cultivated acreage in Hopei (N), Shantung (N), Anhwei (E), and Kwangtung (SE), all areas which one would have expected to register an increase.

Scholars working on Ming acreage data have put forward two explanations for the existence of implausibly high figures for Honan and Hu-kwang. One, advanced by Professor Taiji Shimizu (1942), argues that the larger figures included hilly land and mud flats alongside lakes, land that was cultivated but not normally taxed. There is some basis for believing that there was over-reporting of land for this reason (see discussion of Chekiang below) but, as Professor H. Fujii has pointed out, the amounts of hill land (*shan*) were generally too small to account for more than a small part of the bias.[5]

The second explanation is based on the belief that there are major recording errors in the 1393 figures. As Lien-sheng Yang has pointed out (1961, p. 8), misprints and copyists' errors are very common in Chinese texts. For example, the Chinese characters for 10 (十) and 1,000 (千) are very similar.

Professor Fujii, who based his conclusions on an investigation of more than 200 local histories from the Ming period, argues convincingly that the inconsistency in the Ming data arises out of such recording errors. For Hu-kwang (Hupei-Hunan) (C), Fujii added up the figures appearing in the provincial gazetteers for each district for the years 1472 and 1512 and found that the total was 24 million *mou* in 1472 and 24.4 million *mou* in 1512, as compared to the 220.2 million figure in the *Hui-tien*. In the case of Honan (N), the 1393 figure in the *Hui-tien* was 145 million *mou*, but the figures for taxed land for 1391 and 1412 appearing elsewhere are 27.5 and 27.7 million *mou* respectively.

Fujii also argues that the Kwangtung (SE) acreage figure for 1393 is more consistent with data in other sources than is the 1502 figure. From Table B.4, it is also obvious that the per capita acreage (using 1393 population data) is much too low.

Fujii does not deal with difficulties in the Hopei (N), Shantung (N), and Anhwei (E) estimates. In all three cases, the use of 1502 data result in a much more plausible per capita acreage figure. The high figure for Anhwei in 1393 is due to the fact that Feng-yang Prefecture, one of ten prefectures in Anhwei, reported an acreage of 41,749,300 *mou*, an unreasonably high figure and probably due to the Chinese equivalent of a misplaced decimal point. The low

5. In the examples given by Fujii (1943, 1944, 1947), the percentage of such land ranged from 8 to 26 per cent.

quality of the 1393 Hopei (N) estimate is suggested by the fact that no prefectural breakdown is given for 1393 as it is for 1502 and 1578.

In constructing a revised estimate for cultivated acreage around the year 1400,
I have decided to use the 1502 data except for the provinces of Honan, Hu-
kwang, and Kwangtung, where I follow Fujii's lead. The results appear in
Table B.5. The total is almost exactly half that of the figure normally used for the
late fourteenth century.

The third major land survey under the Ming took place beginning in 1578, as

TABLE B.5. REVISED MING ACREAGE DATA
(c. 1400)

	Total[a] (*1,000 Ming* Mou)	Per Capita[b] (*Ming* Mou)
NW		
Shensi–Kansu	26,066	11.2
N		
Hopei	26,971	13.8
Shantung	54,293	10.3
Shansi	39,081	9.6
Honan[c]	27,705	14.2
E		
Chekiang	47,234	4.5
Anhwei	24,991	8.0
Kiangsu	56,026	7.4
C		
Kiangsi	40,235	4.5
Hupei[d]	13,548	5.1
Hunan[d]	10,428	
SE		
Fukien	13,517	3.5
Kwangtung[e]	23,734	7.9
Kwangsi	10,785	7.3
SW		
Kweichow	—	—
Yunnan	—	—
Szechwan	10,787	7.3
Total (Ming *mou*)	425,401	7.0
Total (Shih *mou*)	370,100	6.1

[a] Except where otherwise noted these are the 1502 data in Liang Fang-chung, 1935.

[b] Per capita figures were obtained by dividing through using 1393 population data.

[c] The Honan figure is that for 1412 in a sixteenth-century edition of the *Honan t'ung chih*
as reported by Fujii.

[d] These Hu-kwang figures were obtained by adding up the prefectural data in a Ming
edition of the *Hunan t'ung chih* as reported by Fujii.

[e] The Kwangtung figure is that for 1393 given in Liang Fang-chung, 1935.

stated above, but the often quoted 1578 data do not reflect the new survey.[6] As Shimizu points out, the 1582 figure for Hu-kwang, according to the governor of the province, was raised by over 50 million *mou* to a figure of 84 million *mou*. Shimizu finds that in all the provinces taken together [except Fukien (SE) and Yunnan (SW)], the land added by the second survey was 147 million Ming *mou*.[7] Thus the true figure for cultivated acreage around 1580 was over 600 million Ming *mou*, more if there was serious under-reporting or *mou* conversion. Unfortunately, the population data for 1578 are wholly unreliable and hence cannot be used as a basis for checking the internal consistency of this 600 million-plus *mou* figure (500 million *shih mou*).

CONSISTENCY OF MING AND PRE-MING DATA

Just as in the case of the Ming population data, it is desirable to check the degree to which the Ming acreage data are consistent with other independently arrived at estimates of the cultivated area.

The Ming T'ai-tsu emperor did not conduct the first land survey in China. Land surveys have regularly been the basis upon which the fiscal system has been built.

The Yuan (Mongol) dynasty, beginning with Khubilai, conducted several land surveys, but these were plagued by fraudulent concealment.[8] The Emperor Jen-tsung, however, made a major effort over a prolonged period of time (1314–1330) to correct these data, including making corrections in the over-reporting of lands held by the poor. Over-reporting of land belonging to the poor was one way in which the rich initially responded to the Emperor's desire to correct for under-reporting. By the late 1320's, with the aid of strong penalties for under-reporting and rewards in the form of tax reductions for self-reported land, the government was satisfied that it had a reasonably accurate picture of the land situation.

The Yuan data for the southern provinces are presented in Table B.6 (data for other provinces could not be found). There was a major revision of provincial boundaries between the Yuan and Ming so that no exact comparison of individual provinces is possible. Since it is unlikely that the Ming T'ai-tsu Emperor made much use of the Yuan surveys in conducting his own land survey, the survey of the 1320's and that of 1398 can be treated as essentially independent of each other.[9] Given a lack of mutual dependence, the two sets of data seem generally consistent with each other.

6. This is the conclusion of both Fujii and Shimizu based on the fact that the survey was carried out in the various provinces over a period of several years.

7. Shimizu, May 1942, 29.2. These data were taken from provincial reports.

8. This discussion of the Yuan land surveys is based on Schurmann, 1956, chap. II, section B. This section, as is much of the rest of the book, is a translation of a part of the *Yuan shih* (History of the Yuan Dynasty).

9. Although the Ming like other dynasties looked to the past, it was to a Chinese past, not a "foreign" (i.e., Mongol) past. Certain distortions, of course, may have consistently entered into both the Yuan and Ming surveys. *Mou* conversion was practiced as early as the Sung and may have persisted in a few areas in the Yuan and Ming. Local *mou* sizes may have caused consistent distortions between Yuan and Ming as well.

TABLE B.6. ACREAGE DATA CONSISTENCY CHECK
(Data in 1,000 *Mou*—Unconverted)

Yuan area	Sung 1082	Yuan early 1300's	Ming 1393
Chiangche (E)[a]	90,437	99,508	97,500
Kiangsi (C)[b]	48,369	47,469	64,000
Honan (N)[c]	133,000	118,077	78,000

SOURCES: *Hsü wen-hsien t'ung-k'ao* (Yuan dynasty) pp. 59–60; Schurmann, 1956, p. 38; Table B.5; and A. Herrmann, 1966, pp. 42–43, 52 and 56.

[a] This area included virtually all of the Ming provinces of Fukien, Chekiang, and all the prefectures south of the Yangtze in Nan-Chihli. The Sung provinces were Liang-che, Fuchien, and Chiang-nan-tung.

[b] This area included roughly the provinces of Kiangsi and Kwangtung in all three periods except that Kwangtung's boundaries in the Ming period included a somewhat larger area than previously. Hence the Ming figure should be reduced somewhat to make it comparable to the earlier data.

[c] Honan in the Yuan period included the Sung areas of Huai-nan, most of Ching-hsi, half of K'aifeng, and perhaps one-third of Ching-hu-pei. In the Ming period, this area was roughly commensurate with Nan-Chih-li north of the Yangtze, the northern one-third of Hukwang and Honan (except for the small area north of the Yellow River). The Ming Honan and Hukwang figures used were the revised figures of Fujii (see text).

Data for the northern provinces can be checked against several kinds of data from the T'ang and Han dynasties. At the beginning of the T'ang Dynasty (A.D. 624), all land in theory belonged to the emperor and was parceled out to individual farmers during their productive life.[10] Although in practice private property was increasingly being recognized, evidence has been found to suggest that this system (the *Chün-t'ien* system) was actually in effect in far northwest China (Turfan and Tun-huang in present-day Sinkiang and Kansu respectively). The land regulations stated that each male between the ages of 18 and 60 was to receive 100 T'ang *mou* of land (one T'ang *mou* = one Ming *mou*). Since the average family of 5-plus persons occasionally had more than one male between the ages of 18 and 60, the average farm size in the far northwest was ideally as much as one and one-quarter times 100 *mou*. In the districts close to Chang-an (in present-day Shensi [NW]), the land allotment fell as low as 20–30 *mou* per adult male, but this was not typical. The rule for areas where land was not a surplus was 60 T'ang (or Ming) *mou* per adult. The principal aspect to note about these various farm sizes is how closely they correspond to the derived figures for the northern provinces during the Ming (multiply the per capita figures by 5 or 6). It should also be noted that in the early T'ang nearly three-quarters of the population was in the northern provinces.[11] This, together with the fact that these particular land regulations were a more or less direct adaptation of the systems developed by the barbarian dynasties of northern China in the fifth and sixth centuries, indicate that they probably were primarily intended for application

10. This discussion of the T'ang land system is based on that of Twitchett, 1963, chap. 1.
11. See Table A.1 in Appendix A.

in the north. Thus the T'ang regulations are a check on the reliability of northern acreage data alone.

Several of the Han dynasty land figures are also worth a brief look. All the data in Table B.7, except the figure for A.D. 2, are for the Later Han Dynasty. During the later part of the Former Han, and throughout the Later Han, the government was plagued by large-scale removal of land from tax registers (Reischauer and Fairbank, 1958, pp. 121–25). It is difficult to say how much this

TABLE B.7. HAN DYNASTY LAND AND POPULATION DATA

Year (A.D.)	2	105	122	144	145	146
Population (1,000)	59,595	53,256	48,961	49,721	49,524	47,567
Families (1,000)	12,233	9,227	9,647	9,947	9,937	9.248
Person per family (no.)	4.87	5.76	5.04	4.99	4.99	5.08
Total Acreage (1,000 Han *mou*)	827,054	732,017	694,289	698,727	695,768	693,012
Total Acreage (1,000 *shih mou*)	570,670	505,090	479,060	482,120	480,080	478,180
Acreage per family (*shih mou*)	47	55	50	48	48	52

SOURCE: Hwang Nai-lung, *Chung-kuo nung-yeh fa-chan shih* (*ku-tai chih pu*), p. 333, whose source in turn was Ma Ch'eng-feng, *Chung-kuo ching-chi shih*, vol. 2. Han *mou* were converted to *shih mou* using the data in Table B.2.

problem is reflected in the land statistics, but it is probable that a large portion of cultivated acreage was not reported. If, as is possible, as much as one-quarter of the land went unreported, the Han data for farm size would be roughly comparable to these of the T'ang and Ming for the northern provinces. The Yangtze valley, of course, was not settled extensively during the Han.

Finally, provincial data for the Sung period can be compared with the Ming estimates. The relevant figures are given in Table B.8. The most improbable figures are those for Shantung (N) and Shansi (N), which show a sharp increase from 1082 to 1400 when one would have expected a decline. It is also clear that no serious effort was made during the Sung period to register the cultivated acreage in Kwangsi (SE) (the reported figure represents only 0.2 of a *mou* per capita). Where there are such significant differences between data for the two periods, the Ming data appear the more plausible (e.g., the per capita acreage in these provinces in Ming times is consistent with that in other similar provinces, whereas this is less true for the Sung data). A more definitive explanation of the differences between the Sung and Ming acreage figures must be foregone until more work is done with the Sung data.

For several provinces, one can also obtain more detailed breakdowns of the Ming acreage data. Two examples are presented in Tables B.9 and B.10. The provinces represented are Chekiang (E), which was heavily settled by Ming times and hence had little good land not under cultivation, and Hupei (C), which north of the Yangtze had been laid waste by the Mongols. For Chekiang,

TABLE B.8. SUNG AND MING ACREAGE DATA

	SUNG[a] 1082 (1,000 *Sung* Mou)	(1,000 Shih Mou)	MING (REVISED)[b] c. 1400 (1,000 *Ming* Mou)	(1,000 Shih Mou)	1957[c] (1,000) Shih Mou)
NW					
Shensi-Kansu	44,710	38,000	26,066	22,680	157,000
N					
Hopei	27,906	23,720	26,971	23,470	132,000
Shantung	26,719	22,710	54,293	47,230	139,000
Shansi	11,171	9,500	39,081	34,000	67,000
Honan	32,668	27,770	27,705	24,100	130,000
E					
Chekiang	36,344	30,890	47,234	41,090	33,000
Anhwei	102,358	87,000	24,991	21,740	88,000
Kiangsu			56,026	48,740	93,000
C					
Hupei	25,989	22,090	13,548	11,790	65,000
Hunan	33,204	28,220	10,428	9,720	58,000
Kiangsi	45,223	38,440	40,235	35,000	42,000
SE					
Fukien	11,092	9,430	13,517	11,760	22,000
Kwangtung	3,146	2,670	23,734	20,650	58,000
Kwangsi	55	50	10,785	9,380	38,000
SW					
Szechwan	23,148	19,680	10,787	9,380	116,000
Total	423,733	360,170	425,401	370,730	1,238,000

[a] *Hsü wen-hsien t'ung-k'ao* (Yuan dynasty), pp. 59–60.
[b] See Table B.5.
[c] See Table B.14.

there is a striking degree of consistency among the prefectural data for the Ming, Ch'ing, and Republican periods. For Hupei, most of the cultivated acreage in Ming times was, as one would expect, south of the Yangtze or in the eastern corner of the province.[12]

Other consistency checks could also be made, but these should be sufficient at least to establish the rough plausibility or even reliability of the revised Ming acreage data. Perhaps the most one can say is that total acreage during the late fourteenth century fell somewhere between 300 and 440 million *shih mou*. Equally important for the purposes of this study, something over half of this total was in the six provinces of the lower Yangtze and southeast coast. The total acreage under cultivation in these six provinces, therefore, was nearly two-

12. One could argue that the consistency in the Chekiang data reflected little more than the tendency of officials to report the same figure whether it was valid or not. But, if so, why didn't Hupei officials follow the same practice, and is it simply a coincidence that the Ming and Ch'ing figures for the province as a whole are very close to those for 1957 (after subtracting out hill land, etc., in earlier data; see Table B.15)?

TABLE B.9. CHEKIANG LAND DATA
(In *Mou*)

	1553[a]	1610[a]	1735[a]	1932[b]
Hang-chow Fu	4,197,388	4,257,457	4,296,328	3,790,563
Chia-hsing Fu	2,910,722	4,323,299	4,356,223	3,943,211
Hu-chow Fu	6,846,523	6,122,873	6,136,078	4,251,817
Ning-po Fu	4,047,156	4,099,180	3,900,593	4,154,450
T'ai-chou Fu	4,110,403	4,195,994	3,492,271	3,561,371
Shao-hsing Fu	6,534,104	6,714,730	6,826,539	7,233,891
Chin-hua Fu	7,356,074	7,374,160	7,440,802	6,552,210
Ch'ü-chou Fu	2,987,214	3,068,821	2,847,134	2,656,020
Yen-chou Fu	2,805,009	2,848,060	2,859,169	2,029,375
Wen-chou Fu	2,609,118	2,608,692	2,133,308	2,345,891
Ch'u-chou Fu	1,237,096	2,250,913	1,740,804	[6,978,653][c] 1,871,175
Total	45,640,807	47,864,179	46,029,249	[47,497,454][c] 42,389,974

[a] These figures are from the *Chekiang t'ung chih* (1736), vol. 67–70, pp. 1304–1353.

[b] *Chung-kuo shih-yeh chih* (*Chekiang Sheng*) (Shanghai: 1933) pp. B, 2–7.

[c] One *hsien* in Ch'u-chou Fu is listed as having 5,674,976 *mou*. I have assumed that the Chinese equivalent of a decimal point was misplaced and revised the figure to read 567,498 *mou*. The totals are calculated using both figures. The provincial total also includes one small *hsien* which was not included by me under a prefecture (*fu*).

TABLE B.10. HUPEI CULTIVATED ACREAGE
(*Mou*)

Prefecture (*Location*)	1472[a]	1930's[b]
Wu-ch'ang (SE)	3,215,721	5,560,000
Han-yang (NE)	422,959	8,060,000
Mien-yang (SC)	844,712	
Hwang-chow (E)	3,614,960	5,730,000
Te-an (NC)	995,135	3,460,000
Shing-chou (SW)	3,139,704	12,120,000[c]
Hsiang-yang (NW)	686,116	8,040,000
Yuan-yang (NW)	148,975	1,350,000
An-lu (C)	480,080	7,640,000
Total	13,548,362	51,960,000

[a] Fujii, 1947. Fujii obtained these figures from the 1522 edition of the *Hu-kwang t'ung-chih*.

[b] Statistical Office of the Hupei Government Secretariat, *Hupei-sheng nien-chien*, pp. 141–142.

[c] I have included the prefectures of Ching-chou, Ching-men, I-ch'ang, and Shih-nan in this total.

thirds of present-day levels. The rest of China, by comparison, was nearly empty, with perhaps a billion *mou* of readily cultivable land not in use. By 1600 total acreage had perhaps risen to 500 (± 100) million *shih mou*.

My own guess is that the "true" figures for 1400 and 1600 are more likely above 370 and 500 million *mou* than below. The principal remaining sources of upward bias not taken into account in making the estimates are the registration of some uncultivated land and the conversion of high-grade land into larger amounts of average-grade land. Against these must be set the unaccounted for downward biases resulting from failure to register land either to avoid taxes or because regulations did not require that the land be recorded.[13] In addition, there was the conversion of several low-grade *mou* into a smaller number of average-grade *mou*. These sources of downward bias probably more than offset whatever upward bias existed.

CH'ING ACREAGE DATA

There is little doubt that Ch'ing acreage data are subject to major biases. For example, between 1724 and 1850 when population at least doubled, cultivated acreage rose, according to official estimates, by only 6 per cent. Between 1766 and 1850 there was actually a slight decline in the reported totals.[14]

By 1850, most of the present acreage under cultivation was already being farmed. The principal exceptions to this statement are found in Manchuria, and in parts of the northwest and southwest. If these were the only areas not being farmed, then total cultivated acreage in 1850 might have been as high as 1,300 million *shih mou*. If one further assumes that biases in the official data are generally downward, the cultivated acreage would have been at least 800–900 million *mou*. The issue we shall deal with here is whether there is any plausible way to further narrow this range.

A number of explanations for the biases in Ch'ing data have been put forward. Ping-ti Ho stressed the conversion of several *mou* of low-grade land into a single fiscal *mou*. There is also evidence to suggest that reported acreage was made to conform to the quotas sent down from central authorities rather than to the actual cultivated area. In addition, even a cursory glance at the data suggests that no real attempt was made to bring the land figures up to date after the middle of the eighteenth century. The estimates for dates after the mid-eighteenth century do vary, but seldom by more than 1 or 2 per cent—except in the case of several provinces where greater percentage declines in acreage are recorded. The provinces showing reduced acreages, however, are ones in which one would have expected increases to have occurred.

Starting with this knowledge, I shall use two independent methods to re-

13. Official or public land of various types did not pay taxes and hence may not have always been fully recorded. All data used in this appendix, however, include official (*kuan*) land explicitly.

14. Ch'ing acreage data can be found in many sources. I have used the data in *CKNY*, vol. I, p. 60, where figures are given for 1661, 1685, 1724, 1766, 1812, 1851, 1873, and 1887.

construct the "true" Ch'ing acreage figures. Two methods are necessary (and even more would be desirable) because none of these computations can be rigorously defended.

In attempting to reconstruct the data, I have started by rejecting all Ch'ing figures after 1766 on the grounds that they were not based on a new survey of any kind. Mid-nineteenth–century estimates will be made in the next section, but by working backward from twentieth-century data, not by using Ch'ing figures.

The first estimate for 1766 is based on Ping-ti Ho's argument that the principal source of under-reporting was due to *mou* conversion. Ping-ti Ho's examples of *mou* conversion indicate that medium-grade land was converted to fiscal *mou* at rates ranging from 1.17 to 2 and even higher. Poor-grade land was converted at rates of 2, 3, and more ranging up to 7 or 8. In addition there were many different grading systems for land. One system in Fukien had nine different grades, while another in Kiangsu had eight (Ho, 1959, pp. 104–116). There are also examples in the literature of a *mou* of good land being converted into several lower-grade *mou*, but these are not so frequent.

Apparently by the late 1920's, the system of grading land had become sufficiently standardized for Buck to estimate the percentage of land in each of five classifications. These figures, which are given in Table B.11, are revealing.

TABLE B.11. LAND CLASSIFICATION (PERCENTAGE)

	GRADES					
	1	*2*	*3*	*4*	*5*	*Other*
All China	52.1	25.3	12.7	4.5	3.3	2.1
Wheat Region	42.3	29.7	17.3	4.4	1.6	4.7
Rice Region	58.2	22.6	9.9	4.6	4.2	0.5

SOURCE: Buck, 1937 (Statistical Volume), p. 38.

Slightly over half the total acreage was in the top grade and 25.3 per cent in the second. Only 20.5 per cent was in the remaining three grades. Thus, if second-grade land had been converted at 2 to 1 and the rest at 4 to 1, total reported acreage would represent about 70 per cent of the true total. If the rates were 1.5 to 1 and 2 to 1, reported land would be 80 per cent of actual cultivated land. The latter guess appears to be more reasonable, given the very small amounts of land in grades 4 and 5 in Buck's data.

Can this 70 or 80 per cent be used as a basis for revising the Ch'ing data? First, Buck's data are taken from *hsien* tax records and hence are from the same source as the *mou* conversion rates. The more serious question is whether a land classification system used in the early 1930's and the percentage distribution of land within that classification system can be assumed to be applicable to a period two centuries earlier. This question cannot be answered in a definitive way, but certain considerations make a qualified "yes" answer appear reasonable. As acreage expands, one expects this to involve utilization of poorer grades of land (hilly, sandy, or easily flooded land, etc.). In China, however, there were forces tending to offset this Ricardian progression. In particular, the opening of new lands in such areas as the southwest initially at least brought proportionately more high-grade land under cultivation. Since none of the forces in either direction were very strong after 1800, it can be reasonably assumed that the percentage classification of land did not change radically over the time span between 1766 and 1930. What cannot be answered is whether there was a fundamental alteration in the classification system itself that would basically change the results. In particular, was first-grade land, as classified in the 1930's, comparable to good land in the eighteenth century, or both medium and good land? There is no satisfactory answer, except to argue that classification systems changed rather slowly in China and usually only with a conscious major effort on the part of the government, something of which there is no evidence for the nineteenth and early twentieth centuries.

The range of estimates obtained by using the 70 and 80 per cent figures and applying them to the official Ch'ing land data for 1766 is from 980 to 1,120 million Ch'ing *mou* or 900 to 1,030 million *shih mou*.

The second method used is to assume that all provinces whose cultivated acreage data indicate little increase between 1685 or 1724 and 1766 had by 1766 reached a provincewide acreage figure which is identical with my estimate for 1873 (i.e., a near saturation figure in most cases). It is also assumed that Shansi (N) and Honan (N) reached the 1873 level in 1766, since the official reported figure for 1766 is quite high, although it did occur prior to 1766. The remaining provinces are left unchanged except for Hunan (C)—which is raised. The results appear in Table B.12.

Given the similarity of the two estimates it seems reasonable to narrow the most probable range of estimates from 800–1,300 million *shih mou* to 900–1,000 million *shih mou* for the year 1766. If one further assumes that the degree of bias in the official figures was fairly constant, then one can use these data as an indication of the percentage increase in acreage during the early Ch'ing period. The derived index is presented in Table B.13. Applying this index to the 950 million *mou* figure for 1766, one can derive an estimate of cultivated acreage for 1685 of 740 million *shih mou*. This would appear to be about as far as one can go with the official Ch'ing data.

ACREAGE ESTIMATES (NINETEENTH AND TWENTIETH CENTURIES)

Fortunately one can obtain some idea of the cultivated acreage in nineteenth-century China by working backwards from State Statistical Bureau estimates of cultivated acreage for 1957. The year 1957 was the high-water mark for the quality of Chinese Communist statistics and all data in Table B.14 for the Communist period are from that year except for six provinces. The Shensi, Shansi, Hopei, and Honan estimates are for 1953 or 1954, and that of Shantung is for 1956.

TABLE B.12

| | 1766[a] | | 1873[b] |
	Official (1,000,000 Ch'ing Mou)	Revised (1,000,000 Shih Mou)	(1,000,000 Shih Mou)
NW			
Shensi	30	59	59
N			
Shansi	55	51	51
Hopei	68	120	120
Shantung	99	121	121
Honan	80	107	107
E			
Kiangsu	67	84	84
Anhwei	41	82	82
Chekiang	46	42	42
C			
Hupei	59	51	51
Kiangsi	47	47	47
Hunan	34	50	66
SE			
Fukien	15	14	29
Kwangtung	34	31	57
Kwangsi	10	9	35
SW			
Kweichow	3	3	17
Yunnan	9	8	11
Szechwan	46	41	105
NW			
Sinkiang	1	1	10
NE			
Kirin	2	2	2
Liaoning	21	19	22
Total	767	942	1,118

[a] Official data are in *CKNY*, vol. I, p. 60. For revisions, see discussion in the text.
[b] For derivation of these figures, see Table B.14.

The 1957 figures are not, of course, accurate in some absolute sense. In early 1958, Hsueh Mu-ch'iao, the director of the State Statistical Bureau, stated that "we are not even clear about such important agricultural questions as the size of territorial area, and the amount of cultivated land."[15] Thus there was room for improvement in the 1957 acreage estimates, but presumably these figures were of higher quality than other rural data. The 1957 estimates are also presumably more reliable than those for 1933. Both land reform and the formation of co-

15. Quoted in Choh-ming Li, 1962, p. 33.

TABLE B.13. OFFICIAL CH'ING
ACREAGE DATA

	1,000,000 Ch'ing Mou	*Index*
1661	549	100
1685	608	111
1725	724	132
1766	781	142
1812	791	144
1851	772	141
1873	770	140
1887	845	154

SOURCE: *CKNY*, vol. I, p. 60.

operatives necessitated a reasonably careful calculation of the amount of cultivated land in each area. By 1957 there were, in addition, many more rural statistical workers than in the 1930's.[16]

The data for 1953 or 1954 are probably not as reliable as those for 1956 and 1957. The rural statistical reporting system was only beginning to be set up and land reform cadres may have submitted incorrect data intentionally or otherwise. Thus the figures in Table B.14 for several provinces in north and northwest China are somewhat less reliable than those for the other provinces. Upward biases in one province, however, are presumably offset by downward biases in others, since the total is almost exactly equal to the official 1957 figure.

For Manchuria, Hopei, and Inner Mongolia there is some incomparability between 1933 and 1957 figures because of the redrawing of provincial boundaries. Parts of Manchuria are now in Inner Mongolia and the old province of Jehol was divided between Hopei, Liaoning, and Inner Mongolia. Elsewhere the boundaries are essentially the same except that Ningsia was incorporated into Kansu and Sikang was divided between Szechwan and Tibet, but the cultivated acreage in Ningsia and Sikang was negligible.

The 1933 acreage estimates are those of T. C. Liu and K. C. Yeh (1965, pp. 129, 227–83) except where otherwise noted. Liu and Yeh investigated six different estimates of cultivated area in the pre-1937 period and arrived at their own estimates by various methods. The care with which they arrived at their estimates together with the high degree of correlation with Communist acreage estimates for 1957 suggest that the Liu-Yeh estimates are generally reliable. In a few provinces, however, I have made minor changes. For Manchuria it seemed more reasonable to use the original Japanese figures for these provinces rather than an aggregated version based originally on these same figures but slightly revised. The cases of Kansu and Tsinghai are discussed in the footnotes to Table B.14.

16. There were some 200,000 statistical workers in 1957, a significant proportion of whom were in the rural reporting system. In the 1930's the NARB had 6,300 reporters. See discussion in Appendix C.

TABLE B.14. CULTIVATED ACREAGE DATA (1873–1957)
(1,000,000 *Shih Mou*)

	1873[a]	1893[a]	1913[a]	1933[b]	1957
NE					
Heilungkiang	—[c]	—[c]	32[d]	58[e]	109[f]
Kirin	2[c]	2[c]	44[d]	74[e]	70[f]
Liaoning	22[c]	30[c]	47[d]	74[e]	71[f]
NW					
Sinkiang	10[c]	10[c]	12[d]	16	26[g]
Tsinghai	2	4	4	5[h]	6
Inner ⌠Suiyuan	27	26	25	24	83[g]
Mongolia ⌡Chahar	18	19	20	19	
Ningsia	3	3	3	3	82[g]
Kansu	42	49	50	50[i]	
Shensi	59	58	56	54	75[j]
N					
Shansi	51	53	56	56	67[k]
Hopei	120	118	120	118	132[k]
Shantung	121	125	127	120	139[g]
Honan	107	106	125	123	130[k]
E					
Kiangsu	84	85	86	92	93[l]
Anhwei	82	87	88	88[m]	88[l]
Chekiang	42	44	31	33[m]	33[l]
C					
Hupei	51	53	55	65[m]	65[n]
Hunan	66	58	59	58[m]	58[n]
Kiangsi	47	47	44	43	42[n]
SE					
Fukien	29	28	27	23	22[o]
Kwangtung	57	58	58	58[m]	58[o]
Kwangsi	35	37	41	43	38[o]
SW					
Kweichow	17	20	21	22	31[p]
Yunnan	11	12	15	36	41[p]
Szechwan	105	108	110	116[m]	116[p]
Residual	—	—	—	—	1.5
Total[q]	1,210	1,240	1,356	1,471	1,677.5

[a] The data for 1873, 1893, and 1913 are derived from the indexes compiled by the Agricultural Economics Department of Nanking University and the National Agricultural Research Bureau (*CKNY*, vol. III, pp. 907–908) except where otherwise noted.

[b] The 1933 estimates are those of Liu and Yeh, 1965, p. 129 except where otherwise noted.

[c] These figures are based on the official Ch'ing estimates of population in Manchuria and Sinkiang (*CKNY*, vol. I, p. 60). I have raised these figures slightly on the belief that there was probably some under-reporting.

[d] These are the official estimates of the Peking government for 1914 (*NSTCP*).

[e] East Asiatic Economic Investigation Bureau, *The Manchuria Yearbook, 1932–1933*, p. 101. The figures are for the year 1930.

f Sun Ching-chih, 1959c, pp. 86, 211, and 394.

g These figures are from Chen, 1967, pp. 291, 293–95. The figures are for the year 1957 except for Shantung which is for 1956. The Kansu figure is actually that for sown, not cultivated area. Chen's official data for Kansu include a much smaller figure for cultivated area (59 million *mou*) which would imply that there was substantial double-cropping in Kansu. According to Buck, there was some double-cropping in Kansu, but a more recent source with greater coverage suggests that generally sown area was smaller than cultivated area in Kansu (Wu Ch'uan-chün, *et al.*, *Hwang-ho chung-yu hsi-pu ti-ch'u ching-chi ti-li* [Peking: 1956] p. 55). Still another source states that Kansu's cultivated acreage was about the same as the province's uncultivated but cultivable acreage, the latter being 97 million *mou* (CIA, "Agricultural Statistics," *Weekly Reports on Communist China*, no. 9, Jan. 15, 1960, p. 24).

h The Liu-Yeh estimate for Tsinghai is 7.8 million *mou*. Estimates for 1949, however, put the total planted area at 4.9 million *mou*, whereas for 1959 the figure is 7.4 million *mou* (CIA, "Agricultural Statistics"). Another source puts the 1955 planted area at 5.55 million *mou* (Shabad, 1956, p. 266). On this basis, I have assumed that the 1957 acreage was 6 million *mou* and that of 1933 was 5 million *mou* (the same as 1949).

i The Liu-Yeh figure for Kansu is 29 million *mou*. Buck's figure, by contrast, is 50 million *mou*. This latter figure, together with the estimate for 1957, is more consistent with a rise in population in Kansu-Ninghsia from 7.5 million in 1933 to 13 million in 1957.

j The Shensi acreage figure is assumed to be 3 million *mou* above the total sown acreage in grain, cotton, and rapeseed in 1954 (T. Shabad, 1956, p. 200).

k The figures for Shansi, Hopei, and Honan are for the year 1953 and were derived from farm population and per capita acreage data in Sun Ching-chih, 1957, pp. 41–42, 53, 90, 100, 154–56.

l Sun Ching-chih, 1959a, pp. 53, 137, and 213.

m These figures were assumed to be the same for 1933 as for 1957. The Liu-Yeh estimates are significantly different from these figures by amounts ranging from 8 to 21 million *mou* (some higher, others lower). Use of the Liu-Yeh estimates would have raised the overall acreage total for 1933 by 46 million *mou*.

n Sun Ching-chih, 1958, pp. 70, 256, and 397.

o Sun Ching-chih, 1959b, pp. 62, 64, 247, and 373.

p Sun Ching-chih, 1960, pp. 351, 509 and 513 (for the year 1958); and Ye A. Afanas'yeskiy, *Szechwan*, translated in JPRS No. 15038, p. 216.

q These totals were obtained by addition except in the case of 1957 where the figure is from *TGY* p. 128.

In the cases of Anhwei and Kwangtung, there is no evidence to suggest that acreage increased between 1933 and 1957. Yet the use of the Liu-Yeh and State Statistical Bureau estimates without adjustment indicate just such an increase. The lack of significant change in acreage between 1873 and 1933, according to the indexes, also suggests that these two provinces had reached a near saturation point by 1933. In the case of Kwangtung, two of the six estimates used by Liu-Yeh are very close to the 58 million figure. The same is true for Anhwei, but one of the two estimates is that of the Peking government (1914–1924), which I argue elsewhere are not very useful for estimating total acreage.[17] Given these considerations, it appeared reasonable to raise the 1933 acreage figures for Anhwei and Kwangtung to the 1957 level.

For four provinces (Szechwan, Chekiang, Hupei, and Hunan), however, I have lowered the Liu-Yeh estimates to make them comparable to the 1957 data. I reduced the Chekiang figure on the assumption that the pre-1957 data included uncultivated but taxed hill land (see Table B.15). For each of the other three provinces, the highest of the six estimates used by Liu and Yeh is well over

17. See Appendix C.

twice the lowest. Liu and Yeh reject the most extreme estimates, and then arrive at their own estimate by a variety of means. For two of the provinces, they use estimates of under-reporting of acreage on several *hsien* as a basis for revising the official land figures upward.

TABLE B.15. CHEKIANG HILL LAND (*Mou*)			
	1735[a]	1932[b]	1957[c]
Cultivated Acreage	33,763,753	32,461,495	33,000,000
Taxed Hill Land	12,265,496	15,229,398	—
Total Taxed Land	46,029,249	47,690,893	—

[a] *Chekiang t'ung chih* (1736) vol. 67–70, pp. 1304–1353.
[b] *Chung-kuo shih-yeh chih* (*Chekiang Sheng*), p. B-7.
[c] Sun Ching-chih, editor, 1959a, p. 213.

Although the early official Nationalist acreage estimates were certainly below the true figure, in most if not all cases a strong case can be made that the use of samples of bias in a few *hsien* as a basis for revising total acreage gives a significant upward bias to the final results. This procedure is least serious for Szechwan, where the sample was quite large (twenty *hsien*) and the existence of under-reporting was so widespread (see Table B.16 for further evidence of this), but it is quite misleading for Hupei where the sample is small (eight *hsien*) and the presence of under-reporting less pronounced.

TABLE B.16. BUCK'S REVISIONS IN OFFICIAL ACREAGE DATA				
	NUMBER OF HSIEN			*Revised Cultivated*
Province	*Unchanged*	*Under Reported*	*Over Reported*	*Acreage (1,000* Mou)
Chekiang	63	10	1	41,658
Kiangsi	73	8	0	43,340
Hunan	65	10	0	50,207
Hupei	49	13	2	64,500
Anhwei	31	28	0	73,128
Szechwan	41	88	5	155,448

SOURCE: Calculated from data in Buck, 1937 (Statistical Volume), pp. 21–29.

Liu and Yeh use estimates of under-reporting to adjust the estimates of cultivated acreage only for Szechwan and Hopei, but Ping-ti Ho (1959, pp. 126–35) uses similar reasoning as a basis for arguing that all 1933 estimates (including Buck's) had a significant downward bias. Some of Buck's data, to be sure, were biased downward, but in certain cases there was a major upward bias as well, particularly in the highest of Buck's four acreage estimates (e.g., Szechwan and Hopei).

Ping-ti Ho presents two kinds of surveys undertaken by the Nationalist government, the results of "land self-reporting" in 22 *hsien* of four provinces (plus all of Chekiang) and air surveys of six *hsien* of Hupei and twelve of Kiangsi. In Kiangsu, where the greatest effort to ensure accuracy was made, the difference between Buck and the self-reported areas is only 5 per cent. For Anhwei, only one *hsien* was surveyed and for Shensi only four. It is also worth noting that of the 22 *hsien* investigated, five actually indicated that cultivated area had been over-reported.

The largest number of *hsien* (ten) investigated was in Yunnan, but Buck himself recognized that his early estimate of Yunnan was well below the true figure. The 35 per cent difference between Buck's and the "self-reported" area is not a bad indicator of the degree of bias, although the actual bias was probably slightly larger, but this would appear to be largely due to luck. The Yunnan ten-*hsien* sample is seriously biased against districts with 5 per cent or less cultivated land (10 per cent of sample versus about 30 per cent of the cultivated area).[18] Since *hsien* with 5 per cent or less cultivated land are usually in out-of-the-way places, one might expect under-reporting to be most serious in such areas. These data on "self-reporting" experiments, therefore, do not prove much about the widespread existence of bias in the 1930's acreage figures that was not taken into account in revisions made in the late 1930's (and hence taken into account by Liu and Yeh).

The results of the air survey of Hupei also doesn't stand up well under close examination. First, Buck's investigators estimated that serious bias in the official data for that province occurred in only 15 of 64 *hsien* (two cases of which were over-reporting). Four of the six *hsien* for which air surveys were made were from among those fifteen *hsien*. But the strangest thing about the Hupei data is that the totals as revised by the Hupei government are almost as large as the total land area (including all uncultivated land) in a province where only 20–30 per cent of the land area was on the average under cultivation in 1957.[19] In Chiang-ling *hsien*, the Hupei government's estimate of cultivated acreage is 108 per cent of Buck's estimate of total land area. Han-ch'uan, Wu-ch'ang, and Han-yang (contiguous *hsiens*) are in a rich area where the 1957 data indicate cultivated acreage can reach as high as 80 per cent of total land area, but the lowest percentage given by the Hupei government is 85 per cent (one is 95 per cent) under cultivation. Sui *hsien* is in an area of north central Hupei which a 1957 Communist map indicates is in no place more than 30 per cent cultivated. In nearly half the *hsien*, less than 10 per cent of the total land area is under cultivation, yet the Hupei government places the figure at 53 per cent. Buck's estimates of total land area may be a little off, but not to the degree necessary to make the air survey data appear reasonable.

The Kiangsi data are not so obviously improbable as are the Hupei figures. As a sample, it is certainly biased since all the *hsien* are either on the western and southern shores of Poyang lake or along the Kan river, hence all in north-central

18. Derived from data in Buck, 1937 (Statistical Volume), pp. 28–29.
19. Sun Ching-chih, 1958. All 1957 data for Hupei and Kiangsi used in this discussion are from this source.

Kiangsi and in an area where the percentage of total land cultivated is the highest in the province. It is interesting to note that of the eight *hsien* whose data Buck corrected, five were also on the shores of Poyang lake. One possible conclusion (although not the only one) is that the only thing wrong with Buck's estimate of acreage in Kiangsi is that he did not carry his revisions in the flat-lands around Poyang lake far enough. If that is the case, then the total bias for the whole province is only 5 or 6 per cent, since 70 per cent of the province's total cultivated acreage is in other regions. This argument proves very little, of course, except that the Kiangsi air survey does not prove very much even about Kiangsi, let alone all China.

If the above arguments are generally correct, then there is no reason to assume that there is a pronounced downward bias in the cultivated acreage estimates for the 1930's that has not already been taken into account either by Liu and Yeh or in my revisions based on the 1957 estimates of the State Statistical Bureau. There is also nothing implausible about revising downward the Liu-Yeh figures for Szechwan, Chekiang, Hupei, and Hunan. Some errors undoubtedly remain, but there is no apparent basis for assuming these errors are significantly biased in one direction or the other.

The estimates for 1873, 1893, and 1913 are derived from the 1933 estimates together with the indexes compiled by the Agricultural Economics Department of Nanking University and the National Agricultural Research Bureau. The only exceptions are Manchuria and Sinkiang, for which no indexes were compiled. The sources of these latter figures are given in Table B.14.

The justification for using the indexes for 1873, 1893, and 1913 is the same as that given for using the population indexes compiled by these same organizations (see Appendix A).

The discussion in this appendix has been long and rather complex. Clearly there are biases and errors in the estimates even after revisions have been made. It is hoped that the analysis above will be sufficient to convince the reader that the data are good enough for the purposes of this study. For easy reference, the totals used in the text are presented in Table B.17.

TABLE B.17. REVISED CULTIVATED ACREAGE
DATA (1400–1957)

Year	(*Million* Shih Mou)	(*Million Hectares*)
1400	370 ($\pm$70)	25
1600	500 ($\pm$100)	33
1685	740 ($\pm$100)	49
1766	950 ($\pm$100)	63
1873	1,210 ($\pm$50)	81
1893	1,240 ($\pm$50)	83
1913	1,360 ($\pm$50)	91
1933	1,470 ($\pm$50)	98
1957	1,678 ($\pm$25)	112

Crop Acreage Data (1914-1957)

The 1914–1957 estimates of the gross value of agricultural output are made up of several components, the most important being the figures for total cultivated acreage by province for 1913, 1933, and 1957 (in Appendix B); estimates of the share of each crop in that acreage (this appendix); and assumptions about yields (Appendix D). No one of these components is particularly reliable, but it is more likely than not that together they give a general picture of trends that did in fact occur.

There are great quantities of data available giving the amount of acreage planted to various crops for years from 1914 to the present. As in the case of population and acreage totals, the 1957 crop acreage data are assumed to be the most reliable figures available for any period and are used as a base against which to check the consistency of statistics for earlier periods.[1]

The 1957 data are not, of course, accurate in some absolute sense. There are numerous statements by Chinese statistical authorities to the effect that they were dissatisfied with the quality of much rural data (see, e.g., Li, 1962, pp. 28, 33, 43). But it is likely that the crop acreage figures were of higher quality than most other rural data. Cropping patterns change rather slowly, particularly those of the major grain crops. Once one knows the total cultivated acreage, it is not too difficult to estimate the percentage share of the various major crops. By 1957, the Chinese State Statistical Bureau had some 200,000 statistical workers (Li, 1962, p. 51), a large but unknown proportion of which were part of the agricul-

[1] The 1957 data used in this study are taken from the various economic geographies edited by Sun Ching-chih and can also be found in Chen, 1967, pp. 300–317.

tural reporting system. In many cases these personnel had little or no formal training, but it is unlikely that it required much training to come up with a reasonably reliable percentage of land planted to, say, rice as against potatoes, provided that a sincere effort was made to come up with a reliable figure.[2] Valuation of rural capital assets or handicraft output, by way of contrast, would be examples of data where more sophisticated techniques would be required (e.g., well-designed sample surveys).

The cropping pattern of cash crops such as sugarcane or tobacco might be more difficult to estimate than grain if it were not for the fact that the bulk of these crops were sold to central marketing organizations (Donnithorne, 1967, p. 284). Thus the statistical authorities had an easy cross-check on cash crop data.

As one moves back in time, one's confidence in the data declines. For the 1930's there are two sets of data that can be used to estimate crop patterns. First, there are the figures of the National Agricultural Research Bureau (NARB) collected under the direction of C. C. Chang.[3] Second, there are the estimates made in a survey directed by John Lossing Buck (1937, Statistical Volume, pp. 174–79). In their pioneering national income study, Ta-chung Liu and Kung-chia Yeh have averaged the estimated percentage of cultivated acreage sown to each crop in the two studies and have used those averages as their own estimates of the various crop acreages (1965, Appendix A).

I have in essence followed the path laid down by Liu and Yeh, but with differences. First, I have relied entirely on the NARB data and have not used the Buck percentages. Second, I have calculated the percentage share of each crop on a province-by-province basis. Liu and Yeh do this for rice only, whereas for the other crops only the national average share is calculated. Finally I have used the 1957 data both as a check for consistency and as the principal basis for arriving at total cultivated acreage estimates for the 1930's (see Appendix B). Liu and Yeh base their total cultivated acreage figures (and hence individual crop acreage figures as well) on an analysis of six different estimates of cultivated acreage made prior to 1949.[4]

Why use only the NARB data? The arguments in favor of using the NARB figures (derived percentages only) are less convincing than the argument against using the Buck data. By 1937 the NARB had some 6,300 crop reporters scattered throughout the country (Chong Twanmo, 1956, p. 44). Although these reporters probably had a better than average education and no apparent interest in biasing their reports, few if any were trained for this task (Chong Twanmo, 1956, p. 44; Kraus, chap. II). If there were errors in the 1957 data when more than ten times the number of personnel were involved and when many of these personnel had training, it would appear that there was an ever greater likelihood of error in

2. The problem in 1958 and 1959 was that no real effort was made to collect reliable data, but instead politics was allowed to "take command" with the result that estimates were greatly inflated.

3. All NARB data used in this study were taken from, Chinese Ministry of Information, 1943, pp. 561–89.

4. The 1957 provincial figures did not become available until the Liu-Yeh study was virtually completed.

the 1930's data.[5] Still, as argued above, estimating the percentage share of each crop was not one of the more difficult tasks and one would expect the NARB personnel to have done a reasonably accurate job.

The Buck data, by contrast, were collected by twelve trained regional investigators who in turn found and trained a larger number of local men to fill out the various forms. Thus the number of investigators was extremely small and the training of many could not have been much better than that of the NARB reporters.[6] As a result, the size of the Buck sample is quite small for a country as large as China. Only some 164 localities were surveyed for an average of less than eight per province. A province with 20 million people was thus represented by eight (of about 40,000) villages.[7] Further, these villages themselves had to be chosen on less than ideal criteria. The average number of villages surveyed per province in the six provinces of the Southeast and Southwest, for example, were only six, while for the small province of Shansi the number was twelve.[8]

The small size of Buck's sample creates more serious problems for the yield estimates, but even for crop-acreage percentages the possibilities of error are sufficiently great to lead me not to use the Buck figures to derive an estimate for the 1930's. This decision does not constitute a criticism of the Buck survey, since it was not designed to produce an estimate of gross agricultural output and no such estimate is given in *Land Utilization in China.*

Thus for the 1931–1937 estimate, the basic assumption made is that the only major source of error in the NARB figures is that the percentages devoted to each crop were applied to incorrect total cultivated acreage statistics. The percentages themselves are assumed to be reasonably accurate and hence can be meaningfully applied to the "improved" cultivated acreage figures presented in Appendix B. The Manchurian estimates (for the year 1930) are, by contrast, used without adjustment.[9]

If there are problems with using the Buck data to derive estimates of total crop acreages, these problems are dwarfed by the difficulties involved in using the 1914–1918 data of the Ministry of Agriculture and Commerce. The cautious thing to do would be to reject the 1914–1918 statistics in their entirety, but I believe there is some value in applying the Liu-Yeh technique to the 1914–1918 as well as the 1931–1937 figures.

5. Crop reporters in the 1950's may have been under greater political pressure to report inflated figures than those in the 1930's. Even if this were the case, however, it is unlikely that such pressure had much effect on crop acreage data, as contrasted to yield estimates.

6. As Buck himself points out, even such comparatively simple tasks as the enumeration of births and deaths in a given locality were not always properly recorded by "enumerators with little experience in making field studies and only a hazy idea of the use to which their reports would be put" (1937, p. 359).

7. The figure of 40,000 is somewhat arbitrary because of problems involved in defining just what constituted a "village" in China. For one estimate of the number of villages (1,250,000) for all of China, see Li, 1962, p. 17.

8. Buck, 1937 (Statistical Volume), pp. 174–79. The selection of villages was apparently also effected by ease of access to the village (both physical and social).

9. The Manchurian data were taken from, East Asiatic Economic Investigation Bureau, *The Manchuria Year Book, 1932–33*, pp. 114–15. The year 1930 was the last year prior to the Japanese seizure of Manchuria and was picked for that reason.

There is very little reliable information on how these 1914–1918 figures were arrived at. Presumably they represent crop reports sent in by various *hsien* (county) governments via the provincial governments to Peking. How the *hsien* personnel made their estimates is unclear. At times their reports must have been filled out in a completely arbitrary fashion. But if they made any attempt at a realistic figure, about the only method they could have used was first to estimate the percentage devoted to each crop and then apply that percentage to an acreage total. Thus applying the Liu-Yeh technique to such data is at least plausible.

But if the resulting percentages are to be of use, there must be some way of separating out the clearly unreliable totals from those that are at least plausible. Fortunately, there are straightforward principles upon which this separation can be made.

First, most of the provinces whose data are not available or are clearly inaccurate are provinces over which the central government in Peking had little or no control. The Kwangsi, Kweichow, and Szechwan data are rejected in their entirety (except for a few individual Kweichow crop figures). Yunnan and Kwangtung, on the other hand, were beyond central government control but did report plausible figures in the years in which they did report (Yunnan data are available for 1914 only and Kwangtung for 1914–1917 only). Hunan and Hupei are cases where there was some central government influence, but the Hupei figures are too poor to use while those of Hunan are usable for only two of the three years for which they are available. For six other provinces, individual year's data were rejected on grounds of implausibility and inconsistency with data for other years for those same provinces. Finally all data for Honan province were rejected. Three of Honan's 108 *hsien* have cultivated acreage totals that are twenty times or more what they should be. These three *hsien*, therefore, completely dominate the crop percentages in such a way as to introduce major biases. Since crop figures are not broken down below a provincewide basis, there is no way to separate out the influence of these three *hsien*, and hence all Honan data are rejected.

This procedure may appear complex, but percentage data for eleven of the 24 provinces has been used without adjustment, whereas that for five provinces has been rejected altogether. Of the remaining eight provinces, one year's data were rejected for three provinces, two years' data for three others, and three years' data for two provinces. The years used for each province are listed in Table C.1.

INTERNAL AND EXTERNAL CONSISTENCY

Given the speculative nature of the 1914–1918 and 1931–1937 provincial crop acreage estimates, it is extremely important to have some basis for appraising the reliability of the results. One such appraisal can be made simply by checking the internal consistency of the 1914–1918, 1931–1937, and 1957 figures. These estimates are presented in Tables C.5 through C.20. Generally, there is a high degree of internal consistency in the sense that provinces with great amounts of land in a particular crop in one period have comparably large acreage figures in

TABLE C.I. DATA USED IN 1914–1918
ACREAGE ESTIMATES

Province	Year
Heilungkiang	1914–1915, 1917–1918
Liaoning	1914–1915, 1917–1918
Kansu	1914–1915, 1917–1918
Sinkiang	1914–1915, 1917–1918
Shensi	1914–1915, 1917–1918
Shansi	1914–1915, 1917–1918
Hopei	1914–1915, 1917–1918
Chekiang	1914–1915, 1917–1918
Anhwei	1914, 1917–1918
Kiangsi	1914–1915, 1917
Kwangtung	1914–1915, 1917
Kirin	1914–1915
Hunan	1914, 1917
Chahar	1917–1918
Suiyuan	1917–1918
Kiangsu	1917–1918
Shantung	1918
Fukien	1914
Yunnan	1914
Hupei	Assumed to be same as 1931–1937
Kwangsi	Assumed to be same as 1931–1937
Kweichow	Assumed to be same as 1931–1937
Szechwan	Assumed to be same as 1931–1937
Honan	Assumed to be same as 1931–1937

the other two periods as well (and similarly for provinces with small acreages in a particular crop). The provincial estimates from year to year are not, of course, identical. There are certainly substantial errors in some of the figures, but much of the difference is probably a result of minor shifts in cropping patterns. Given the degree of internal consistency that does exist, it seems reasonable to argue that even the 1914–1918 figures were arrived at (for selected provinces) by individuals who made a genuine effort to present a picture of the crop pattern as it actually existed.

A second check of the data in Tables C.5 through C.20 can be made by comparing indicated trends in these tables with trend estimates made in the Buck study. The Buck figures were obtained from areas in which a particular crop was extensively grown and hence are indicative of trends in such areas only.

Most of the Buck figures are also based on very small samples (seven observations in the case of sesame and soybeans, ten for barley, up to a maximum of 29 for cotton and wheat). Since the samples are small and confined to major producing areas, the potential bias is very large. Further, the Buck data are for the early 1930's (1929–1933), whereas those in the tables in this appendix are for

1931–1937. Nevertheless, the trends indicated by the two sets of data differ in only two cases (barley and soybeans), although the magnitude of the trend differs substantially for cotton, sweet potatoes, and wheat. The two sets of indexes are presented in Table C.2.

Neither of these checks for consistency "proves" the reliability of the crop acreage estimates used in this study. Perhaps the most that can be said is that they lend these estimates a degree of credibility.

TABLE C.2. CROP ACREAGE TRENDS
(1914–1930's)[a] (1914–1919 = 100)

Crop	Estimate	1914–1919	1930's
Barley	Buck	100	83
	Table C.11	100	110
Corn	Buck	100	121
	Table C.7	100	145
Cotton	Buck	100	143
	Table C.16	100	101
Kaoliang	Buck	100	70
	Table C.8	100	86
Millet	Buck	100	94
	Table C.9	100	96
Peanuts	Buck	100	137
	Table C.14	100	109
Rice	Buck	100	98
	Table C.5	100	94
Sesame	Buck	100	113
		100	225[b]
	Table C.19	100	273
Soybeans	Buck	100	89
	Table C.13	100	120
Sweet Potatoes	Buck	100	118
	Table C.10	100	217
Wheat	Buck	100	100
		100	104[b]
	Table C.6	100	126

[a] The Buck figures are derived from Buck, 1937, p. 217. The remaining figures are taken from various tables in this appendix. These latter figures exclude all estimates for Manchuria, Inner Mongolia, Sinkiang, Tsinghai, and Kansu.

[b] These indexes were derived using 1904–1909 as a base rather than 1914–1919.

ADDITIONAL ADJUSTMENTS

The figures in Tables C.5 through C.20 could undoubtedly be improved by a detailed crop-by-crop and province-by-province analysis. Such an analysis would involve the use of voluminous qualitative as well as quantitative materials. The materials available and the effort involved would justify another book-length manuscript. I shall not undertake such a task here.

A careful study of cotton acreage by Richard Kraus does provide a check on the quality of the estimate for that one crop in Table C.16. According to Kraus, the average cotton acreage in China in the years 1931–1936 was 79.5 million *shih mou*,[10] a figure significantly higher than the 70 million *shih mou* in Table C.16. Kraus uses the Liu-Yeh provincial cultivated acreage figures to derive his estimates, but this at most accounts for only 2 million *mou* of the difference.[11] The use of Buck's estimates, it should be pointed out, would have led to an even lower acreage total than the 70 million *mou* of Table C.16.

Whether there are similar biases in the other acreage estimates in this appendix, I have no way of knowing. It is likely that if cotton acreage were underestimated, as seems to be the case, then some other crop was overestimated, but even that need not be true.

The only other crop that I shall look at in any detail is rice, partly because it was by far the most important single crop and partly because there are cases of significant discrepancies in the data for the various periods that cannot be explained away by such things as increased double-cropping.

The basic problem is that the 1931–1937 estimates for Kiangsu, Kiangsi, Hunan, and Fukien appear to be too low. Kiangsi and Hunan, to be sure, experienced an expansion in the double-cropping area, but not one large enough to account for all the difference between the 1931–1937 and 1957 figures (see Table III.2). The revised figures for Hunan and Kiangsi were obtained by adding the difference between total grain and economic crop acreage in 1931–1937 and 1957 and then subtracting any increase in double-cropping. The 1931–1937 figures for Kiangsu and Fukien were assumed to be the same as in 1957 (in neither case was there an increase in double-cropping). These are not the only discrepancies in the 1931–1937 figures, but they are the only ones which I could deal with with some degree of confidence. The original and revised figures are presented in Table C.3.

I have also revised the Anhwei rice acreage figure for 1914–1918 downward to the 1931–1937 level. This revised figure and the corrected rice acreage total are presented in Table C.4.

The province-by-province rice acreage figures (uncorrected) are presented in Table C.5. For purposes of comparison, I have also presented the 1933 estimates of Liu and Yeh.

10. Richard Kraus, chap. II. Kraus has converted his data into old *mou* using a conversion ratio of one old *mou* equals 1.209 *shih mou*. The average figure for 1931–1936 in old *mou* would be 65.7 million *mou*.
11. Of the major cotton producing provinces, the Liu-Yeh total cultivated acreage differ significantly from those in Appendix B only in the case of Hupei province.

TABLE C.3. CORRECTED RICE
ACREAGE DATA (1931–1937)
(1,000 *Mou*)

Province	Uncorrected Figure	Revised Figure
Hunan	34,580	46,520
Kiangsi	22,060	31,640
Kiangsu	24,720	32,690
Fukien	12,310	21,466
Total	353,150	391,796

TABLE C.4. CORRECTED RICE
ACREAGE DATA (1914–1918)
(1,000 *Mou*)

Province	Uncorrected Figure	Revised Figure
Anhwei	41,540	26,540
Total	430,010	415,010

All other data are left without adjustment and are presented in Tables C.6 through C.20. Except where otherwise noted, the absolute figures or percentages used in calculating the provincial crop acreage figures were derived from data in the following sources:

a. (1914–1918) the 1914, 1915, 1917, and 1918 editions of *Nung-shang t'ung-ch piao* (*NSTCP*).

b. (1931–1937) Chinese Ministry of Information, *China Handbook, 1937–1943*, pp. 561–89, and East Asiatic Economic Investigation Bureau, *The Manchuria Year Book, 1932–1933*, pp. 114–15.

c. (1957) the following economic geographies edited by Sun Ching-chih whose data can also be found in Chen, 1967, pp. 300–17.

(1) *Hua-chung ti-ch'u ching-chi ti-li*, translated in JPRS No. 2227-N.

(2) *Hua-hsi-nan ti-ch'u ching-chi ti-li*, translated in JPRS No. 15, 069.

(3) *Hua-nan ti-ch'u ching-chi ti-li*, translated in JPRS No. 14, 954.

(4) *Hua-tun ti-ch'u ching-chi ti-li*, translated in JPRS No. 11, 438.

(5) *Hua-tung-pei ti-ch'u ching-chi ti-li*, translated in JPRS No. 15, 388, and

(6) *Hua-pei ching-chi ti-li*.

TABLE C.5. RICE ACREAGE STATISTICS
(1,000 *Mou*)

Province	1914–1918 Average	1931–1937 Average	Liu-Yeh[a] 1933	1957
NE				
Heilungkiang	30	170	—	3,850
Kirin	290	1,510	—	4,252
Liaoning	1,310	1,480	—	4,200
NW				
Kansu	830	330[b]	200[b]	—[c]
Inner Mongolia	920	500[h]	200[d]	—[c]
Sinkiang	1,100	—	—	—[c]
Tsinghai	—	0	—	2,000
Shensi	3,320	1,920	1,100	—[c]
N				
Shansi	2,610	90	100	18,355[c]
Hopei	2,700	1,440	1,200	—
Shantung	1,900	220	200	880
Honan	[2,340]	2,340	5,500	6,200
E				
Kiangsu	33,590	24,720	33,100	32,690
Anhwei	41,540	26,540	23,200	33,720
Chekiang	32,470	25,860	31,200	24,430
C				
Hupei	[26,730]	26,730	31,300	32,530
Hunan	50,390	34,580	60,300	56,690
Kiangsi	43,820	22,060	25,800	44,140
SE				
Fukien	20,000	12,310	13,700	22,117
Kwangtung	[68,050]	68,050	62,900	72,707
Kwangsi	[31,060]	31,060	24,100	33,909
SW				
Kweichow	[7,740]	7,740	12,900	13,420
Yunnan	8,520	14,660	20,400	15,930
Szechwan	[48,840]	48,840	69,800	62,250
Total	430,100	353,150[e]	417,200[e]	483,620[f]
Revised	[415,100]	[391,796]		

[a] Liu-Yeh, 1965, p. 285.

[b] Includes Ningsia.

[c] The 1957 estimate for Shensi, Shansi, Hopei, Kansu, Inner Mongolia, and Sinkiang is a residual.

[d] Chahar and Suiyuan only.

[e] Obtained by addition.

[f] *TGY*, p. 129.

TABLE C.6. WHEAT ACREAGE STATISTICS
(1,000 *Mou*)

Province	1914–1918 Average	1931–1937 Average	1952[a]	1957[b]
NE				
Heilungkiang	6,430	11,310	—	13,890
Kirin	5,870	785	1,757	731
Liaoning	1,560	1,580	2,110	1,005
NW				
Kansu	24,500	16,430	—	—
Inner Mongolia	7,950	9,800[c]	11,660	19,004
Sinkiang	5,690	—	—	10,328
Tsinghai	—	2,540	—	—[d]
Shensi	29,540	23,050	—	—
N				51,640
Shansi	15,060	17,494	16,960	
Hopei	24,970	45,100	31,300	—
Shantung	45,470	60,420	57,660	187,340
Honan	[68,980]	68,980	72,100	—
E				
Kiangsu	28,550	35,970	—	31,640
Anhwei	22,730	35,180	—	40,210
Chekiang	5,540	8,350	—	4,680
C				
Hupei	[17,490]	17,490	—	17,340
Hunan	3,630	4,720	—	5,000
Kiangsi	430	6,550	—	2,260
SE				
Fukien	2,650	3,440	1,564	2,466
Kwangtung	600	2,920	1,100	3,591
Kwangsi	[4,770]	4,770	—	2,913
SW				
Kweichow	[2,840]	2,840	—	4,030
Yunnan	1,470	5,210	—	5,010
Szechwan	[20,360]	20,360	14,550	20,040
Total	347,080[e]	405,289[e]	371,700[f]	413,120[f]

[a] These figures are also from the regional geographies edited by Sun Ching-chih. The Hopei, Shansi, Shantung, and Honan figures are actually those for 1953 and the Kwangtung figure is for 1949.

[b] In addition to the regional economic geographies, these figures were also taken from Chin Shan-pao, *Chung-kuo hsiao-mai tsai-p'ei hsueh*. The estimate for Honan, Shantung, and part of Hopei is actually a residual, but is consistent with other information in the Chin Shan-pao book.

[c] This figure is that for Chahar and Suiyuan only multiplied by the rather arbitrary conversion rate of 2.

[d] Wheat acreage in the Tsinghai–Tibetan region was negligible. Part of Tsinghai is in the northern spring wheat area, the total acreage of which is recorded under Kansu and Inner Mongolia.

[e] These data were obtained by addition.

[f] *TGY*, p. 129.

TABLE C.7. CORN ACREAGE STATISTICS
(1,000 *Mou*)

Province	1914–1918 Average	1931–1937	1952	1957
NE				
Heilungkiang	3,060	2,080	15,000	19,200
Kirin	5,550	3,520	12,454	13,615
Liaoning	4,250	8,750	8,800	10,459
NW				
Kansu	2,190	3,090	—	[4,000][a]
Inner Mongolia	30	840	—	7,000
Sinkiang	3,290	—	—	—
Tsinghai	—	10	—	—
Shensi	2,880	4,380	—	[5,000][a]
N				
Shansi	1,850	4,000	—	5,000
Hopei	11,400	17,700	—	19,000
Shantung	1,460	10,170	—	13,500
Honan	[11,480]	11,480	—	14,000
E				
Kiangsu	4,780	6,490	—	9,380
Anhwei	970	2,210	—	[4,000][a]
Chekiang	2,110	1,040	—	2,390
C				
Hupei	[1,630]	1,630	—	6,920
Hunan	340	770	—	2,490
Kiangsi	120	90	—	260
SE				
Fukien	10	20	—	[300][a]
Kwangtung	230	290	—	[1,500][a]
Kwangsi	[2,730]	2,730	—	8,329
SW				
Kweichow	[2,300]	2,300	—	11,310
Yunnan	2,960	7,050	—	13,880
Szechwan	[13,380]	13,380	—	24,600
Total	79,000	104,020[b]	188,490[c]	196,133[b]

[a] Conservative guesses based on an assumed increase over the 1931–1937 estimates.
[b] These totals were obtained by addition.
[c] Official figures from sources given in Wu Yuan-li, 1956, p. 158.

TABLE C.8. KAOLIANG (SORGHUM) ACREAGE STATISTICS
(1,000 *Mou*)

Province	1914–1918 Average	1931–1937 Average	1952	1957
NE				
Heilungkiang	3,240	7,570	—	8,890
Kirin	9,000	13,790	13,536	10,696
Liaoning	21,980	24,470	23,100	19,004
NW				
Kansu	1,110	3,290	—	[3,000]ᵃ
Inner Mongolia	2,510	8,920	—	5,600
Sinkiang	470	—	—	—
Tsinghai	—	—	—	—
Shensi	850	2,490	—	[2,400]ᵃ
N				
Shansi	10,600	6,980	—	4,000
Hopei	23,220	16,180	—	12,240
Shantung	25,780	21,190	—	20,460
Honan	[15,480]	15,480	—	13,400
E				
Kiangsu	7,010	5,950	—	3,290
Anhwei	7,480	7,830	—	[5,000]ᵃ
Chekiang	110	210	—	—
C				
Hupei	[2,670]	2,670	—	—
Hunan	910	480	—	500
Kiangsi	70	80	—	—
SE				
Fukien	10	30	—	300ᵇ
Kwangtung	230	120	—	1,500ᵇ
Kwangsi	[510]	510	—	1,000ᵇ
SW				
Kweichow	[360]	360	—	500ᵇ
Yunnan	240	720	—	—
Szechwan	[5,850]	5,850	—	6,000ᵇ
Total	139,690	145,070ᶜ	140,910ᵈ	117,780ᶜ

ᵃ These figures are arbitrary guesses included in order to make the total for all provinces comparable to that in earlier years.

ᵇ The various regional economic geographies give an acreage figure for "miscellaneous grains" and also state that one of those grains was kaoliang. If four types are listed, the "miscellaneous" total was divided by four, and the resulting figure entered into the table.

ᶜ These totals were obtained by addition.

ᵈ Wu Yuan-li, 1956, p. 158. This is an official Chinese government figure.

TABLE C.9. MILLET ACREAGE STATISTICS
(INCLUDING PROSO MILLET)
(1,000 *Mou*)

Province	1914–1918 Average	1931–1937 Average	1952	1957
NE				
Heilungkiang	6,270	10,080	—	11,680
Kirin	3,950	13,950	13,113	12,652
Liaoning	4,920	9,480	12,540	9,500
NW				
Kansu	2,740	14,880	—	—
Inner Mongolia	8,620	16,350	—	—
Sinkiang	120	—	—	—
Tsinghai	—	420	—	—
Shensi	2,060	9,850	—	—
N				
Shansi	33,350	15,720	—	10,880
Hopei	23,980	27,460	—	19,040
Shantung	13,970	23,050	—	16,740
Honan	[20,310]	20,310	—	13,390
E				
Kiangsu	7,740	2,120	—	—
Anhwei	550	830	—	—
Chekiang	1,010	480	—	—
C				
Hupei	[2,430]	2,430	—	1,600
Hunan	300	330	—	280
Kiangsi	1,700	850	—	710
SE				
Fukien	570	640	—	300
Kwangtung	680	470	—	1,500
Kwangsi	[520]	520	—	1,000
SW				
Kweichow	[390]	390	—	—
Yunnan	700	670	—	—
Szechwan	[1,680]	1,680	—	1,500
Total	138,560	172,960[a]	146,400[b]	145,750[c]

[a] This figure was obtained by addition.

[b] Wu Yuan-li, 1956, p. 158. This is an official Chinese government figure.

[c] This figure was obtained by taking the difference between the 1931–1937 and 1957 figures for individual provinces (where figures were available) and subtracting that amount from the 1931–1937 total.

TABLE C.IO. POTATO ACREAGE STATISTICS
(1,000 *Mou*)

Province	1914–1918 AVERAGE Sweet	1914–1918 AVERAGE Irish	1931–1937[a] AVERAGE	1957 Sweet	1957 All Tubers
NE					
Heilungkiang	0	340	—[b]	—	3,490
Kirin	310	90	—[b]	—	1,609
Liaoning	0	100	—[b]	400	2,625
NW					
Kansu	0	260	330	—	—
Inner Mongolia	0	1,010	80	—	—
Sinkiang	0	0	—	—	—
Tsinghai	—	—	—	—	—
Shensi	120	90	460	—	—
N					
Shansi	0	200	270	—	2,500[c]
Hopei	350	160	3,170	4,000[c]	6,000[c]
Shantung	760	250	4,020	20,000[d]	20,000[d]
Honan	60	190	5,080	16,000[d]	16,000[d]
E					
Kiangsu	1,010	900	2,890	5,320	5,320
Anhwei	90	60	2,200	11,320[e]	11,320
Chekiang	390	860	1,540	2,660	2,660
C					
Hupei	1,350		1,350	2,850	2,850
Hunan	300	1,300	3,190	6,210	6,610
Kiangsi	90	690	1,540	2,664	2,960
SE					
Fukien	0	410	1,840	4,215	4,519
Kwangtung	1,510	830	5,220	16,208	18,630
Kwangsi	2,250		2,250	4,000	6,270
SW					
Kweichow	[280]		280	1,130	2,210
Yunnan	0	90	560	470	2,770
Szechwan	[8,680]		8,680	20,000[f]	23,700
Residual	—	—	—	—	15,377[g]
Total (Sweet Potatoes)	—	—	44,950[h]	117,447[h]	—
(Irish Potatoes)	—	—	10,000[i]	—	40,000[j]
Total (All Tubers)	25,380[k]		54,950[k]		157,420[l]

ᵃ The 1931–1937 estimates are for sweet potatoes only.

ᵇ No data for Manchurian sweet potato cultivation are given in the *Manchurian Yearbook*. Irish potato data for Manchuria are included in the total for the country as a whole.

ᶜ The Shansi-Hopei figures are rough estimates based on circle graphs in Sun Ching-chih, 1957, pp. 61 and 108. The data are for the year 1953.

ᵈ The Honan-Shantung figures are an average of the sweet potato acreages in 1953 and 1959. The 1953 data are in the source referred to in note "c" and the 1959 data are from CIA, "Agricultural Statistics," *Weekly Reports on Communist China*.

ᵉ According to the relevant regional economic geography, Anhwei sweet potato acreage rose from 7 million *mou* prior to 1949 to 17 million *mou* in 1958. It thus appears reasonable to assume that all potato acreage in 1957 was in sweet potatoes.

ᶠ This figure was arbitrarily chosen except that it is known that most potato acreage in Szechwan was in sweet potatoes.

ᵍ Derived by addition of the provincial totals and then subtracting from the grand total.

ʰ Derived by addition of the provincial figures.

ⁱ The 1931–1937 Irish potato figure is based on data in Liu-Yeh, 1965, p. 300.

ʲ The difference between the sweet potato and total potato acreage is assumed to be Irish potato acreage. This estimate probably somewhat exaggerates the Irish potato acreage as there were also other kinds of tubers.

ᵏ Derived by addition.

ˡ *TGY*, p. 129.

TABLE C.11. BARLEY ACREAGE STATISTICS
(1,000 *Mou*)

Province	1914–1918 Average	1931–1937 Average	1957
NE			
Heilungkiang	3,300	—[a]	—
Kirin	1,730	—	—
Liaoning	720	—[a]	—
NW			
Kansu	1,950	3,340	[2,000][b]
Inner Mongolia	2,970	6,830	[4,000][b]
Sinkiang	180	—	—
Tsinghai	—	1,580	[1,000][b]
Shensi	4,200	5,340	[4,000][b]
N			
Shansi	6,940	3,160	—[c]
Hopei	3,500	6,490	—[c]
Shantung	6,350	5,810	—[c]
Honan	[12,450]	12,450	4,000[d]
E			
Kiangsu	14,530	16,920	11,020
Anhwei	13,050	12,190	8,000[b]
Chekiang	3,320	4,920	3,040
C			
Hupei	[15,930]	15,930	8,730
Hunan	4,070	2,680	2,210
Kiangsi	760	3,330	1,060
SE			
Fukien	1,190	1,780	200[e]
Kwangtung	1,450	2,900	—
Kwangsi	[2,750]	2,750	1,000[e]
SW			
Kweichow	[2,510]	2,510	1,610
Yunnan	840	2,800	3,120
Szechwan	[15,860]	15,860	7,000[e]
Total	120,550[f]	129,570[f]	61,990[f]

[a] *The Manchurian Yearbook* makes no mention of barley.

[b] These figures represent rough guesses made on the assumption that barley acreage in these provinces declined at the same rate as the rest of the country or perhaps a little less.

[c] No mention of barley is made for these three provinces in Sun Ching-chih, 1957.

[d] The Honan figure is a rough estimate derived from circle graphs in Sun Ching-chih, editor, 1957, p. 163.

[e] The regional economic geographies for these provinces state that barley was one of the lesser crops in these provinces. When four crops were said to be included under "miscellaneous grains," barley was assumed to be one-quarter of the total acreage in "miscellaneous grains."

[f] The totals were obtained by addition.

TABLE C.12. MISCELLANEOUS GRAINS
(Field Peas, Broad Beans, Oats, Buckwheat)
(1,000 *Mou*)

Province	1914–1918 Average	1931–1937[a] Average	1957
NE			
Heilungkiang	2,780	5,810	5,767
Kirin	2,950	6,780	7,256
Liaoning	1,830	9,960	15,233
NW			
Kansu	6,210	5,890	—
Inner Mongolia	15,040	18,070	38,120
Sinkiang	670	—	—
Tsinghai	—	1,880	34,086[b]
Shensi	6,750	3,890	—
N			
Shansi	6,890	8,540	16,840
Hopei	10,460	2,490	7,140
Shantung	14,990	2,810	7,304
Honan	[8,030]	8,030	9,250
E			
Kiangsu	18,320	12,490	21,800
Anhwei	8,950	8,880	17,130
Chekiang	5,830	6,990	3,690
C			
Hupei	[12,170]	12,170	10,330
Hunan	2,860	7,980	7,430
Kiangsi	1,570	4,510	3,450
SE			
Fukien	730	810	750
Kwangtung	1,780	2,260	—
Kwangsi	[4,120]	4,120	1,731
SW			
Kweichow	[2,620]	2,620	4,010
Yunnan	3,570	10,880	8,840
Szechwan	[23,130]	23,130	17,300
Total	162,250	170,990[c]	237,457[d]

[a] Except for Manchuria, these figures do not include buckwheat.

[b] The estimate for Kansu, Sinkiang, Tsinghai, and Shensi is a residual obtained by subtracting the estimates for the other provinces from the overall total.

[c] This figure was obtained by addition.

[d] This total was derived by subtracting the estimates for kaoliang, millet, corn and barley from the total figure for "miscellaneous grains" in *TGY*, p. 129.

TABLE C.13. SOYBEAN ACREAGE STATISTICS
(1,000 *Mou*)

Province	1914–1918 Average	1931–1937 Average	1952	1957
NE				
Heilungkiang	6,700	20,490	—	22,760
Kirin	8,580	26,420	—	13,607
Liaoning	8,740	15,370	—	10,940
NW				
Kansu	910	1,340	—	—
Inner Mongolia	400	2,210	—	—
Sinkiang	20	—	—	14,100[a]
Tsinghai	—	20	—	—
Shensi	670	1,480	—	—
N				
Shansi	930	1,730	—	4,500
Hopei	6,510	6,110	—	8,000[b]
Shantung	22,990	22,910	—	31,060
Honan	[13,530]	13,530	—	26,780
E				
Kiangsu	8,940	14,310	—	14,050
Anhwei	8,040	10,700	—	15,545
Chekiang	2,020	2,860	—	1,990
C				
Hupei	[3,170]	3,170	—	5,280
Hunan	1,420	1,340	—	2,540
Kiangsi	600	3,020	—	4,560
SE				
Fukien	970	840	—	1,410
Kwangtung	830	900	—	1,660
Kwangsi	[1,860]	1,860	—	[3,000][b]
SW				
Kweichow	480	1,230	—	2,310
Yunnan	410	2,980	—	2,100
Szechwan	[5,750]	5,750	—	5,040
Total	104,470[c]	160,570[c]	175,191[d]	191,233[d]

[a] This figure is a residual.

[b] These figures are rough guesses based on material in the regional economic geographies.

[c] This figure was obtained by addition.

[d] CIA, "Agricultural Statistics," *Weekly Reports on Communist China*, No. 20, April 11, 1960, p. 87.

TABLE C.I4. PEANUT ACREAGE STATISTICS
(1,000 *Mou*)

Province	1914–1918 Average	1931–1937 Average	1957
NE			
Heilungkiang	0	—	—
Kirin	310	—	—
Liaoning	70	[2,000]	2,235
NW			
Kansu	0	—	—
Inner Mongolia	0	110	—
Sinkiang	0	—	—
Tsinghai	—	—	—
Shensi	50	230	—
N			
Shansi	70	100	—
Hopei	2,360	4,430	3,300
Shantung	2,920	5,190	9,300
Honan	[2,810]	2,810	2,000
E			
Kiangsu	2,670	2,360	2,510
Anhwei	3,170	2,020	[3,000]
Chekiang	470	330	250
C			
Hupei	[960]	960	1,100
Hunan	500	720	500
Kiangsi	500	820	680
SE			
Fukien	1,050	710	1,107
Kwangtung	3,540	2,600	3,787
Kwangsi	[1,830]	1,830	2,357
SW			
Kweichow	190	320	—
Yunnan	60	190	—
Szechwan	[3,160]	3,160	1,700
Total	26,690[a]	30,890[a]	38,124[b]

[a] These figures were obtained by addition.
[b] Chen, 1967, p. 287.

TABLE C.15. RAPESEED ACREAGE STATISTICS
(1,000 *Mou*)

Province	1914–1918 Average	1931–1937 Average	1957
NE			
Heilungkiang	—	—	—
Kirin	—	—	—
Liaoning	—	—	—
NW			
Kansu	—	1,860	—
Inner Mongolia	—	3,730	1,600
Sinkiang	—	—	—
Tsinghai	—	510	—
Shensi	—	3,710	980
N			
Shansi	—	1,810	—
Hopei	—	1,570	—
Shantung	—	630	—
Honan	—	2,110	450
E			
Kiangsu	—	4,130	2,100
Anhwei	—	6.840	[3,500][a]
Chekiang	—	5,700	2,456
C			
Hupei	—	4,620	2,640
Hunan	—	8,400	2,940
Kiangsi	—	7,680	5,150
SE			
Fukien	—	710	449
Kwangtung	—	1,470	350
Kwangsi	—	3,560	349
SW			
Kweichow	—	2,670	3,780
Yunnan	—	2,060	[1,190][a]
Szechwan	—	14,430	2,800
Residual	—	—	3,875
Total	n.a.	78,200[b]	34,619[c]

[a] These figures were estimated on the assumption that the decline in rapeseed acreage in these two provinces more or less matched the national rate of decline.

[b] This figure was obtained by addition.

[c] Chen, 1967, p. 287.

TABLE C.16. COTTON ACREAGE STATISTICS
(1,000 *Mou*)

Province	1914–1918 Average	1931–1937 Average	1952–1953	1957
NE				
Heilungkiang	0	—	—	—
Kirin	0	—	—	—
Liaoning	340	—	6,000	2,925
NW				
Kansu	10	430	—	600
Inner Mongolia	0	—	—	—
Sinkiang	470	—	—	—
Tsinghai	—	—	—	800
Shensi	9,950	7,000	—	5,000
N				
Shansi	2,140	2,700	3,650	5,000
Hopei	5,030	12,160	14,960	15,000
Shantung	15,240	6,630	9,300	10,000
Honan	[8,490]	8,490	10,500	13,000
E				
Kiangsu	11,880	12,650	—	11,840
Anhwei	1,230	3,320	—	3,008
Chekiang	1,440	1,880	—	1,129
C				
Hupei	[7,190]	7,190	—	8,750
Hunan	1,530	1,930	—	1,210
Kiangsi	590	1,210	—	1,090
SE				
Fukien	0	40	—	—
Kwangtung	50	70	—	—
Kwangsi	[640]	640	—	114
SW				
Kweichow	[260]	260	—	300
Yunnan	90	190	—	800
Szechwan	[3,240]	3,240	—	6,000
Total	69,810[a]	70,030[a]	(1952) 83,640[b]	83,630[b]
	—	(Kraus) 79,500[c]	(1953) 77,700[b]	—

[a] These figures were obtained by addition.
[b] Chen, 1967, pp. 286–87.
[c] Richard Kraus, chap. II.

TABLE C.17. TOBACCO ACREAGE STATISTICS
(1,000 *Mou*)

Province	1914–1918	1931–1937	1957
NE			
Heilungkiang	180	—	—
Kirin	550	—	140
Liaoning	90	—	285
NW			
Kansu	10	770	—
Inner Mongolia	20	190	—
Sinkiang	20	—	—
Tsinghai	—	10	—
Shensi	210	610	—
N			
Shansi	150	380	—
Hopei	220	470	—
Shantung	130	920	740
Honan	0	1,050	—
E			
Kiangsu	520	100	—
Anhwei	290	570	409
Chekiang	490	270	—
C			
Hupei	[360]	360	—
Hunan	2,450	940	160
Kiangsi	590	240	—
SE			
Fukien	160	160	96
Kwangtung	440	290	374
Kwangsi	[560]	560	145
SW			
Kweichow	[560]	560	930
Yunnan	80	400	—
Szechwan	[2,500]	2,500	—
Total	10,580[a]	11,350[a]	8,130[b]

[a] Obtained by addition.
[b] Chen, 1967, p. 287.

TABLE C.18. FIBER ACREAGE STATISTICS
(Including Jute, Hemp, Ramie, and Flax)
(1,000 *Mou*)

Province	1914–1918	1931–1937	1957
NE			
Heilungkiang	290	—	500
Kirin	1,230	—	567
Liaoning	140	—	[140]
NW			
Kansu	110	—	[110]
Inner Mongolia	360	—	[360]
Sinkiang	10	—	[10]
Tsinghai	—	—	—
Shensi	270	—	[270]
N			
Shansi	670	—	900
Hopei	540	—	500
Shantung	250	—	300
Honan	[600]	—	600
E			
Kiangsu	90	—	450
Anhwei	530	—	513
Chekiang	120	—	770
C			
Hupei	[330]	—	330
Hunan	1,470	—	250
Kiangsi	400	—	290
SE			
Fukien	160	—	97
Kwangtung	660	—	424
Kwangsi	[130]	—	125
SW			
Kweichow	[110]	—	110
Yunnan	60	—	[60]
Szechwan	880	—	[880]
Total	9,410[a]	[9,000][b]	8,560[c]

[a] Obtained by addition.

[b] Assumed to be a rounded average of the 1914–1918 and 1957 figure.

[c] Obtained by addition after assuming that fiber acreage in 1957 was the same as in 1914–1918 when there was no other evidence available.

TABLE C.19. SESAME CROP ACREAGE DATA
(1,000 *Mou*)

Province	1914–1918	1931–1937	1957
NE			
Heilungkiang	40	—	—
Kirin	10	—	118
Liaoning	10	—	—
NW			
Kansu	0	10	—
Inner Mongolia	0	90	—
Sinkiang	110	—	—
Tsinghai	—	0	—
Shensi	140	1,000	—
N			
Shansi	10	630	—
Hopei	1,010	3,390	660
Shantung	380	2,410	—
Honan	[2,810]	2,810	3,550
E			
Kiangsu	690	2,230	170
Anhwei	850	3,670	approx. 1,500
Chekiang	40	260	approx. 200
C			
Hupei	[2,380]	2,380	3,090
Hunan	0	440	220
Kiangsi	130	1,480	1,350
SE			
Fukien	0	60	43
Kwangtung	20	120	under 200
Kwangsi	0	450	405
SW			
Kweichow	0	170	under 100
Yunnan	0	60	—
Szechwan	0	1,550	—
Total	8,630[a]	23,210[a]	14,130[b]

[a] Obtained by addition.
[b] Chen, 1967, p. 287.

TABLE C.20. SUGARCANE ACREAGE
(1,000 *Mou*)

	1914–1918	1932[a]	1957
Kwangtung	1,100	674	1,760
Szechwan	—	567	620
Kwangsi	(350)[b]	—	562
Yunnan	105	696	300
Fukien	490	175	372
Chekiang	60	142	129
Kiangsi	330	172	80
Hunan	130	526	—[c]
Honan	—	121	—
Kweichow	—	0	50
Anhwei	30	26	—
Residual	—	—	126
Total	(3,600)[d]	3,099	3,999[e]
		(3,600)[d]	

[a] The NARB apparently did not publish information on sugarcane acreage. These figures are from a 1932 survey undertaken by the government accounts office (*Kuo-fu chu-chi ch'u*) and published in *Chung-kuo ching-chi nien-chien*, vol. I, pp. F, 138–39. Buck gives some data on sugarcane acreage in China which give a national total similar to the one used here, but Buck's estimate is completely dominated by one *hsien* in Kwangtung where 41 per cent of the crop acreage was in sugarcane.

[b] Although I have generally not used Kwangsi data for the 1914–1918 period, figures are available for 1914–1915 which provide us with the estimate in the table.

[c] Although no figure is given for Hunan, acreage in that province must have declined if the overall total is correct. Independent evidence that sugarcane production in Hunan declined can be found in production data for 1952 and 1957 which show a sharp drop (see Chen, 1967, p. 357).

[d] I have assumed that sugarcane acreage was the same in the 1914–1918 and 1931–1937 periods. To obtained the 1931–1937 (or 1932) total, I have assumed that sugarcane acreage in Kwangsi in 1931–1937 was something over 500 thousand *mou*.

[e] This figure is an official estimate and appears in Chen, 1967, p. 287.

Crop Yield and Output Data (1914-1957)

Given the crop acreage estimates in Appendix C, the remaining steps in an estimate of the gross value of agricultural output are estimates of crop yields, output, and prices.

Prices can be dealt with quite easily. Liu and Yeh (1965, pp. 341–56) provide all the price data needed for the estimate in this appendix in their national income study. Their purchase price data for 1933 were selected for use here on the grounds that price data for that year are more complete and reliable than are the figures for 1952 and 1957. The year 1933 is also midway between 1914 and 1957, but this is not really much of an advantage because there are no serious index number problems when one is dealing with a single sector such as agriculture. The relevant price estimates are presented in Table D.31 near the end of this appendix.

Yield figures, by contrast, are very difficult to estimate reliably. Problems peculiar to particular crops will be discussed individually below, but a few general remarks are in order here.

With some exceptions, the gross value output index at the end of this chapter is constructed by assuming that the average yield for a particular crop in a single province did not change over time. Thus the index is a measure of the impact on output of changes in the cropping pattern and in the size and quality of the cultivated acreage. It is, in effect, a trend line upon which either I or the reader can impose a variety of alternative assumptions about yield behavior.

There are many reasons why yield figures are so difficult to estimate correctly. Perhaps most important, yield data tend to vary widely over time and between regions. Thus a millet field in a drought may yield little or nothing and the next year a bountiful harvest. Hill land or land full of rocks may produce per acre only a small percentage of that produced by irrigated lowlands only a few hundred yards away. Furthermore, it is much easier for a farmer to intentionally understate his actual yield (or for a village head to understate the average yield in his village) than it is to deliberately falsify cultivated acreage.

Thus a badly designed sample or one carried out by poorly trained investigators could very easily end up being seriously biased. A small sample, even if unbiased, is likely to have such a large margin for error that little confidence can be placed in the results. Such biases and errors are particularly serious if one is attempting to construct an index of movement over a fairly short period of time when one can assume that "normal year" yields[1] could not have changed much either up or down. Under such circumstances, sample biases can completely dominate the index turning what was in reality a rise in output into a decline and vice versa.

The relevance of these remarks to any attempt to independently estimate yield figures for each of the three periods, 1914–1918, 1931–1937, and 1957, is apparent when one compares the figures of Buck, the NARB, and the State Statistical Bureau (for the 1950's). The national average yields for rice, wheat, millet, corn, and soybeans are presented in Table D.1. The coverage of the figures on the first four of these crops is not the same (the 1950's estimates include Manchuria for all crops except soybeans), but this difference in coverage is significant only for corn and millet. The rice and wheat acreage of Manchuria

TABLE D.I. NATIONAL AVERAGE YIELD COMPARISONS
(1931–1958)
(Catties per *Mou*)

	Buck[a] 1929–1933	*NARB*[b] 1931–1937	STATE STATISTICAL BUREAU[c]		
			Pre-1958 high	*1957*	*1958*
Rice	446	342	359	359	463
Wheat	141	144	121	114	145
Millet[d]	148	157	152[e]	—	—
Corn	177	184	191	191	—
Soybeans	112	155	—	81[f]	—

[a] Buck, 1937 (Statistical Volume), p. 209.

[b] Chinese Ministry of Information, 1943, pp. 561–73.

[c] Chen, 1965, p. 319.

[d] Includes both millet and proso millet. I have used the NARB production figures for these two crops to weight the Buck yield estimates.

[e] This figure is for 1952 and may or may not be the pre-1958 high. This is an official estimate which is quoted in Wu, 1956, p. 163.

[f] This figure excludes Manchuria. See Table D.15.

1. The term "normal year yields" is in effect meant to be an average of yields on a particular plot of land over a period of time when the only variable allowed is weather.

amounted to only about 3 to 4 per cent of the national total acreage in each case.

Two points arise out of an analysis of the data in Table D.1. First, some of the NARB estimates are higher than those of Buck and some are lower. There are no consistent biases but, in the case of rice and soybeans, there are large discrepancies (in opposite directions). Second, the State Statistical Bureau estimates for the pre-1958 period are generally lower than those of Buck and the NARB although there are significant exceptions.

The most serious differences between the figures for the 1930's and those for the 1950's are for rice and wheat, two crops that together accounted for about 60 per cent of all grain output. The Buck estimates, in particular, are almost as high as the State Statistical Bureau figures for 1958, a year in which virtually everyone in or out of China acknowledges that the yield and output estimates were grossly inflated. The most reasonable explanation for this phenomena would appear to be either that the Buck estimates were derived from samples biased toward accessible and hence high-yield areas or that the Buck samples were so small that random sampling error could account for much or all of the discrepancy. The Buck wheat estimate was based on 118 observations, rice on only 72 observations.

The 1914–1918 yield data, not surprisingly, are the poorest of all. Only occasional references are made to these estimates in the discussion of individual crops below.

The rather large potential errors and biases in the figures for the various periods, therefore, are the basic reasons behind my decision to use yield estimates for only one period or year. The year I have picked is 1957.

The provincial yield data for the year 1957 are the most complete available for the post-1949 period. As indicated in the discussion of crop acreage data in Appendix C, by 1957 the crop-reporting system appears to have reached a peak in terms of the probable degree of reliability of its data. It is possible, of course, that yield estimates in 1957 were slightly inflated in an attempt to make the performance of the agricultural producers' cooperatives look better than it in fact was. I doubt that such was the case, however. The 1957 yield figures for the various crops are very similar to and often below those for the year 1955, the last year before the cooperatives replaced individual peasant agriculture.

In the remaining discussion, each crop is analyzed individually.

RICE YIELDS

The similarity between the national average rice yield estimate of the NARB and that of the Communists' for the 1950's is deceptive. The provincial estimates for the two periods have little in common. Some of the 1930's figures are higher than those for 1957, others much lower. Buck's national average yield figure, as already pointed out, is nearly equal to that of the Communists' greatly exaggerated figure for 1958.

The Liu-Yeh solution was to average the NARB and Buck estimates except for Hupei, Kweichow, and Szechwan where other procedures were followed.

Although the Liu-Yeh method seems to improve some individual provincial estimates, the use of the Buck data appears overall to lend an upward bias to the 1930's data. The bias would be even greater if Liu and Yeh had not departed from the averaging of the Buck and NARB figures for the three provinces already mentioned. If the 1957 data are a closer approximation of actual yields, this departure lends a downward bias to the Hupei, Kweichow, and Szechwan estimates which partially, but not wholly, offsets the upward bias for the other provinces (see Table D.3).

Given that the 1957 national average yield was the highest post-1949 estimate except for the falsified 1958 and 1959 data, it would seem improbable that the average yield throughout the 1930's would be any higher. It is possible that the weather throughout the 1930's was better than the best post-war years, but not very likely. It can be argued that the cooperatives had a negative effect on grain output, but in 1955, the year before cooperatives were established and a year in which the weather was very good, the national average rice yield was only 357 catties per *mou*.

The procedure followed here is to assume that the 1957 provincial yield figures are generally valid for the 1930's and for 1914–1918 as well. If there was a gradual increase in yields between 1914 and 1957, then this assumption lends a modest upward bias to the rice yield figures for the 1914–1918 and 1931–1937 periods. The provincial data (rather than the national average) are used in order not to eliminate the effects of shifts in the relative positions of certain provinces (e.g., Kiangsu and Szechwan).

WHEAT YIELDS

The highest national average wheat yield reported by the State Statistical Bureau prior to the exaggerated estimates of 1958 was 121 catties per *mou* for 1956. Prior to 1954 (and after 1949) the wheat yield estimate never exceeded 100 catties per *mou*. In contrast, as pointed out above, both Buck's estimate (141) and that of the NARB (144) are virtually identical to the 1958 figure (145).

In Table D.2, 1957 figures from a 1961 book on wheat are compared with the Buck figures for 1929–1933. The regional breakdown in both periods is that originally devised by Buck. In each of the six areas for which Buck gives an estimate, his estimates are higher than those for the year 1957. Although this situation could arise as a result of random error, it is more likely that either the Buck wheat figures have a systematic upward bias or those of 1957 a systematic downward bias. Bias in this case could have resulted from sampling only higher- (or lower-) yielding areas or from the selection of yields from a year when the wheat harvest was abnormally good or bad. I find it easier to believe that there is an upward bias in the 1929–1933 estimates for whatever reason than that there is much of a downward bias in the figures for 1957.

Because I could not find wheat yield data for many of the major wheat-producing provinces in the north, I have not followed the procedure used for rice, but instead have multiplied total wheat acreage in each of the three periods

TABLE D.2. WHEAT YIELDS
(Catties/*Mou*)

Area Classification	1929–1933 (Buck)	Number of Observations	1957	1957 per cent of total wheat acreage
Spring Wheat	152	12	146	8.5
Winter Wheat—Millet	120	19	92.5	12.5
Winter Wheat—*Kaoliang*	131	36	111	46.5
Yangtze Rice—Wheat and Rice—Tea	124	35	109.4	22.7
Szechwan	198	7	177	4.2
Double Cropping and Southwest	182	11	63	4.4
Sinkiang	—	—	169	2.5
Manchuria (1930)	131	—	123	3.9
National Average	141		114	

SOURCES: The 1929–1933 data and number of observations are from Buck, 1937 (Statistical Volume), pp. 209–210. The 1957 data are derived from material in Chin Shan-pao, *Chung-kuo hsiao-mai tsai-p'ei hsüeh*, pp. 29–43. The Manchuria figure for 1930 is derived from the *Manchuria Yearbook 1932–33*, pp. 106 and 108.

by an estimate of the national average yield. The estimate I have used for all three periods is the 1957 yield figure of 114 per *mou*. The use of a national average would introduce a systematic bias into the earlier period estimates if there was a significant shift in wheat acreage away from high-yielding or low-yielding areas (i.e., Szechwan and the spring wheat region). As far as I can tell, no such major shift in wheat acreage occurred in this period (see Table C.6).

CORN YIELDS

Data on corn yields for 1957 are less complete than those available for wheat and rice. What figures there are suggest that 1931–1937 yields and 1957 yields are not very different (see Table D.6). The 1914–1918 yield figures are much lower on the average than those for later years, but the data for several provinces are higher than their 1931–1937 counterparts. There may have been some increase in yields in the 1920's, but it is unlikely that it was very dramatic. In computing corn output data, therefore, the yields of 230 catties per *mou* for Manchuria and 180 catties per *mou* for the rest of the country are used for all years (see Table D.7). The results would not have been altered much if I had used 191 catties per *mou* for all provinces instead.

POTATO YIELDS

Scattered yield data on potatoes can be found for the 1950's as well as the 1930's. The potato yield data are presented in Table D.8. I have followed the practice of the State Statistical Bureau and converted potatoes into grain equivalents at the rate of four catties of potatoes (gross weight) to one catty of grain. The 1957 national average yield for potatoes was 278 catties per *mou*. That figure is also assumed to be valid for 1914–1918 and 1931–1937 (see Table D.9.).

Kaoliang, MILLET, BARLEY, AND MISCELLANEOUS GRAIN YIELDS

The State Statistical Bureau considers corn, *kaoliang*, millet, barley, field peas, broad beans, oats, and buckwheat to be "miscellaneous grain." Except for corn, no 1957 national average yields are available for these crops individually, although there are a few figures available for earlier years (e.g., 1952).

To obtain a rough idea of the performance of each of these crops, I have rounded off the Liu-Yeh estimates of *kaoliang*, millet, and barley yields (1965, p. 300) and applied these yields to the acreage figures for all three periods. The 1957 output of other "miscellaneous grain" crops was estimated by subtracting the 1957 output of corn, barley, millet, and *kaoliang* from the official total for "miscellaneous grain" (*TGY*, p. 119). The average "miscellaneous grain" yield was then obtained by dividing estimated output by the relevant acreage figure in Appendix C and this yield estimate was then applied to the 1914–1918 and 1931–1937 acreage data as well. The results of these various calculations are presented in Tables D.10 through D.13. Total grain output is then presented in Table D.14.

SOYBEAN YIELDS

One of the largest discrepancies between the yield estimates of Buck, the NARB, and the State Statistical Bureau is that of soybean yields. The NARB figures, in particular, are extraordinarily high. The Buck estimates are closer to those of the State Statistical Bureau, but still there is a nearly 40 per cent differential.

The clearest discrepancy is between the Buck and State Statistical Bureau estimates for Shantung, one of the major soybean producing provinces. The Buck figure is 78 per cent higher than an estimate for the early 1950's. The difference cannot be accounted for by regional biases in one or the other sample since the average yields in the various regions of Shantung in 1953 were all well below the Buck provincewide average (see Table D.16). The simplest explanation would appear to be that the Buck sample is biased upward by a few atypically high figures. In calculating the soybean output figures in Table D.17, I have used the 1957 average yield of 105 catties per *mou* for all periods.

OIL-BEARING SEED YIELDS

The Communist yield figures for peanuts, sesame, and rapeseed in the 1950's are significantly lower than those of both the NARB and Buck (Buck did not estimate sesame seed yield). Of the three crops, a drop in rapeseed yields is the most plausible. Total rapeseed acreage in 1957 was less than half that in 1931–1937, but more important the weight of such low-yield areas as Kweichow and Kiangsi had increased sharply relative to that of Szechwan, probably a high-yield area. In contrast, the relative position of the various provinces in the production of peanuts and sesame did not change dramatically. What change there was, if anything, favored comparatively high-yielding areas (e.g., Shantung in the case of peanuts and Hupei in the case of sesame seeds).

It is possible that yields did drop precipitously because the weather was particularly unfavorable or for other similar reasons, but it is more plausible to argue that the 1930's yield estimates are too high. No definitive proof of this proposition can be given, but a brief look at the Buck peanut yield estimate for Shantung is revealing. Buck's sample in this largest of the peanut-producing provinces consists of only five observations—but this total sample has only 28 observations, so there is no bias there. According to data for 1954, most of Shantung's peanut output (78.9 per cent: Sun Ching-chih, 1957, pp. 128, 133–35) is grown in the central South district and on the end of the Shantung peninsula, but only two of Buck's five observations are from these two areas. Two of Buck's observations are from a single *hsien* in western Shantung, a section where less than 10 per cent of Shantung's peanut production is located.

It is also possible that cooperatives had a particularly damaging effect on oil-bearing crops. I have in fact argued elsewhere that such was the case (1966, pp. 70–71). This reasoning is sufficient to explain why yields dropped from 1955 to 1957, but the 1952–1955 yields are all still well below the 1931–1937 estimates.

In light of these considerations, I have decided that it was more plausible to use the 1952–1955 average yield for rapeseed and peanuts as a substitute for the NARB figures for the period 1914–1937. Comparable data for sesame seeds are not available so the NARB 1931–1937 estimates are used. Yield data and output estimates are presented in Tables D.18 through D.21.

COTTON YIELDS

Cotton is one of the few crops whose estimated yield per *mou* for 1957 is substantially higher than estimated yields for the 1930's. Cotton data generally are of a higher quality than other crop figures for the pre-1949 period because a greater effort was made to collect reliable statistics. In addition, a careful re-working of the figures for the 1930's by Richard Kraus is now available. As a result, it appears to me that the increase in yields between 1931–1937 and 1957 indicated by the data in Table D.22 did in fact occur. Output estimates using Kraus' 1931–1936 yield figure for the 1914–1937 period and the State Statistical Bureau figure for 1957 are presented in Table D.23.

HEMP FIBERS AND TOBACCO YIELDS

It is not possible to estimate a meaningful average yield for fibers with the degree of reliability of estimates for other major crops. One source does give an average yield for 1952–1955 of 259 catties per *mou* (*Jen-min shou-ts'e, 1957*, pp.

470–71), but this estimate excludes hemp and flax. There are also scattered yield figures in a book written about such fibers (Liu Hung-chu, 1956) and in the economic geographies edited by Sun Ching-chih, but these figures range from 37 catties to well over 200 catties per *mou* and do not cluster around any obvious point. I have used the figure of 150 catties per *mou* because it seems to be somewhere near the median of these scattered estimates.

The tobacco yield estimates of Buck (147), the NARB (153), and the State Statistical Bureau (1952–1955 average of 153 catties per *mou*) are so close that it is reasonable to use 150 catties per *mou* for all three periods.

The resulting output estimates for fibers and tobacco are presented in Tables D.24 and D.25.

SUGAR CANE AND SUGAR BEET YIELDS

Data on sugar cane output and yields are quite poor. Some 80 per cent of total output came from the three provinces of Kwangtung, Szechwan, and Fukien, but the data for the 1930's and 1957 for these provinces are not consistent. I have assumed 1914–1918 output was the same as in 1931–1937, and that 1931–1937 output can be obtained by multiplying the 1931–1937 acreage (Table C.20) by the 1957 yield. The relevant data are presented in Table D.26.

Attempts to develop a sugar beet industry began as early as 1906 and beets were grown and refined in the 1910's and 1920's, but the amounts were negligible and the enterprises involved failed under the impact of the world depression.[2] The growing and refining of beets was again pushed in the 1940's by the Japanese, but output did not really reach significant levels until 1954 or 1955. The 1957 estimate is presented in Table D.27.

TEA AND SILK OUTPUT

There are great quantities of data available for estimating tea and silk output, but these figures are not always consistent with each other. There is no question, however, that there was a sharp drop in tea and silk output during the 1940's and that production recovered only slowly in the 1950's. The assumptions used in reconstructing output figures for the various periods are presented in Tables D.28 and D.29.

LIVESTOCK

The various estimates of the number of livestock in China are presented in Table D.30 without adjustment not because the figures are reliable, but because it is difficult to come up with a meaningful basis for making such an adjustment. The 1914–1918 figures, in particular, are probably underestimates, but one cannot be certain.

2. See discussion in T. Hoshino, 1920, pp. 195–97 and *The Manchuria Yearbook 1932–33*. pp. 227–28.

THE GROSS VALUE OUTPUT ESTIMATE

Although the above discussion covers most of the products produced by China's agricultural sector, a number of items have been left out. The gross value output estimate in Table D.32, therefore, is lower than what it would be if coverage were complete. The items left out, however, should not significantly affect the figures for percentage increase over time. The significance of the results appearing in Table D.32 are discussed in Chapter II.

SOURCES

Except where otherwise stated in the footnotes to the tables, the 1931–1937 and 1957 yield figures are from the same sources as the acreage figures for those periods (see Appendix C).

TABLE D.3. RICE YIELDS
(Catties/*Mou*)

Province	1931–1937	Buck	Liu-Yeh	1957
NE				
Heilungkiang	235	—	—	253
Kirin	199		—	295
Liaoning	196	—	—	310
NW				
Kansu	169	—	169	—
Inner Mongolia	136	—	136	—
Sinkiang	—	—	—	—
Tsinghai	—	—	—	—
Shensi	280	343	312	—
N				
Shansi	72	—	72	—
Hopei	196	352	274	—
Shantung	94	—	94	—
Honan	252	143	198	233
E				
Kiangsu	371	429	400	416
Anhwei	290	325	308	362
Chekiang	334	294	314	489
C				
Hupei	304	569	404	465
Hunan	388	420	404	341
Kiangsi	332	359	346	283
SE				
Fukien	373	407	390	296
Kwangtung	342	274	308	274
Kwangsi	309	349	329	259
SW				
Kweichow	290	812	369	501
Yunnan	317	420	369	467
Szechwan	383	595	445	459
National Average	342	447	369	359

TABLE D.4. RICE PRODUCTION (1914–1957)
(1,000,000 Catties)

Province	1914–1918 Average	1931–1937 Average	1957
NE			
Heilungkiang	10	40	974
Kirin	90	300	1,254
Liaoning	410	460	1,300
NW			
Kansu			
Inner Mongolia			
Sinkiang			
Tsinghai			
Shensi	4,510	1,520	6,179
N			
Shansi			
Hopei			
Shantung			
Honan	550	550	1,445
E			
Kiangsu	10,400	10,280	13,599
Anhwei	10,860	9,610	12,207
Chekiang	15,880	12,650	11,946
C			
Hupei	12,430	12,430	15,111
Hunan	17,190	15,860	19,333
Kiangsi	12,400	8,950	12,474
SE			
Fukien	5,920	6,630	6,354
Kwangtung	18,650	18,650	19,922
Kwangsi	8,040	8,040	8,780
SW			
Kweichow	3,870	3,870	6,710
Yunnan	3,980	6,850	7,439
Szechwan	22,420	22,420	28,573
Total	147,610	139,110	173,600

TABLE D.5. WHEAT PRODUCTION
(1914–1957)

Year	Yield (Catties/*Mou*)	Production (1,000,000 Catties)
1914–1918	114	39,570
1931–1937	114	46,200
1957	114	47,100

TABLE D.6. CORN YIELDS
(Catties/*Mou*)

Province	1931–1937	Buck	1952	1957
NE				
Heilungkiang	223	—	175	196
Kirin	241	—	—	204
Liaoning	243	—	—	293
NW				
Shensi	162	—	—	—
N				
Shansi	141	—	—	—
Hopei	166	—	156	—
Shantung	183	—	—	—
Honan	133	—	—	—
E				
Kiangsu	217	—	—	187
Anhwei	175	—	—	—
Chekiang	170	—	—	215
C				
Hupei	160	—	—	173
Hunan	200	—	—	230
Kiangsi	152	—	—	135
SE				
Fukien	260	—	—	—
SW				
Kweichow	235	—	—	197
Yunnan	144	—	—	193
Szechwan	271	—	—	173
Average (22 provinces only)	184	177	—	—
National Average	193	—	179[a]	—

[a] Wu Yuan-li, 1956, p. 163.

TABLE D.7.
CORN PRODUCTION
(1914–1957)
(1,000,000 Catties)

Year	Production
1914–1918	14,680
1931–1937	20,440
1957	37,470

TABLE D.8. POTATO YIELDS
(Catties/*Mou*)*

	1931–1937 Sweet Potatoes	Buck Sweet Potatoes	1957 Sweet Potatoes	1957 All Potatoes
Province				
NE				
Heilungkiang	—	—	—	259
Kirin	—	—	—	213
Liaoning	—	—	—	297
E				
Kiangsu	367	—	194	—
Anhwei	164	—	—	285
Chekiang	265	—	621	—
C				
Hupei	210	—	314	—
Hunan	262	—	527	—
Kiangsi	241	—	—	246
SW				
Kweichow	189	—	366	—
Yunnan	217	—	—	243
Szechwan	195	—	326	—
Average (22 provinces only)	263	269	—	—
National Average	—	—	—	278

* All potato yield figures have been converted to one-quarter of their actual weight to conform to the practices of the State Statistical Bureau.

TABLE D.9.
POTATO
PRODUCTION
(1914–1957)
(1,000,000 Catties
in Grain
Equivalents)

Year	Production
1914–1918	7,060
1931–1937	15,280
1957	43,800

TABLE D.10. KAOLIANG
PRODUCTION (1914–1957)

Year	Yield (Catties/*Mou*)	Production
1914–1918	170	23,750
1931–1937	170	24,680
1957	170	20,030

TABLE D.II. MILLET PRODUCTION
(1914–1957)

Year	Yield (Catties/*Mou*)	Production (1,000,000 Catties)
1914–1918	160	22,180
1931–1937	160	27,680
1957	160	23,330

TABLE D.I2. BARLEY PRODUCTION
(1914–1957)

Year	Yield (Catties/*Mou*)	Production (1,000,000 Catties)
1914–1918	150	18,090
1931–1937	150	19,440
1957	150	9,300

TABLE D.I3.
MISCELLANEOUS GRAIN
PRODUCTION
(1914–1957)

Year	Production (1,000,000 Catties)
1914–1918	10,370
1931–1937	10,940
1957	15,170

TABLE D.I4. TOTAL GRAIN
OUTPUT (1914–1957)
(1,000,000 Catties)

Year	Production (1,000,000 Catties)	Production Per Capita (Catties)
1914–1918	283,300	675
1931–1937	319,960	615
1957	370,000	571

TABLE D.15. SOYBEAN YIELDS
(Catties/*Mou*)

Province	1931–1937	Buck		1957
NE				
Heilungkiang	171	—	—	149
Kirin	179	—	—	—
Liaoning	156	131	(1)	233
NW				
Kansu	136	64	(1)	—
Inner Mongolia	99	—	—	73
Sinkiang	—	—	—	—
Tsinghai	—	87	(2)	—
Shensi	109	73	(3)	—
N				
Shansi	104	78	(8)	—
Hopei	127	139	(12)	—
Shantung	179	148	(14)	83
Honan	128	90	(4)	104.3
E				
Kiangsu	172	123	(6)	100
Anhwei	135	109	(7)	—
Chekiang	129	87	(6)	112
C				
Hupei	157	118	(1)	114
Hunan	174	110	(5)	71
Kiangsi	140	93	(3)	85
SE				
Fukien	165	—	—	—
Kwangtung	171	74	(1)	—
Kwangsi	204	60	(1)	88
SW				
Yunnan	225	197	(2)	—
Szechwan	220	—	—	—
Kweichow	—	60	(1)	111
National Average (22 provinces only)	155	112	(78)	81
National Average (Incl. Manchuria)	162	—	—	105

( ) Figures in parentheses indicate the number of observations in the Buck sample.

TABLE D.16.
SHANTUNG
SOYBEAN YIELDS
(1953)
(Catties/*Mou*)

Area	Yield
1	?
2	102
3	72
4	64
5	102
Province Average	83

SOURCE: Sun Ching-chih, 1957, pp. 132–35.

TABLE D.17.
SOYBEAN
PRODUCTION
(1914–1957)
(1,000,000
Catties)

Year	Production
1914–1918	10,970
1931–1937	16,860
1957	20,100

TABLE D.18. OIL SEED YIELD DATA USED
IN THIS STUDY
(Catties/*Mou*)

Year	Rapeseed	Sesame	Peanuts
1914–1937	65	78	170
1952–1955	65	—	170
1957	51	44	135

TABLE D.19. PEANUT YIELDS
(Catties/*Mou*)

Province	1936[a]	1931–1937	Buck	1954	1957
N					
Shantung	300	285	250 (5)	181	—
Hopei	236	238	—	—	190[b]
C					
Hupei	267	240	—	—	248
Hunan	225	210	—	—	150
Kiangsi	267	229	—	—	170
Wheat Region	—	—	210 (9)	—	—
Rice Region	—	—	212 (19)	—	—
National Average	250	242	196 (48)	176[c]	135[d]

( ) Figures in parentheses indicate the number of observations in the Buck sample.
[a] International Trade Office of the Ministry of Industries, *Hua-sheng* (Changsha: 1940), pp. 31–32.
[b] CIA, "Agricultural Statistics."
[c] *Jen-min Shou-ts'e*, 1957, pp. 470–71.
[d] Derived from data in Table C.14 and *TG Y*, p. 124.

TABLE D.20. SESAME AND RAPESEED YIELDS
(Catties/*Mou*)

| Province | SESAME | | RAPESEED | | |
	NARB 1931–1937	1957	NARB 1931–1937	Buck	1957
Kirin	—	16	—	—	—
Hupei	84	68	72	72 (2)	40
Hunan	56	53	80	122 (4)	38
Kiangsi	44	73	81	65 (5)	33
Chekiang	—	—	76	71 (6)	55
Kiangsu	—	—	89	160 (2)	70
Kweichow	—	—	75	215 (1)	44
Wheat Area	—	—	—	118 (2)	—
Rice Area	—	—	—	90 (34)	—
National Average	78	44	87	92	51[a]

( ) Figures in parentheses indicate the number of observations in the Buck sample.
[a] These figures were derived by dividing the total acreage estimates in Tables C.15 and C.19 into total rapeseed (*TG Y*, p. 124) and sesame seed output. The sesame seed output figure for 1957 is an estimate by Liu and Yeh, 1965, pp. 380 and 397.

TABLE D.21. OIL SEED CROP PRODUCTION
(1,000,000 Catties)

Crop	1914–1918	1931–1937	1957
Peanuts	4,540	5,250	5,142
Rapeseed	3,800[a]	5,080	1,775
Sesame	670	1,810	625
Total	9,010	12,140	7,542

[a] There are no rapeseed acreage figures for 1914–1918 in Appendix C. For lack of a better alternative, I have used an index derived from data in Buck, 1937, p. 217 as a basis for estimating 1914–1918 rapeseed output.

TABLE D.22. COTTON YIELDS
(Catties/*Mou*)

Province	1931–1937	Buck	1952	1957
Liaoning	—	—	—	—
Kansu	28	—	—	28
Shensi	21	—	—	57
Shansi	24	—	46	39
Hopei	30	—	38	42
Shantung	33	—	27	36
Honan	24	—	23	—
Kiangsu	31	—	—	—
Anhwei	29	—	19	32
Chekiang	33	—	—	78
Hupei	29	—	—	52
Hunan	29	—	—	36
Kiangsi	25	—	—	47
Fukien	24	—	—	—
Kweichow	28	—	—	18
Szechwan	28	—	—	23
National Average	28.5	25	31	38
Kraus estimate	23.1[a]	—	—	—

[a] Richard Kraus, chap. II. I have converted Kraus' figure into *shih* catties per *shih mou*.

TABLE D.23. COTTON PRODUCTION
(1914–1957)

Year	Yield (Catties/*Mou*)	Production (1,000,000 Catties)
1914–1918	23	1,606
1931–1937	23	1,888
1957	38	3,280

TABLE D.24. FIBER PRODUCTION (HEMP, RAMIE, ETC.)

Year	Yield (Catties/*Mou*)	Production (1,000,000 Catties)
1914–1918	150	1,410
1931–1937	150	1,350
1957	150	1,290

TABLE D.25. TOBACCO PRODUCTION (ALL TYPES)

Year	Yield (Catties/*Mou*)	Production (1,000,000 Catties)
1914–1918	150	1,590
1931–1937	150	1,830
1957	150	1,220

TABLE D.26. SUGARCANE YIELDS AND PRODUCTION

	1932[a]		1952[b]	1957[b]	
	Yield (Catties/*Mou*)	Output (1,000,000 Catties)	Yield (Catties/*Mou*)	Yield (Catties/*Mou*)	Output (1,000,000 Catties)
SE					
Kwangtung	1,960	1,320	5,828	7,300	10,008
Fukien	2,360	413	—	6,647	2,471
SW					
Szechwan	900	508	4,960	5,529	3,445
Yunnan	1,350	943	—	3,078	1,509
Kweichow	—	—	—	3,801	176
C					
Kiangsi	3,210	552	—	4,794	404
Hunan	1,680	875	—	—	116
N					
Honan	1,080	121	—	—	—
Residual	—	135	—	—	2,656
Total	1,577	4,867 (18,720)[c]	5,200	5,198	20,785

[a] *Chung-kuo ching-chi nien-chien*, vol. I, pp. F, 138–39.

[b] These figures are from the economic geographies edited by Sun Ching-chih except for the figure for Hunan and the national figures which are in Chen, 1967, pp. 319, 331, and 339.

[c] This figure was obtained by assuming a yield of 5.200 catties per *mou* on 3.6 million *mo u* (see Table C.20).

TABLE D.27. SUGAR BEET PRODUCTION
(1,000,000 Catties)

	1914–1918	1931–1937	1957[a]
Heilungkiang	—	—	2,100
Kirin	—	—	434
Inner Mongolia	—	—	442
Other	—	—	26
Total	*[b]	*[b]	3,002

[a] These figures are from the economic geography for the northeast edited by Sun Ching-chih and from Chen, 1967, pp. 339 and 342.

[b] See text.

TABLE D.28. TEA PRODUCTION
(1,000 *piculs* or 100,000 Catties)

Province	1914–1918[a]*	1932–1933[b]*	1949–1950[c]	1957[c]
Shensi	10	[10][d]	—	—
Shantung	1	[1][d]	—	—
Honan	1	4	—	—
Kiangsu	6	1	—	20
Anhwei	414	320	100	400
Chekiang	436	563	245	466
Hupei	503	436	30	300
Hunan	2,300	1,942	—	approx. 450
Kiangsi	210	120	20	approx. 100
Fukien	181	170	—	139
Kwangtung	100[e]	[100][e]	—	approx. 100
Kwangsi	40[e]	64	—	—
Kweichow	10[e]	5	—	—
Yunnan	10[e]	16	—	—
Szechwan	230	240	—	—
Total	4,452	3,992	820	2,230

* Converted to *shih piculs* (1 old *picul* = 1.2 *shih picul*).

[a] *NSTCP* (1914, 1915, 1917, 1918). The total was obtained by addition. For several provinces, highly improbable and inconsistent figures were eliminated before averaging.

[b] Chu Mei-yu, 1937, pp. 49–50. The total was obtained by addition.

[c] Taken from various issues of the economic geographies edited by Sun Ching-chih.

[d] No data available so these were assumed to be the same as in 1914–1918.

[e] The output data available in *NSTCP* were inconsistent with each other and generally improbable. I have used the reported number of families in the tea growing business (same source) as a rough guide to output in the area by assuming per person output was the same as in the major tea producing provinces.

[f] The figure for Kwangtung in the source mentioned in note b is much too high. I have assumed output to be the same as in 1914–1918.

[g] *TGY*, p. 125.

TABLE D.29. SILK COCOON PRODUCTION
(1,000 *Piculs* or 100,000 Catties)

Province	1914–1918[a]	Early 1920's[b]	Early 1930's	1949–1950[c]	1957[c]
Liaoning	200[c]	[200]	—	10	1,000
Shantung	96	72	—	—	—
Honan	50	120	—	1	—
Kiangsu	680	420	—	25% of Prewar	25% of Prewar
Anhwei	160	36	100[c]	1	35
Chekiang	1,160	1,200	—	233	490
Hupei	[120]	120	—	—	—
Hunan	30	24	—	—	—
Kwangtung	[1,200]	1,200	—	14% of Prewar	28% of Prewar
Szechwan	280	720	560[d]	—	—
Other	[80]	84	—	—	—
Total	4,060[e]	4,200[e]	4,190[f]	860[g]	2,250[g]
Exports	2,070	2,320	1,390	—	—

[a] Averages derived from data in *NSTCP* (1914, 1915, 1917, 1918) except for bracketed figures which are assumed to be the same as in the early 1920's and Liaoning which is the 1915 estimate from the Northeast economic geography edited by Sun Ching-chih. Extreme figures appearing in *NSTCP* were eliminated before averaging.

[b] These data are estimates made by a Shanghai investigation and now appear in *CKNY*, vol. III, p. 222, except Liaoning which is assumed to be the same as in 1915.

[c] These data are from various issues of the economic geographies edited by Sun Ching-chih.

[d] *CKNY*, vol. III, p. 628.

[e] These totals were obtained by addition.

[f] This is the average of 1931 and 1935 (*CKNY*, vol. III, p. 924) plus Liaoning. The figures originally given are for silk and have been converted to cocoons at the ratio 13 : 1 (Liu-Yeh, 1965, p. 314).

[g] *TGY*, p. 125.

[h] Official trade returns for 1914–1918, 1921–1925, and 1931–1935. They originally were given in silk and I have converted them to cocoons at the ratio 13 : 1. Data are from D. K. Lieu, 1941, p. 265.

TABLE D.30. LIVESTOCK POPULATION
(1,000 Head)

	1914–1918[a]	*1931–1937*[b]	*1955*[c]	*1957*[c]
Hogs	63,500	68,358 (70,200)	87,920	145,900
Sheep and Goats	26,400	48,100 (72,200)	84,218	98,580
Oxen and Water Buffaloes	23,000	37,900 (40,100)	65,951	63,612
Horses	5,000	6,690 (8,400)	7,312	7,302
Mules and Donkeys	5,000	14,400 (13,100)	14,125	12,543

[a] Taken from *NSTCP*. These figures are the averages of the years 1914–1915, and 1917–1918. Where data for particular provinces were missing, the estimate was based on what data were available.

[b] The figures for China proper are from *China Handbook, 1937–1943* and the *Manchurian Yearbook 1932–33* (data for 1930). The figures in parentheses are the Liu-Yeh estimates for 1933 (1965, p. 308).

[c] Chen, 1967, p. 340.

TABLE D.31. 1933 FARM PRICES
(*Yuan*/Catty)

Crop	Price
Rice	0.035
Wheat	0.045
Corn	0.029
Potato	0.040
Kaoliang	0.028
Millet	0.036
Barley	0.038
Miscellaneous Grain	0.035
Soybeans	0.039
Cotton	0.031
Peanuts	0.052
Rapeseed	0.059
Sesame	0.080
Tobacco	0.170
Fibers	0.202
Sugarcane	0.006
Sugar Beets	0.006
Tea	0.258
Silk Cocoons	0.250

	(*Yuan*/Head)	(Utilization Rate)
Hogs	17.4	80%
Sheep and Goats	3.5	40%
Oxen and Water Buffaloes	50.0	15%
Mules and Donkeys	48.0	10%
Horses	48.0	10%

SOURCE: Liu-Yeh, 1965, Appendix B. Where their prices were broken down into more precise categories, I have simply averaged the relevant figures.

TABLE D.32. GROSS VALUE OF MAJOR FARM OUTPUT
(1914–1957)
(Millions of 1933 *Yuan*)

Crop	1914–1918	1931–1937	1957
Rice	5,166.4	4,869.6	6,078.1
Wheat	1,780.7	2,079.0	2,119.5
Corn	425.7	592.8	1,086.6
Potatoes	282.4	611.2	1,752.0
Kaoliang	665.0	691.0	560.8
Millet	798.5	996.5	839.9
Barley	687.4	738.7	353.4
Miscellaneous Grain	363.0	382.9	531.0
Total Grain	10,169.1	10,961.7	13,321.3
Soybeans	427.8	657.5	783.9
Peanuts	236.1	273.0	267.4
Rapeseed	224.2	716.3	455.3
Sesame	53.6	144.8	50.0
Cotton	497.9	585.3	1,016.8
Fibers	284.8	272.7	260.6
Tobacco	270.3	311.1	207.4
Sugarcane	112.3	112.3	124.7
Sugar Beets	0	0	18.0
Tea	114.9	103.0	57.5
Silk	101.5	104.8	56.3
Subtotal	2,323.4	3,280.8	3,297.9
Hogs	883.9	951.6	2,030.3
Sheep and Goats	37.0	67.3	138.0
Oxen and Water Buffaloes	172.5	284.3	477.1
Mules and Donkeys	24.0	69.1	60.2
Horses	24.0	32.1	35.0
Total Animals	1,141.4	1,404.4	2,740.6
Total	13,633.9	15,646.9	19.359.8

Urban Population Statistics (1900-1958)

Prior to the 1930's, the Chinese government did not systematically collect urban population statistics. Instead official figures were compiled for *hsien* (counties) and only rarely did a *hsien* boundary coincide with that of a city. For the 1930's and 1950's, in contrast, there are large quantities of data available, even if their quality is not always very high. The most complete compilation of these figures appears in a study by Morris B. Ullman (1961), and his estimates for the years 1938, 1953, and 1958 are presented in Table E.1.

For the purposes of this study, particularly Chapter V, it is desirable to have some notion of the number of people in large urban centers in the several decades prior to 1938 as well. To obtain such data, one is forced to rely on rough estimates by Chinese officials and foreign observers. At first glance, reliance on estimates of this type might appear rather unrewarding. For several reasons, however, sifting out the unreliable from the reliable figures in order to obtain some idea of the size of major urban centers about 1900 is not as difficult a task as one might suppose.

First, for a number of cities there are several more or less independent estimates which can be checked against each other and against more recent figures for internal consistency. In addition, there are various other kinds of information that are available, such as whether or not a particular city was growing or whether it was larger or smaller than some other urban center. The various estimates can be checked for consistency with these data as well.

Second, much of the growth in urban population in the twentieth century has taken place in a few key cities (Shanghai, Peking, etc.) where somewhat greater efforts were made to get reliable figures. For example, about 20 per cent of the population in cities of over 100,000 in 1958 was in Shanghai, Peking, Tientsin, and Nanking alone.

Third, there were some sixteen cities with a population of 5 million (in 1958) which did not even exist in 1900, except perhaps as rural villages, and a great many others whose population was so small that even a 100 or 200 per cent error would not greatly affect the totals.

For the 1900 total to be far enough off to affect the conclusions reached in Chapter V and elsewhere, one must assume the existence of a consistent downward bias in the population estimates for the fifteen cities with over 300,000 people, a bias of at least 30 to 40 per cent. An error of this magnitude for a single city is certainly possible, but that all or most of the figures are this bad or that the bias is consistently on the side of underestimation appears improbable.

At first glance, the large increase in population between 1938 and 1953 appears to be too large, but not when one takes into account the fact that many cities saw their population decrease in 1938 as a result of the Japanese invasion and that by 1953 Communist China's industralization effort was underway. Much more important, the principal increases in population took place in cities where one would expect a substantial rise, such as the Manchurian cities and Kunming, Chungking, and Chengtu (a total rise of 8,000,000), or cities whose population figures are comparatively reliable such as Shanghai, Tientsin, and Peking (whose population rose by 5,500,000).

It must be emphasized that the figures for any one city are less reliable than the various subtotals. With the subtotals, errors probably, at least to some degree, cancel each other out. Although further research could undoubtedly improve on both the individual figures and the totals, the data in Table E.1 appear to be sufficiently reliable for the purposes to which they are put in this study.

TABLE E.I. URBAN POPULATION DATA (1900–1958)
(Cities of over 100,000 in 1958)
(1,000's of inhabitants)

	c. 1900–1910	early 1920's	1938	1953	1957	1958
Manchuria (NE)						
Shenyang	200	200	772	2,300	2,411	2,423
Harbin	30	300	468	1,163	1,552	1,595
Luta	50	100	637	892	1,508	1,590
Fushun	*	—	215	679	985	1,019
Ch'angch'un	35	100	360	855	975	988
Anshan	*	—	120	549	805	833
Tsitsihar	40	40	97	345	668	704
Kirin	100	100	132	435	568	583
Pench'i	*	—	66	449	500	[449]
Chinchou	†	†	105	352	—	400
Antung	140	140	211	360	—	370
Fouhsin	*	*	160	189	—	290
Chihsi	*	*	—	20–50	—	253
Mutanchiang	30	—	100	151	—	251
Chiamussu	*	—	71	146	—	232
Hokang	*	*	20	90	—	200
Ich'un	*	*	—	20–50	—	200
Liaoyuan	*	*	32	120	—	177
Liaoyang	100	150	90	147	—	169
Yingk'ou	†	100 +	160	131	—	161
T'unghua	2	—	42	129	—	158
Ssup'ing	—	—	56	126	—	130
Shuangyashan	*	*	—	20–50	—	110
Subtotal	[800]	—	3,914	9,703	—	13,285
Shensi (NW)						
Sian	400	200	217	787	1,310	1,368
Paochi	*	—	—	130	—	180
I.M.A.R. (NW)						
Paotou	†	†	70	149	—	490
Huhehot	200	50 +	94	148	—	320
Chining	—	—	—	30	—	100
Kansu (NW)						
Lanchou	80	80	122	397	699	732
Yumen	—	†	—	—	—	200
Tsinghai (NW)						
Hsining	60	—	—	94	—	150
Sinkiang (NW)						
Urumchi	50	30	45	141	—	320
Kashgar	60–70	60	—	91	—	100
Subtotal	[855]	—	[450]	1,967	—	3,960

	c. 1900–1910	early 1920's	1938	1953	1957	1958
Shantung (N)						
Tsingtao	120	120	592	917	1,121	1,144
Tsinan	100	280	472	680	862	882
Tzupo	—	†	—	184	806	875
Weifang	100	97	98	149	—	190
Chefoo	82	90	166	116	—	140
Subtotal	[450]	—	[1,400]	2,022	—	3,231
Honan (N)						
Chengchou	—	†	197	595	766	785
Loyang	—	†	73	171	—	500
K'aifeng	200	—	303	299	—	318
Chiaotso	*	—	—	20–50	—	250
Hsinhsiang	—	—	—	170	—	203
Shangch'iu	—	†	73	134	—	165
Anyang	—	†	94	125	—	153
Subtotal	[500]	—	[850]	1,529	—	2,374
Hopei (N)						
Peking	700	1,181	1,574	2,768	4,010	4,148
Tientsin	750	840	1,223	2,694	3,220	3,278
T'angshan	50	—	146	693	800	812
Shihchiachuang	†	—	194	373	598	623
Kalgan	30	75	146	229	—	480
Hantan	†	—	—	90	—	380
Paoting	80	100	216	197	—	250
Ch'inhuantao	5	5	47	187	—	210
Ch'engte	†	80	43	93	—	120
Subtotal	[1,900]	—	3,589	7,324	—	10,301
Shansi (N)						
Taiyuan	230	220	177	721	1,020	1,053
Tat'ung	†	20+	70	228	—	243
Yangch'uan	*	—	—	177	—	200
Ch'angchih	—	20+	—	98	—	180
Yutzu	*	—	—	60	—	100
Subtotal	[300]	—	[400]	1,284	—	2,776
Kiangsu (E)						
Shanghai	840	1,750	3,595	6,204	6,900	6,977
Nanking	350	400	950	1,092	1,419	1,455
Suchow	40	—	205	373	676	710
Soochow	500	600	388	474	633	651
Wuhsi	200	—	272	582	613	616
Ch'angchou	†	—	125	296	—	300
Nant'ung	†	150	155	260	—	240
Hsinhailien	†	—	—	208	—	210
T'aichou	†	—	81	160	—	200
Chenchiang	168	103	213	201	—	190
Yangchou	100	250	127	180	—	160
Chengshu	†	—	94	101	—	[101]
Subtotal	[2,800]	—	6,205	10,131	—	11,810

	c. 1900–1910	early 1920's	1938	1953	1957	1958
Anhwei (E)						
Hofei	—	—	94	184	—	360
Pangfou	—	70	136	253	—	330
Huainan	*	*	*	287	—	280
Wuhu	137	127	168	242	—	240
Anch'ing	40	100 +	117	105	—	129
Subtotal	[300]	—	515	1,071	—	1,339
Chekiang (E)						
Hangchow	350	600	575	697	784	794
Ningpo	260	465	247	238	—	280
Wenchow	80	100	237	202	—	210
Shaoshing	500	—	149	131	—	160
Chiahsing	†	†	92	78	—	132
Huchou	100	100 +	66	63	—	120
Subtotal	[1,400]	—	1,366	1,409	—	1,696
Kiangsi (C)						
Nanch'ang	300	210	275	398	508	520
Chingtechen	[200]	100 +	125	92	—	266
Hupei (C)						
Wuhan	1,300	1,500	1,242	1,427	2,146	2,226
Huangshih	†	—	—	100	—	135
Hunan (C)						
Ch'angsha	500	536	464	651	703	709
Hsiangt'an	300	300	103	184	—	247
Hengyang	20	—	122	235	—	240
Chuchou	*	—	—	127	—	190
Shaoyang	†	—	83	118	—	170
Subtotal	[2,800]	—	[2,500]	3,342	—	4,703
Szechwan (SW)						
Chungking	600	500	528	1,772	2,121	2,165
Chengtu	450	700	458	857	1,107	1,135
Tzukung	†	—	176	291	—	280
Nanch'ung	†	—	55	165	—	206
Ipin	150	150	78	178	—	190
Neichiang	†	—	—	190	—	180
Wut'ungchaio	†	—	—	199	—	140
Luchou	130	—	68	289	—	130
Subtotal	[1,800]	—	[1,800]	3,941	—	4,426
Yunnan (SW)						
Kunming	45	120	184	699	880	900
Kochiu	—	†	—	160	—	180
Kweichow (SW)						
Kweiyang	100	100	145	271	504	530
Tsuni	45	50 –	72	—	—	200
Subtotal	[250]	—	[500]	[1,250]	—	1,810

	c. 1900–1910	early 1920's	1938	1953	1957	1958
Kwangsi (SE)						
Nanning	25	67	101	195	—	260
Liuchou	35	—	—	159	—	190
Kweilin	80	80	88	145	—	170
Wuchou	65	50	103	111	—	120
Fukien (SE)						
Foochow	624	500	343	553	616	623
Amoy	114	260	177	224	—	308
Ch'uanchou	†	75	57	108	—	110
Kwangtung (SE)						
Canton	900	750	1,022	1,599	1,840	1,867
Haik'ou	12	30	52	135	—	402
Swatow	60	100	196	280	—	250
Chanchiang	190	189	245	166	—	170
Foshan	200	—	135	122	—	120
Chiangmen	†	100 +	55	85	—	110
Ch'aochou	†	300	152	101	—	[101]
Hong Kong	254	625	1,007	2,000 +	—	3,133
Subtotal	[2,700]	—	[3,834]	3,983	—	4,801
Subtotal—with Hong Kong	[2,950]	—	[4,841]	5,983	—	7,934
Total (without Hong Kong)	16,851	—	27,323	48,946	—	66,512
Total (with Hong Kong)	17,105	—	28,330	50,946	—	69,645

* City did not exist or was little more than a village.
† City existed, but no data on its population are available.
[ ] Subtotals with brackets include estimates for cities for which no data are available.

PRINCIPAL SOURCES:

1. 1938–1953, and 1958: Ullman, 1961, pp. 35–36.
2. 1957: *TGY*, p. 12.
3. Early 1920's: Arnold, 1926, including Rand McNally map insert.
4. Circa 1900–1910: Based on reports from officials and issued in 1906 and appearing in among other places, *Shina Nenkan, No. 1* (Tokyo: 1912), pp. 8–9.
5. For general information about various cities, I referred to Shabad, 1956.

OTHER SOURCES AND NOTES:

Manchuria: James, 1888, the record of a journey made through much of Manchuria in 1886 and an insert map from the Proceedings of the Royal Geographic Society, 1887. Population figures for certain cities in 1931 appearing in, *The Manchuria Year Book, 1932–33*, p. 14 were used to check for consistency.

Hopei: Some of the Tientsin and Peking figures are from, Kung, 1937, pp. 305, 307, except for Kung's figure for Tientsin in 1900 which seemed to be too low (320,000). Kung's figures are local police estimates. The figure for T'angshan is based on the fact that the Kaiping mines in 1900 had 9,000 workers plus rather arbitrary assumptions about the number of nonworkers and the rate of growth between 1900 and 1920 (the 1900 workers figure is in Carlson, 1957, p. 45).

Shansi, Shensi: Tat'ung, Yangchuan, and Ch'angchih all owe their development to nearby coal mines, although Tat'ung and Ch'angchih were towns before coal became important. Yutzu is a major railroad junction and Paochi is a railroad station which is a major transshipment point to surrounding provinces. The population estimates for Sian are puzzling. The 1906 semi-official figure is 1,000,000, but this is certainly too high. An American visitor to Sian in 1901 felt the figure was exaggerated and guessed that the correct figure was more like 700,000 (Nichols, 1902, p. 167). If this figure is correct, then the estimates for the 1920's and 1930's must be too low, even when allowance is made for the famine conditions then prevailing. I rather arbitrarily compromised on 400,000 as a more likely estimate for 1900.

I.M.A.R. (Inner Mongolian Autonomous Region): Paotou was apparently a market town of no great significance until it became, for a time, the terminal point of the Peking–Suiyuan railroad. Chining also apparently owes its rise to being on the same railroad line.

Kansu: Although Yumen appears on maps of the 1920's, it was a town of no real significance until the discovery and development of petroleum in the area. The most often quoted population figure for Lanchou is 500,000, but this is improbably high. Rockhill states its population was only 70,000 to 80,000 (quoted in Couling, 1917, p. 286).

Shantung: Tzupo existed (as Poshan) in the 1920's, but it owes its principal growth to the coal fields in the area and the construction of a railroad to Poshan which was in operation at least by the early 1920's.

Honan: Although no estimates of the population of Chengchow before 1938 could be found, it is clear that most of its development resulted from the fact that it was a junction of two main rail lines. Chiaotso owes its growth to coal beds nearby and Hsinhsiang is another rail junction. Anyang also owes its growth to nearby coal fields. Loyang, although a former seat of emperors, was described as a "sleepy agricultural town" prior to 1955. It is unlikely that the total population of all these cities together (except K'aifeng) exceeded 300,000 persons.

Anhwei: Huainan was set up after 1949 when the center of coal mining operations in the area was shifted to that location (Shabad, 1956, p. 130). Hofei is the provincial capital and probably did not change much in size between 1900 and 1938. Pangfou owes its growth to being a major railroad junction.

Kiangsu: Ullman's figure for Nanking in 1938 appears too low. I have substituted Kung's figure for 1935. Such cities as Ch'angchou, Nant'ung, and T'aichou are agricultural centers and were probably of substantial size by 1900. The case of Hsinheilien is less clear because its owes much of its importance to being a port at the end of a rail line.

Kiangsi: One source (Richards, 1908, p. 144) states that Chingtechen employed 160,000 people around 1900.

Hupei: I have used the figure in Couling, 1917, p. 224 for Wuhan rather than the somewhat higher figure in the 1906 reports (1,770,000). Huangshih is a port of call on the Yangtze originally opened by treaty.

Hunan: Chuchou owes its growth to the fact that it is a rail junction.

Szechwan: Tzukung has long been a large city. It is the center for salt production in Szechwan. Neichiang has long been a large sugar center. Nanch'ung is a regional center and Wut'ungchiao is another salt center. The figures for Ipin and Luchow (1900–1910) are from Bishop, 1899, pp. 471, 477, collected on a trip made in 1898.

Yunnan: Kochiu owes its existence to tin. In the early 1920's the mines employed between 20,000 and 50,000 workers and virtually the entire product was exported. The mines at Kochiu were worked only by native methods before 1911. The mines were given a major stimulus with the opening of the Yunnan railway (before 1917).

Chekiang: The figure for Shaohsing is probably high and that for Hangchow low, but the errors offset each other.

Fukien: R. M. Martin (1847, vol. 2, p. 287) estimates the population of Amoy in 1840 at 250,000.

Kwangtung: There are many estimates of the population of Canton including one for the 1840's of 1,236,000 (R. M. Martin, 1847, vol. 2, p. 28). The 1920's figure used here is from Kung, 1937, p. 310. The figures for Haik'ou and Chiangmen are from *China Proper* (Geographical Handbook Series, 1945), pp. 237, 249.

Hong Kong: The Hong Kong figures are for 1898, 1921, 1937, a rough average of the 1945 and 1956 figures, and 1960. (Endacott, 1958, pp. 276, 289 and 305, and *Hong Kong Report for the Year 1961*, 1962, p. 24). The figures are for the whole territory, but approximately 70 per cent (in 1960) lived in the urban center (Victoria and Kowloon) and many of the remainder could also be said to be urban residents.

Grain Consumption Data

A key assumption in Chapter I is that per capita grain production in China during the past six centuries varied within a narrow range. If, instead, grain output per capita declined markedly over this period, the conclusion that per acre yields must have risen would be less plausible. A marked increase in per capita grain production over time would be less serious in that it would re-inforce the case for rising per acre yields. The purpose of the discussion in this appendix is to present evidence that tends to support the assumption made in Chapter I that per capita grain consumption changed little over time, but to the degree that it did change it is more likely to have risen than fallen.

The argument is presented in three parts. In the first, scattered pieces of direct evidence on rural consumption and income are presented. This evidence is generally consistent with a picture of unchanged consumption standards, but there is not enough of it to say anything very concrete. The second step is to look at the range of grain-consumption levels within China and in the world as a whole during selected years of the twentieth century. These data suggest that average per capita grain consumption in China in 1957 was quite high by world standards. If grain production levels had been significantly higher in the past, therefore, most of the increased output would presumably have been used for fodder and, to a lesser extent, alcohol, and not consumed directly. The third step in the analysis is to present scattered evidence that suggests that the number of hogs and work animals per capita in the past was probably not greatly different from the number today.

As already indicated, the direct data on historical grain consumption levels is not impressive. Four different sources for separate periods state that a man consumed one *sheng* ($\frac{1}{100}$ *shih*) per day. Two of these sources are for the Sung-Yuan period in Kwangtung and Chekiang Provinces,[1] a third is for Shantung in 1785,[2] and the fourth for Ningpo (Chekiang) in 1840 (R. M. Martin, 1847, p. 310). One source states that this figure is for husked rice,[3] the others are not specific. A fifth source uses three *shih* of husked rice to represent typical annual grain consumption levels in Anhwei Province in 1844.[4] One *sheng* per day, on an annual basis, would be 3.65 *shih*. The one *sheng* per day figure was probably only a shorthand way of referring to amounts 20 or 30 per cent above or below that level. Further, the statistic in some (but not all) cases was apparently intended to indicate adult consumption during a reasonably good year.[5]

A source of the Ming period indicates that field hands (heavy labor) received 1.5 *sheng* per day[6] while another observer in the 1840's puts the figure for field hands at three *sheng* per day (R. M. Martin, 1847, p. 310). In an area of Shensi in the twentieth century, by way of contrast, a typical individual could obtain 2.4 *shih* of grain per year, but he could survive on only 1.3 *shih*.[7]

In the Sung period, one *sheng* per day converts to 2.4 *shih* per year in twentieth century units, whereas the same one *sheng* per day in the Ming is 3.9 *shih* per year in twentieth-century units, and, in Ch'ing, 3.8 *shih*.[8] Depending on what assumptions one makes about the weight per *shih* and whether the grain was husked or unhusked, one can arrive at per capita consumption levels ranging from 500 to 750 catties (250 to 375 kilograms).[9] Given the lack of uniformity of weights and measures in China, and more important, the vagueness of these consumption estimates as to whether they were for adults only or included children, or were for husked or unhusked grain, and the off hand way the estimates were made in the first place, trends in these figures over time are meaningless. What these data do indicate is that most people throughout Chinese history have consumed large quantities of grain. From all appearances, therefore, the principal source of Chinese energy (calories) was grain. Direct evidence that meat was not a major alternative energy source will be presented below.

There are also scraps of evidence on the wages of farm labor, one of the poorest groups in the society. Figures for the eighteenth and early nineteenth

1. *Sung hui yao chi kao*, vol. 6, p. 5865 (for Kwangtung) and Fang Hui, *Hsu ku chin kao* (for Chekiang).
2. *Kao-t'ang chou chih* (1835) 3.24a.
3. *Sung hui yao chi kao*, vol. 6, p. 5865.
4. Amano Gennosuke, 1962, p. 340, who in turn is quoting Pao Shih-chen.
5. The figure in the *Sung hui yao chi kao* is for a man 15 years old or more. In Fang Hui, on the other hand, the 3.6 *shih* figure is stated to be the average per capita consumption of a family of five, presumably including children.
6. Quoted in T. Nishiyama, "An Investigation of Landlords in Chiang-nan in the Ming Period," *Nōgyō sōgō kenkyu*, vol. 4, special, March 1950, pp. 243–51.
7. *T'ung-kuan hsien chih* (1944) 10.5a.
8. These figures are based on conversion data in Wu Ch'eng-lo, 1957, p. 71.
9. A figure of 3.8 *shih* of unhusked rice (at 130 catties per *shih*) is equivalent in weight to 494 catties, and 2.4 *shih* of husked rice (at 200 catties of unhusked rice per *shih* of husked) is equivalent in weight to 480 catties. On the other hand, 3.9 *shih* of husked rice converts to 780 catties of unhusked rice.

TABLE F.1. RURAL LABOR WAGE DATA

Year	Wage per month (In *Cash*)
1737	450[a]
1740	[2,000][b]
1741	300
1752	680
1789	300[a]
1797	670
1797	600
1798	600
1798	180
1798	300
1799	500
1801	330
1801	470
1802	250
1803	300[a]
1804	480
1809	1,000
1810	500
1818	440

SOURCE: Li Wen-chih, 1957, pp. 652–53.
[a] These rates are stated to be for short-term employment.
[b] This figure is in small (*hsiao*) cash.

centuries are presented in Table F.1. There is considerable variation in these figures, but no discernible trend. One cause of this variation is the fact that in many cases these wages were for short-term employment which was generally paid less. The average wage is roughly 465 *cash* per month or 5.6 *taels* per year or, in real terms, about six *shih* of husked rice.[10] Total annual income from all sources was undoubtedly substantially higher. Wages in the mid-seventeenth century in Chekiang were also similar to those in later periods. One estimate puts total outlay on a long-term male worker in the silk industry at 12.7 *taels* which in real terms would be about 12–13 *shih* of rice.[11] What these various wage figures seem to indicate is that workers in Chinese society in the late Ming and Ch'ing periods must have spent a high proportion of their income on grain for themselves and their families, perhaps more than half.[12] Rural China was not rich enough to spend any large sum on meat or other luxury items.

10. In the early eighteenth century, the average price of husked rice was a little over one *tael* per *shih* (see Chart V.1).
11. These value and quantity figures are from Ch'en Heng-li, 1958, pp. 93–94.
12. How high a portion one gets depends on whether one assumes the worker had or had not other sources of income and on how many mouths that worker's wage had to support. If that wage was the sole support of 2½ persons (half of a family of five) who consumed 3 *shih* each, then the portion of income spent on grain would be 7.5/12.7, or 59 per cent. These figures are intended only to be illustrative.

Given the proposition that grain was the major historical source of energy in China, what is the probable range in which national average grain consumption might have varied in the past. For twentieth-century China, there are two relevant kinds of data. First are the consumption data of J. L. Buck for the 1930's, and second, there are per capita grain production figures for 1957 by province. The Buck data, which are presented in Chart F.1, are expressed in terms of daily adult per capita grain (including potatoes, beans, and peas)

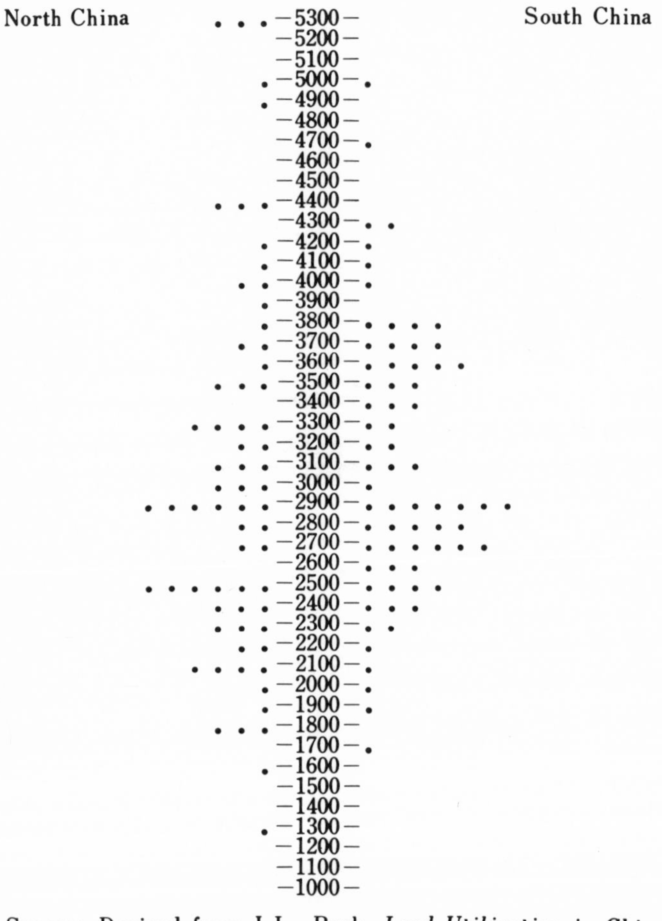

North China   • • • —5300—   South China
—5200—
—5100—
• —5000— •
• —4900—
—4800—
—4700— •
—4600—
—4500—
• • • —4400—
—4300— • •
• —4200— •
• —4100— •
• • —4000— •
• —3900—
• —3800— • • • •
• • —3700— • • • •
• —3600— • • • • •
• • • —3500— • • •
—3400— • • •
• • • —3300— • •
• • —3200— • •
• • —3100— • • •
• • —3000— •
• • • • • • —2900— • • • • • • •
• • —2800— • • • • •
• • —2700— • • • • • •
—2600— • • •
• • • • • • —2500— • • •
• • —2400— • • •
• • —2300— • •
• • —2200— •
• • • • —2100— •
—2000— •
• —1900— •
• • • —1800—
—1700— •
• —1600—
—1500—
—1400—
• —1300—
—1200—
—1100—
—1000—

Source: Derived from J. L. Buck, *Land Utilization in China*
(Statistical Volume) p. 73.
Chart F.1
Grain Consumption Data
(calories per adult per day)

consumption (in calories). Although three areas consumed as much as 5,303 to 5,357 calories of grain per capita per day and one area as little as 1,340 calories, some 93 per cent of Buck's 137 samples range between 1,823 and 4,434 calories and 81 per cent between 1,880 and 3,846 calories. At a rate of 3,400 calories per kilogram of grain,[13] and given Buck's estimate of 77 adult equivalents for a total population of 100 (including children), these figures can be converted into ranges of 151 to 366 kilograms (93 per cent) or 155 to 317 kilograms (81 per cent) of grain consumed per year.

These figures probably cover a wider range than would "national average grain consumption per capita in a normal year," the concept that is most relevant to the calculations in Chapter I. First of all, Buck's samples appear to be for actual consumption in some particular year (usually 1929, 1930, 1931, or 1932) whether or not that year was abnormally good or bad for the village surveyed.[14] Second, many of the high consumption figures may have represented conditions peculiar to certain areas. For example, the four highest figures recorded in Buck's survey all come from the far north (two from Suiyuan and two from one *hsien*, Chang-li, in northern Hopei). It is likely that these high grain-consumption levels resulted from special living conditions this far north (cold weather?) and hence it is unlikely that national average consumption levels could have ever been so high.

Provincial average figures for 1957 are likely to be more representative of possible ranges in national average per capita consumption than are surveys of individual villages (as in the case of Buck's survey). The year 1957 was neither unusually good or unusually bad in most of China. Further, I suspect that province wide data are subject to smaller percentage errors due to improper estimating procedures than are surveys of a single village by individuals of varying competence.

Unfortunately, the only provincial data available are for production, not consumption. These data are presented in Table F.2. In 1957 provincial average per capita grain output (including potatoes) ranged from 207 kilograms in Hopei to 426 kilograms in Heilungkiang. Fifteen of the 24 provinces fall between 299 and 367 kilograms per capita. Of the eight provinces with less than 299 kilograms per capita, several are major grain importers (Hopei, Kiangsu, and Liaoning) whereas Heilungkiang, the only province with more than 367 kilograms per capita, was a major grain exporter.[15] Thus the range in the available grain supply per capita was less than that of production.

Both the Buck and provincial data indicate that per capita grain availability (output + imports) seldom fell below 180–240 kilograms (unhusked) during the twentieth century. The upper end of the range is more ambiguous. With minor exceptions maximum grain availability (output − exports) probably did not exceed 340 kilograms if the provincial production data are used. But Buck's data indicate an upper range as high as 380 to 440 kilograms.[16]

For the purposes of this study, it is important to establish the implausibility

13. Buck gives figures for calories per kilogram for the various crops. I have weighted these with national output figures in Appendix D to obtain an average of 3,400 calories per kilogram counting 1 kilogram of potatoes as only $\frac{1}{4}$ kilogram of grain).

14. It would appear that Buck's survey is more likely to have recorded some villages in abnormally good years than villages in the midst of famine. Even if local famines did exist in the years surveyed by Buck, it is doubtful that Buck's field workers visited any such villages.

15. For the grain trade of the various provinces, see Chapter VII.

16. These estimates are all based on an assumption that only small amounts of grain, 10 to 20 per cent of the total, were used for seed, fodder, and alcohol.

TABLE F.2. GRAIN OUTPUT DATA BY PROVINCE (1957)
(Unhusked)

	Grain Output[a] (1,000's of Metric Tons)	Population[b] (1,000's)	Per Capita Output[c] (Kilograms)
NE			
Heilungkiang[d]	6,150	14,860	426
Kirin[d]	4,275	12,550	263
Liaoning[d]	5,935	24,095	247
NW			
Kansu[e]	4,250	12,800	332
Inner Mongolia[e]	2,811	9,200	306
Ninghsia	—	1,810	—
Sinkiang[e]	2,034	5,640	361
Tsinghai[e]	640	2,050	343
Shensi[e]	4,500	18,130	248
N			
Shansi[f]	4,335[a]	15,960	272
Hopei (+Peking)[g]	10,100[a]	48,730	207
Shantung[g]	12,100[a]	54,030	224
Honan[g]	17,300[a]	48,670	355
E			
Kiangsu (+Shanghai)[g]	11,780	52,130	226
Anhwei[g]	11,495	33,560	343
Chekiang[g]	7,793	25,280	316
C			
Hupei[h]	10,966	30,790	356
Hunan[h]	11,234	36,220	310
Kiangsi[h]	6,832	18,610	367
SE			
Fukien[i]	4,377	14,650	299
Kwangtung[i]	12,200	37,960	321
Kwangsi[i]	5,400	19,390	278
SW			
Kweichow[i]	5,255	16,890	311
Yunnan[i]	6,250	19,100	327
Szechwan[i]	22,799	72,160	319
Tibet	—	1,270	—
	(190,991)[a]	(646,535)	—
Nationwide	185,000	646,530	286

[a] Most grain figures exclude soybeans. But the north China data (Hopei, Shantung) include soybeans. As these provinces were major producers of soybeans, inclusion of soybeans in their output accounts for most of the difference between the official national grain output figure (185 million tons) and that obtained by adding the provincial totals (191.0 million tons).

[b] *TGY*, p. 11.   [c] Obtained by dividing output by population.

[d] Sun Ching-chih, 1959c, pp. 63, 90, 216, and 407 and Chen, 1967, p. 347.

[e] Chen, 1967, pp. 343, 348, 349, 352–54.   [f] Wang Shih-ying, 1957, p. 74.

[g] Chen, 1967, pp. 344, 350, and 356.

[h] Sun Ching-chih, editor, 1959a, pp. 61, 78, 222, 265, 390, and 406.

[i] Chen, 1967, pp. 355, 359, 360–61.

for China of levels of output per capita much above 350 kilograms (unhusked). Data on per capita grain supply and consumption in a number of countries around the world are presented in Chart F.2 and Table F.3. From these international comparisons, it is apparent that the available grain supply per capita in China in the twentieth century was quite high by world standards. In fact China ranks with such countries as Italy, Japan, Syria (a major grain exporter), Greece, Brazil, and the UAR, most of whom had much higher per capita incomes than China. In terms of husked grain consumption per person, China ranks below only Japan (in 1934), the UAR, Turkey and Yugoslavia. Most nations normally thought to be at a comparable level of development with China turn out to consume 10 to 30 per cent less grain than China.

There are undoubtedly many explanations for China's relatively high level of grain consumption. The weather in many of the other developing countries may be less severe, the average height of their adult population may be less than in China, and their bone structure may be more slight. Higher rates of population growth than in China may make for a large proportion of children in the population.[17] But when all these qualifications are made it is difficult to avoid the conclusion that the Chinese population on the average in 1957 had about as much grain as they could directly consume. Further increases in output per capita would have pushed China into the ranks of countries which use large portions of their grain supply to feed cattle for meat or milk.

This conclusion may seem odd given that grain was rationed in China in 1957. But a closer look at rationing in that year suggests that it was rather relaxed and people seem to have been able to buy all the grain they needed.[18] Even a drop in per capita availability of grain in 1960 of some 20 per cent from the levels of 1957, for example, did not cause starvation in China, at least not on any scale.[19]

Given this situation, it seems reasonable to argue that if the available supply of grain in China in previous centuries had been much above present-day levels, a significantly large proportion of that grain would have gone to feed hogs (for meat) or draft animals. The precise level at which this shift would have occurred cannot be fixed, but it is unlikely it would have been much above 300 or 350 kilograms of output per capita.[20]

17. Other possible explanations for the discrepancy are the greater degree of income and grain distribution in China and differences in eating tastes between China and the rest of the world.

18. For a more substantial discussion of grain rationing in China, see Perkins, 1966, pp. 177–87. Some of the excess demand for grain, to the degree it existed at all, may have resulted from the government's decision to freeze grain prices at a low level while allowing other farm product prices to continue to rise.

19. Mao Tse-tung told Viscount Montgomery that in 1960 grain output had fallen to 150 million tons. In per capita terms, this would be about 220 kilograms or just over 20 per cent less than in 1957. Although certain kinds of malnutrition did exist in China at this time, my impression is that shortages of edible oils, sugar, and other similar foods had more to do with whatever malnutrition that did exist than did shortages of grain.

20. It is possible that grain output per capita could have been a little higher in the past than in 1957 without causing a shift to fodder. Slower population growth in the past, for example, could have caused the proportion of children in the population to be lower than in 1957.

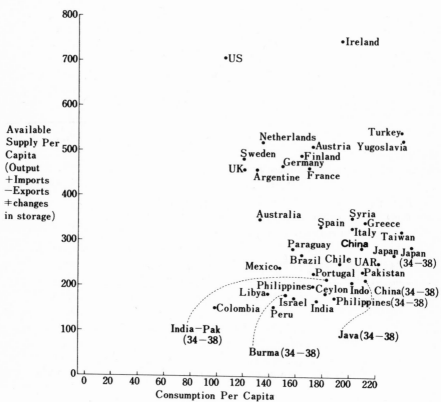

Sources: Food and Agricultural Organization of the United Nations,
Food Balance Sheets(Washington: 1949) and *Food Balance
Sheets, 1957—1959 Averge* (Rome: 1963).

Chart F. 2
Grain Consumption and Supply (Per Capita)
(unhusked in kilograms)

TABLE F.3. GRAIN OUTPUT, AVAILABILITY AND CONSUMPTION DATA (1957–1959)[a]
(Kilograms per Capita)

			CONSUMPTION[b]	
	Output [b] (Gross)	*Available Supply*[b] (Gross)	(Gross)	(Net) of Processing loss
Argentine	708	446	177	133
Australia	705	355	134	98
Austria	390	504	177	137
Brazil	256	281	161	114
Canada	1,348	944	112	86
Ceylon	86	187	180	131
Chile	258	259	195	152
Colombia	134	147	100	82
Finland	406	494	166	137
France	518	480	170	134
Germany	364	448	148	123
Greece	322	339	214	178
India	183	191	174	134
India-Pak (1934–1938)	202	208	183	147
Indo China (1934–1938)	313	217	197	148
Ireland	635	744	197	133
Israel	41	174	161	119
Italy	311	333	202	154
Japan	246	289	234	165
Japan (1934–1938)	246	286	248	202
Japan (1947–1948)	213	230	209	151
Java, Madura (1934–1938)	225	221	207	167
Libya	69	187	140	119
Mexico	218	236	150	126
Netherlands	239	513	135	108
Pakistan	215	230	209	154
Paraguay	255	287	159	141
Peru	130	164	143	117
Philippines	178	200	176	131
Philippines (1934–1938)	180	191	180	134
Portugal	230	228	176	148
Sweden	436	482	118	97
Syria	519	360	201	164
Turkey	563	559	242	210
UAR	232	260	220	187
UK	288	468	119	108
US	902	705	106	79
Yugoslavia	585	535	244	203
China (1957)[c]	286	285	217	167

[a] The term grain as used here follows the Chinese practice of including potatoes at one-fourth their actual weight.

[b] Except where otherwise noted, all data were taken or derived from Food and Agri-

cultural Organization of the United Nations, *Food Balance Sheets* (Washington: 1949) and *Food Balance Sheets, 1957–1959 Average* (Rome: 1963). All "gross" figures are for unprocessed grains. Where the FAO tables record only processed grain, I have used common processing rates to convert the data into unprocessed grain equivalents.

c For output per capita, see Table F.2. Net grain exports from China were approximately 700 thousand tons. I have followed Liu and Yeh, 1965, p. 29 in assuming that 76 per cent of the gross grain output was consumed as food and that the average extraction rate was 77 per cent. Their calculation was based on a weighted average of 1933 data, but the error introduced by applying this percentage to 1957 data is probably very small.

What evidence we have, however, suggests that the number of hogs and draft animals per capita in the past was not very different from the situation in 1957 or 1931–1937. Draft animals were apparently introduced into China in the first millennium B.C. (Chi Ch'ao-ting, 1936, pp. 56–57), and have been used ever since. But if draft animals were known and used, that use was limited. Animals, for example, were used to supply power to pump water for irrigation, but, if the agricultural handbooks are any guide, man power still turned many if not most of China's irrigation devices.[21]

There are also occasional references in historical records to the number of *mou* that could be cultivated by a single man or by one draft animal. In Shensi province, for example, one draft animal was sufficient for 250 *mou* of cultivated land whereas by 1748 the amount cultivated by a single animal was 200 to 300 *mou*.[22] In 1931–1937, the average for the province as a whole was one ox for about 60 *mou*.[23]

In the south in the Kiangsu area, in A.D. 1135 there were five draft animals for every 500 *mou* according to one source. In 1957 the average number of draft animals per 500 *mou* was ten rather than five (Hwang Yü-chia, 1940, pp. 6–8; Sun Ching-chih, 1959a, p. 68). In Yunnan in the late eighteenth or early nine-teenth centuries, two draft animals were used with three men whereas in Szechwan in 1667 one animal was used with two men.[24] In the 1930's there was about one draft animal for every three farm families,[25] but this was a province-wide average, whereas the figures for earlier years may have represented best practice rather than average practice. In Chekiang in late Ming, draft animals were used on wet fields, but not on dry fields.[26]

It is not possible from these data to derive any precise index of changes in the ratio of farm labor to draft animals over time. The figures do suggest, however, that China prior to the twentieth century used draft animals in much the same way as in recent decades. It is unlikely that in Ming times a much larger portion of the grain crop was used to feed such animals.

In most of China, the only other large consumers of grain, in addition to

21. See list of agricultural handbooks in Chapter III.

22. *Shensi t'ung chih* (1748) 38.7a and 45.15a.

23. Cultivated acreage data can be found in Table B.14. The number of oxen in Shensi in 1931–1937 can be found in, *China Handbook, 1937–1943*, p. 580.

24. *Yunnan t'ung chih* (1835) 30.40b; and *Szechwan t'ung chih* (1816) 87.7b.

25. This estimate is based on population data in Table A.5 and some simple assumptions about the percentage share of the rural population together with the number of oxen and water buffaloes listed in *China Handbook, 1937–1943*, pp. 579–80.

26. *Chekiang t'ung chih* (1736), p. 1825.

people and draft animals, were hogs. But as argued in Chapter IV, the consumption of pork per capita over the past several centuries does not appear to have changed much, although there may have been a slight rise. Further, hogs have generally fed more on garbage and chaff together with limited amounts of barley. Rice and wheat, for example, don't seem ever to have been used for fodder in any significant amount.

Uses of grain for purposes other than human or animal food could not have changed much over time. Foreign trade in grain was negligible until the twentieth century and alcohol consumption probably cannot have changed enough over time to make a difference. Seed grain and feed for horses used by the military were probably a constant or declining small percentage of output. Wastage due to rats and sparrows may have been reduced in the 1950's but not before.

Thus it appears reasonable to argue that Chinese grain consumption habits have not changed radically over time. If this statement is valid, then it seems reasonable to set both lower and upper limits on per capita grain output in China in the past. The lower limit would seem to be around 200 kilograms, the upper perhaps 350 kilograms.

Pre-1900 Crop Yield Data

A principal argument of this study is that Chinese grain yields per *mou* or acre increased significantly over a period of several centuries prior to 1900. Assuming that the Chinese 1390's acreage and population data are roughly accurate and that per capita output of grain did not decline dramatically over the centuries intervening, it follows that an increase in per acre yields has to have occurred. In this appendix an attempt is made to support this proposition with direct evidence.

Nearly 900 observations have been collected, primarily from *hsien*, prefecture (*fu*), and provincial histories, either by my assistants, Mr. Yeh-chien Wang, Mrs. Kuo-ying Wang Hsiao, and Miss Ming Su, or, in the case of the Sung dynasty data, by Japanese scholars. Given the incompleteness of and biases in the data, it is possible to establish only that rice yields in a number of key provinces were rising during various periods in Chinese history and to date roughly when the principal increases occurred. In no case is it possible to estimate precisely the average degree of rise for an entire province from these data. In the case of north-China data on wheat and miscellaneous grain yields, even these limited objectives are unachievable.

There are three key problems in the use of yield data culled from local histories. They are (1) the lack of standardized weights and measures over time and among different areas; (2) the presence of various biases and errors in the samples; and (3) the question of how to use rent data to estimate yield. These issues will be taken up in turn.

1. *Lack of standardized weights and measures.* At first glance, the lack of

standardized weights and measures in China appears to present an insurmountable obstacle to the estimation of yields prior to 1900. It is known from any number of sources that the Chinese land measure (the *mou*) and capacity measure (the *shih*) differed from area to area. Further, there is ample evidence that the size of these measures changed over time. Add to these problems the task of converting *shih* (a capacity measure) of husked rice to catties (a weight measure) of unhusked rice and there seems to be little point in even beginning the exercise. If the analyst is careful, however, the problem of converting historical yield data to a contemporary standard measure is not as difficult as these remarks imply.

The least serious problems involve the conversion of husked to unhusked rice, and capacity measures (*shih*) to weight measures (catties). The methods of husking rice in China did not change much over time and hence the commonly used conversion ratio of two *shih* of unhusked rice to one *shih* of husked rice can presumably be used for all periods. Similarly, the weight of a given capacity unit of grain could not have changed much either. Hence, if the capacity measures can be converted into a common or standard unit, these standard units can be converted to weights without the danger of introducing biases. This conversion is necessary because Chinese yield data for the 1930's and 1950's are expressed in catties per *mou*, whereas those for the pre-1900 periods are generally in *shih* per *mou*.

Differences over time and among areas in the principal land measure, the *mou*, are more difficult, but not impossible, to deal with. The problems involved have already been discussed in Appendix B and need not be repeated here. Changes over time in the "standard" *mou* have been carefully researched by scholars such as Wu Ch'eng-lo and his results are used in this study (see Table G.1).

Differences among areas in the 1930's, according to the Buck data presented in Appendix B, were commonly 10 or 20 per cent above or below the "standard" *mou*. What the situation was in the Ming and Ch'ing periods cannot be known precisely. Similarities between earlier and later cultivated-area estimates for districts with stable populations, however, do suggest that the situation in Ming and Ch'ing may not have been much different from that in the 1930's.

Further, when districts did use a land measure that was radically different from the "standard," they often called it by some other name. Several examples were given in Appendix B. Where conversion ratios are given, I have used the data. But occasionally no such ratios are available. In other cases the local measure is not a constant unit of land area at all. In Hunan (C) and Hupei (C) provinces, for example, the quantity of land is often given in terms of the amount of seed required in sowing. Thus several *mou* of land may be equivalent to one *shih* or several *shih*, depending on sowing practices. Land areas so calculated were not normally used in the estimates made in this appendix.

Changes over time in the "standard" capacity measure, the *shih*, are dealt with by referring to the work of Wu-Ch'eng-lo (Table G.1), but differences within and between provinces are much the most serious problem of all.

Differences between provinces are less of a problem than those within provinces. As long as the *shih* measure within a province was reasonably uniform and stable, then changes over time in yields would not be exaggerated (or understated) by changes in the measurement unit. Problems would arise only when one attempted to compare yields in different provinces or when one converted the pre-1900 yield data into *shih* catties per *shih mou*.

Some data on regional differences in the basic capacity measures in nineteenth-century China were compiled by H. B. Morse.[1] Most of the data he collected were for the provinces of Kiangsu (E), Chekiang (E), and Kwangtung (SE), although a few figures for several other provinces were also presented. In the three eastern and southeastern provinces, differences in capacity measures are not great. The standard Ch'ing *shih* measure was equivalent to 103.55 liters. The average of 23 observations for various parts of Kiangsu was 111.7 liters, or 7–8 per cent above the standard. Only two of the 23 observations were more than 10 to 14 per cent above or below the average. The average of three observations for Chekiang was 90.6 liters (13 per cent below the standard), and that of four observations for Kwangtung 120.5 liters (17 per cent above the standard).

Differences between the standard and local *shih* in other areas such as Shantung (N), Shansi (N), and Yunnan (SW) are much greater, but only one or two observations each are available for these provinces.

Pressures for standardization of weights and measures were probably much greater in the provinces along the Yangtze River and the southeast coast than elsewhere. These were the provinces where long-distance commerce was most developed (see Chapters VI–VII). Long-distance commerce by its nature requires agreement on the meaning of weights and measures between widely separated regions. A merchant ordering rice from Hunan must have a precise knowledge of the quantity he is going to receive. The easiest way to handle such a problem is for the parties at both ends of the transaction to agree on a single measure.

Another element tending to encourage standardization in several of these same provinces was the government collection and shipment of "tribute" rice to Peking. There was a standard measure for tribute shipments and this standard probably influenced local measures as well in regions affected. Most tribute shipments, however, came from the Yangtze River provinces and hence the tribute measure probably had little influence on local *shih* in the north, southwest, and southeast.

Tax payments in kind during the Ming and early Ch'ing period were presumably calculated using a common measure as well.[2] Otherwise tax evasion would have been an extraordinarily simple matter for landowners. Certainly the government added up the totals received from various areas as if they were measured in comparable units. Minor variations could be and undoubtedly were ignored by those keeping the financial records, but it is less likely that a responsible official would knowingly add tax payments from different areas that were measured in units differing by 50 or 100 per cent or more.

---

1. H. B. Morse, 1889, vol. 2, pp. 90–92. These data are based on a circular sent to foreigners residing in various parts of China.
2. This statement should not be understood literally, since there were many minor adjustments made in local tax measures.

The land tax in kind, however, was of much less importance in the Ch'ing than the Ming periods. Its greatest influence on local measures was thus during the Ming period when the population of China was concentrated along the lower reaches of the Yangtze River and the southeast coast.

From this discussion it would appear that the principal pressures for standardization applied mainly to the provinces in central, east, and southeast China. Fortunately, as it turns out, most of the data on yields that are reported in this appendix are from these same provinces. The principal exceptions are the rice yield data for Szechwan and Yunnan and the wheat and miscellaneous grain yield data for Shensi. This is only one of several problems that make it difficult to draw much of significance from northern yield data. Other problems will be dealt with in subsequent sections of this appendix.

Although Szechwan figures are presented in the summary table, Table G.2, it may well be that the *shih* measure used for this province was as much as 100 per cent or more above the standard.[3] For example, I have references to *shih* (market), *hsiang* (rural), and *ching* (capital) capacity measures for rice, but no conversion figures for any.[4] The last of the three is presumably the standard measure, but the first two appear in the same source along with an equivalent value in silver. A *hsiang shih* is, according to this source, worth 75 per cent more than a *shih shih*. Given these considerations, it would appear that the Szechwan estimates should be used with much greater caution than those for the other provinces in Table G.2. For Yunnan, fortunately, virtually all the data are explicitly given in *ching* (capital) *shih*, which I assume to be the "national standard" *shih*.

2. Biases and errors in the sample. There are two major sources of bias or error in the samples used for the individual provinces, and several more possible minor biases.

Data for the northern provinces may refer to wheat, corn, millet, or even rice yields. Often the source does not specify which crop is involved. Because wheat yields are much lower than those of millet and corn, a sample made up of a higher proportion of wheat yields would be lower than one with a large number of millet yields. In addition, crop yields in the north fluctuate more than in the south and one often cannot discover what kind of a year the figure in the source is meant to refer to.[5] There is no obvious bias in the data for Shensi in Table G.13, but one can conclude that the variance around the mean is so large that changes in the provincewide averages over time may simply reflect this variance and not changes in the true mean.

The principal source of bias in the rice yield samples is geographic in nature.

3. This is the tentative opinion of Mr. Yeh-chien Wang based on a study he is presently undertaking.

4. The data in this and the subsequent four sentences are from the *Kao hsien chih* (1866) 15.9b and the *Wu-shan hsien chih* (1893) 16.21a.

5. It was more common in the north to fix rents on the basis of a percentage of the crop rather than as a fixed amount. Hence rents in any given year would also fluctuate according to whether the crop was good or bad.

The Kiangsu sample is taken almost entirely from the rich Soochow Sung-chiang delta area south of the Yangtze river. The Chekiang and Kiangsi figures are all from the richer northern portion of these two provinces, and the Kwangtung data are concentrated in the Swatow and Canton areas, the former being the highest rice-yield area in all China as well as Kwangtung. The Szechwan yields are from three *hsien* and it is not clear whether these *hsien* were above or below average. Only the Hupei, Kwangsi, Yunnan, and perhaps the Hunan rice-yield samples cover anything like the entire province. The Hunan figures, however, seems to be biased toward Ch'ang-sha prefecture.

Given this bias toward high-yield areas, one would expect that the sample average would be higher than the true average yield for the province as a whole. This bias would seem to provide an adequate explanation for the existence of higher average yields in the nineteenth century than in 1957 in several of the provinces.

Another possible source of bias arises from the use of so much data from public land, particularly school land. Some scholars believe that school land was generally poor land. A downward bias from this source would not be serious if school-land data were distributed fairly evenly among periods for a particular province. This is the case in most of the provinces where school-land data are important. But, in my own opinion, the case that school-land yields are generally lower than the average on land used for other purposes is yet to be proved. For Kwangtung province (SE), for example, school-land data are fairly evenly distributed among the sixteenth, seventeenth, eighteenth, and nineteenth centuries. In each century the average yield on school land is slightly above, not below, the average yield on other kinds of land. For Yunnan province (SW), eight pieces of school land are stated to be high-grade, nine middle-grade, and only five low-grade rice land. The quality of the other Yunnan observations is not specified. School land may well be worse than the best land, but not worse than average quality land.

An additional source of some upward bias in earlier years may exist if observers at the time in question only saw fit to comment on particularly high yields. For example, three of seven observations for sixteenth- and seventeenth-century Hunan are explicitly stated to be yields in a good year or on high-grade land. One advantage of public-land data over statements in memorials and elsewhere regarding the yield in a particular area is that one knows that the yield was recorded because it was an official duty to keep records for such land, not because yields or rents on such land were unusual in some respect.

3. *The use of rent data.* A large number of the yield observations for various provinces were derived by doubling figures for rent. The practice in twentieth-century China was to charge a rent which amounted to half of the normal yield of the principal summer-fall crop. The winter crop commonly was the sole possession of the tenant. There is a great deal of evidence with which to support the belief that rents have for many centuries amounted to about half the yield of the main summer crop (if there were two or more rice crops, then rent was half of the output of both crops).

For example, data collected for the period 1796–1820 indicate that in 19 of 34 cases, rent was exactly 50 per cent, in 11 cases below and 4 above 50 per cent. One suspects that the 15 cases above and below were generally divided on a 60–40 or 55–45 basis (Li Wen-chih, 1957, p. 613). Similar examples of 50–50 or 60–40 divisions are found in Sung materials according to Sudo Yoshiyuki (1954, p. 613). Data for the 1880's indicate that rents throughout the country were about half of the rice yield, but since rents were fixed, in a good year the real rate might be only one-third (Jamieson, 1890, pp. 59–117). These examples could readily be increased several-fold. Further evidence of the rough validity of doubling rent data to obtain an estimate of yields is provided in subsequent tables. Where there are substantial amounts of both rent and yield data for a particular period and province, the two different kinds of data give roughly similar results (see Kiangsu, Kwangtung, and Hunan) although in Kiangsu and nineteenth-century Hunan the rent estimates tend to be lower, whereas in Kwangtung the opposite is the case.

CONCLUDING APPRAISAL

When all the above qualifications have been made, it is still reasonable to argue that errors and biases in the data would not upset the principal conclusion of this appendix, that grain yields per acre rose slowly but significantly over periods of several centuries. If anything, known biases in the data tend to reinforce this conclusion.

The lowest-quality data in Table G.2 are probably those that make up the nineteenth-century estimate for Szechwan (SW). For Szechwan, the capacity measure (the *shih*) may have been radically different from the "national standard," or the three *hsien* from which the data were taken may have been atypical.

The Kwangsi (SE) eighteenth-century figures are also a puzzle. Yields derived from school-land data are less than half those derived from a much larger sample of sacrifice-land data. My initial reaction was to assume that the sacrifice-land figures must be yields (the source is not explicit on this point). But in all other provinces this land was let out to tenants and the figures recorded in the local histories are explicitly stated to be rents. Hence I have treated the Kwangsi data as rents.

For the remaining seven provinces listed in Table G.2, there are an average of 108 observations per province, ranging from a minimum of 60 (for Hupei) to 169 (for Kiangsu). Further, except for Yunnan, the observations are scattered over a period of several centuries. As a result, it is possible to obtain a picture of change (or the lack of it) without converting the figures to *shih* catties per *shih mou* and comparing those figures with the cultivated acreage yield derived from 1957 data. Conversion is bound to introduce some error due to differences in regional weights and measures. In addition, the 1957 provincial averages include many regions not covered by averages derived from rent and yield data in the local histories.

If the rice-yield figures are useful for certain limited purposes, the same cannot be said for wheat and miscellaneous grain yields. In the rice-producing provinces of the Yangtze river on south, there are very few wheat-yield figures. Because rent was generally paid on the basis of the main summer crop (i.e., rice), there are also very few wheat-rent observations and it is seldom clear from the observations that do exist just how much land was actually planted in wheat.

Northern yield and rent data are not much better. Perhaps the most useful estimate is that for Honan (N) in the Chin period (A.D. 1262) because it is, according to the original source, the average yield on a very large amount of land (96 million *mou*). The Shensi (NW) figures are in sufficient number (48 observations) and generally low enough so that one can tentatively conclude that yields must have risen in that province in the late nineteenth and twentieth centuries. The Liaoning (NE) figures for the 1640's are interesting, but not significant because the province was so sparsely populated in the seventeenth century. There are too few Shantung (N) observations (7) to conclude much from them.

Local histories for provinces not included in this appendix were surveyed, but either there was little or no yield or rent data to be found or, as in the case of Fukien (SE), the rents were generally paid in money or were measured in special units which I was unable to convert into standard units.

TABLE G.I. YIELD CONVERSION RATIOS

Period	One mou = —acre[a]	One old shih = —shih shih[b]	No. of catties of rice per shih[c]	One old shih per old mou = —shih catties per shih mou[d]
Sung	0.1399	0.664	—	102
Yuan	0.1399	0.949	—	145
Ming	0.1434	1.074	—	160
Ch'ing	0.1518	1.036	—	146
Present	0.1647	1.000	130	130

[a] Table B.2.

[b] Wu Ch'eng-lo, 1957, p. 71.

[c] This figure is for unhusked rice and is in *shih* catties. There are 150 *shih* catties per *shih shih* of husked rice. Ch'en Heng-li, 1958, p. 25.

[d] The formula used in arriving at these figures was, using Ming as an example:

$$\frac{0.1647}{0.1434} \times 1.074 \times 130 = 160$$

TABLE G.2. RICE YIELDS

(*Shih* Catties per *Shih Mou*—Unhusked)

Province	SUNG 960–1279	YUAN 1280–1367	1368–1499	MING 1500–1599	1600–1699	CH'ING 1700–1799	1800–1899	1957
E								
Chekiang	402 (115)*	473 (28)	—	—	600	—	—	685
Kiangsu	326 (143)	347 (3)	—	450 (11)		550 (6)	501 (8)	433
C								
Kiangsi:								
North	—	—	—	400 (13)		423 (22)	423 (64)	400 +
Entire	—	—	—			—	—	343
Hunan	255 (2)	—	—	288 (7)	249 (10)	321 (16)	467 (50)	426
Hupei		—	—	250 (5)		267 (41)	555 (2)	517
SE								
Kwangtung:								
Swatow	—	—	—	512 (3)	484 (8)	486 (12)	1,299 (6)	900 +
Entire	—	—	—	416 (14)	512 (11)	447 (37)	1,037 (19)	455
Kwangsi	—	—	300 (1)	—	—	438 (73)	—	400
SW								
Szechwan	178 (1)	—	—	—	—	—	263 (15)	641
Yunnan	—	—	—	—	380 (130)		—	447

* Figures in parentheses ( ) are the number of observations used in obtaining the average figure in the table.

TABLE G.3. RICE YIELDS (CHEKIANG) (E)

PERIOD

Area	SUNG[a] 960–1279 (Shih per Mou—husked Rice)	YUAN 1280–1367	LATE MING 1500–1643 (Shih per Mou—Unhusked)	CH'ING 1644–1699	CH'ING 1700–1799	1900–1960[b] (Catties per Mou—Unhusked)
Chekiang						
Shao-hsing Fu	2.5–3.0	—	—	—	—	500
Cheng hsien	2.0 (1)	—	—	—	—	300
Shan-yin hsien	2.1 (17)*	2.6 (3)*c	—	—	—	—
Yu-yau hsien	1.5 (43)*	5.5 (5)*d	—	—	—	700
Hui-chi hsien	—	2.4 (4)*c	—	—	—	—
Ning-po Fu	—	2.7 (1)d	—	—	—	—
Yin hsien	2.5 (15)*	—	—	—	—	450
Ting-hai hsien	2.3 (12)*	—	—	—	—	280
Feng-hua hsien	2.7 (6)*	—	—	—	—	550
Tzu-chi hsien	2.9 (7)*	6.0 (1)e	—	—	—	250
Hsiang-shan hsien	2.5 (2)*	—	—	—	—	210
Chang-ku hsien	2.3 (4)*	—	—	—	—	—
Hu-chou Fu	1.2 (6)*	4.0 (1)*e	—	—	—	200
Hu-chou Fu	0.9 (2)*f	—	—	—	—	—
Chang-hsing chou	—	2.6 (13)*a	—	—	—	—
Lung-chuan hsien	—	—	—	—	2.8g	—
Chia-hsing	—	—	520–680 (catties)h	—	2.0i	527h
T'ung-hsiang hsien	—	—	—	6.0j	—	550h
P'ing-hu hsien	—	—	—	2.0*j	—	420h
Chiang-hsiang hsien	—	—	1.6*k	—	0.7*k	—
Average	1.97 (115)	3.26 (28)	—	—	—	(sown area) 489
Average	—	—	—	—	—	(cult. area) 685

* These estimates were derived from rent data on the assumption that rent constituted half of the total yield. Rent figures in husked rice were multiplied by four instead of two.

( ) Figures in parentheses are the number of observations used in deriving the average figure presented in the table.

[a] These Sung yield and rent data (principally for the early thirteenth century) were collected from the original sources by Sudo Yoshiyuki, 1954, pp. 650–66, and the same author's 1965, pp. 911 and 919; and by Amano Gennosuke, 1962, pp. 255–56.

[b] The figure for Chekiang province as a whole is for 1957 and is taken from Sun Ching-chih, 1959a, pp. 215–17. Except where otherwise noted, the remaining data are from *Chung-kuo shih-yeh chih (Chekiang Sheng)*, pp. D. 18–22 and for the early 1930's.

[c] *Shao-hsing hsien chih t'zu-liao* (1938) 4.125a–126a, 137ab, and 138a.

[d] Sudo Yoshiyuki, 1965, pp. 881 and 918. It is not clear whether the Yu-yao figure is husked or unhusked rice. I have assumed it is unhusked. The Ning-po (Kuang-yuan) figure is for unhusked rice.

[e] *Ibid.*, pp. 874 and 889.

[f] *Wu-hsing chih* (1201), 8.7a and 11.11ab.

[g] *Lung-ch'uan hsien chih* (1878), 4.1b.

[h] Ch'en Heng-li, *Fu nung shu yen-chiu*, pp. 28–33. The early period data are either late Ming or early Ch'ing, but in either case are for the seventeenth century.

[i] Amano, 1962, p. 363.

[j] In Ch'en Chen-han, pp. 274 and 278.

[k] *Chiang-shan hsien chih* (1873), 4.25a.

TABLE G.4. RICE YIELDS (KIANGSU) (E)

Area	SUNG[a] 960–1279 (Shih per Mou—Husked Rice)	YUAN 1280–1367	1500–1699	1700–1799	1800–1899[b]	1957 (Catties per Shih Mou)
			PERIOD (Shih per Mou—Unhusked Rice)			
Soochow Fu	2.0–3.0	1.4–1.8*c	2.0d	—	2.0e	—
Soochow Fu	—	—	2.1*d	—	—	—
Chang-chou	1.8 (48)*	—	—	—	1.6*f	—
Kun-shan	1.3 (6)*	2.0*g	—	—	—	—
Wu-chiang	—	—	4.0*h	1.0–3.6*i	—	—
Wu	2.4 (13)*	—	—	—	—	—
Chang-shou	1.2 (19)*	—	2.0*	—	—	—
Wu-hsi	1.4 (56)*	—	—	—	3.0–6.0	—
Chen-tse	—	—	—	1.0–3.6*j	—	—
Chiang-yin	—	—	6.0h	—	—	—
Yuan-ho	—	—	—	4.0 (3)*k	—	—
Soochow-Sung-chiang	—	0.8–2.0*l	2.0*m	—	1.5–2.0m	—
Soochow-Sung-chiang	—	—	3.0–5.0h	—	—	—
Soochow-Sung-chiang	—	—	2.0–6.0h	—	—	—
Sung-chiang Fu	—	—	—	—	3.9 (2)	—
Hua-t'ing	—	—	1.5–3.0o	—	—	—
Hua-t'ing	—	—	2.0–3.2*p	—	—	—
Shang-hai	—	—	1.2–2.4*p	—	1.5–4.0	—
T'ai-tsang	—	—	—	4.8–7.2q	—	—
Huai-an Fu	—	—	—	—	3.0–12.0	—
Average	1.6 (143)	1.7 (3)	3.0 (11)	3.8 (6)	3.4 (8)	433r
Average (rent data only)	—	—	2.4 (6)	3.0 (6)		
Average (yield data only)	—	—	3.65 (5)	4.0 (8)		

* These estimates were derived from rent data on the assumption that rent constituted half of the total yield. Rent figures in husked rice were multiplied by four instead of two.

( ) Figures in parentheses are the number of observations.

a See Table G.3, footnote a.

b Except where otherwise noted, nineteenth-century data are from *CKNY*, Vol. I, pp. 619–20.

c Lu Jung, *Shu yuan tsa chi*, pp. 53–54. This figure is based on rent on land confiscated from rich families. The date is early Ming or late Yuan.

d Ku Yen-wu, *Jih-chih-lu chi-shih*, 4.56.

e Pao Shih-chen, *An-Wu szu chung*, vol. 26. This is stated to be the yield for an average harvest.

f Wu Ta-ken, *Chang yuan wu feng pei i tsang ch'uan an hsü pien*, 2.1b, 3.14b–3.68b. This figure is derived from the average rent on land owned by a Soochow granary.

g Wang Hung-hsü, ed. *Ming shih kao* (1697), 60.4b.

h See Table G.3, footnote j.

i *Wu-chiang hsien chih* (1747), 38.7a.

j *Chen-tse hsien chih* (1842 edition, compiled in 1746), 25.8a.

k *Yuan-ho hsien chih* (1761), 5.22b–23a.

l *Hsü wen hsien t'ung k'ao* (Commercial Press edition, 1936), 2,788.

m Lu Shih-i, *Su-Sung fou-liang k'ao*, 3.2a–b. This yield is stated to be for good land in a good harvest.

n Tseng Kuo-fan, "Memorials on the Suffering of the People," in *Huang-chao tao hsien t'ung kuang tsou-i* (Shanghai: 1902), 30.3a.

o *Sung-chiang fu chih* (1662–1722) 6.31b. The figures are for 1511.

p Yeh Meng-chu, 1935, 1.18a.

q Amano, 1962, p. 361.

r Sun Ching-chih, 1959a, p. 57. The figure is the rice yield on the cultivated acreage.

TABLE G.5. RICE YIELDS (KIANGSI) (C)

	Ming (Shih per Mou—Unhusked Rice)	1700–1799	1800–1899	1957 (Catties per *Shih Mou*)
Area		PERIOD		
Nan-ch'ang fu[a]	2.85 (4)*	1.9 (4)*	3.0 (4)*	—
Yuan-chou fu[b]	2.0 (6)*	2.6 (1)*	2.1 (1)*	—
Lin-chiang fu[c]	4.6 (1)*	—	2.0 (3)*	—
Chi-an fu[d]	—	3.4 (2)*	—	—
Kuang-hsin fu[e]	2.0 (2)*	2.7 (7)*	2.5 (2)*	—
Chiu-chiang fu[f]	—	3.9 (4)*	—	—
Nan-k'ang fu[g]	—	3.0 (4)*	3.3 (9)*	—
Fu-chou fu[h]	—	—	2.9 (45)	—
Average (North)	2.5 (13)	2.9 (22)	2.9 (64)	400–600[i]
Average (Province)	—	—	—	343[i]

* These estimates were derived from rent data on the assumption that rent constituted half the total yield.

( ) Figures in parentheses are the number of observations used in deriving the average figure appearing in the table.

[a] *Nan-ch'ang fu chih* (1873) 12.12b–13a, 16.24b, 16.61a, 16.81a, 17.2b, 17.12b, 17.15a–16b, and 17.55b. The four Ming figures are not dated more precisely. The other figures are for the years 1724, 1774, 1775, 1779, 1803, 1833, 1837, and 1839. Two of the Ming figures are for school land and one for temple land. Three of the other figures are also for school land. Seven of the observations are stated to be in unhusked rice (*ku*). The other five are also presumably unhusked since I have seen no Kiangsi figures given in husked rice.

[b] *Yuan-chou fu chih* (1874) 2.20a–22b and 4.36a–40b. Four of the Ming figures are for 1596 and one each for 1611 and 1616. The other data are for 1741 and 1872. All data except for the 1611 figure are for school land. With two exceptions these figures are given in terms of *t'ung* per *mou*, but data in this and other sources seems to indicate that a *t'ung* is the same as a *tou* (one-tenth of a *shih*). For example, this same source cites the following figure: 16.8 *shih*, 6 *t'ung*, 6 *sheng* (4.38a). Other sources give the rent total in terms of *shih* and *tou* and then add that the figure is in official *t'ung* (*kuan-t'ung*) (*Nan-k'ang fu chih* [1862–1874] 7.2a).

[c] *Lin-chiang fu chih* (1871) 7.15b. These data are for 1570 and 1817–1872 (three). All are in unhusked rice and are rents on school land.

[d] *Chi-an fu chih* (1875) 19.48b–49a and 118b. These data are school land rents (× 2) for 1745 and 1775.

[e] *Kuang-hsin fu chih* (1736–1795) 7.43a–44b, 7.52a–53b, 7.64a–b, and 7.66a. No dates are given for two figures and I have assumed they were for the eighteenth century. The other figures are for 1534, 1585, 1717, and 1781 (three). A 1770 and two 1870 figures are in *Kuang-hsin fu chih* (1862–1874) 2.52b–53a and 4.11b. The data in both sources are either for school or temple land.

[f] *Chiu-chiang fu chih* (1873) 11.3a–4a, 13.2a, and 13.37a. These figures are for temple land in 1723, 1726, 1727, and 1757.

[g] *Nan-k'ang fu chih* (1862–1874) 7.2a–3a, 7.5a, 7.9a–10a, 7.32–85a, and 9.46a–b. These figures were rents on temple or unspecified land in the years 1733 (two), 1734, 1853 (two), 1861 (two), 1874 (two) and 1872 (four).

[h] Ho Kang-te, *Fu chün nung ch'an k'ao lüeh*, (1903 Preface) rice types section, 1–4. These yield figures are presumably for the late nineteenth century. Seven of the estimates are for low-grade land, eight for medium-grade, and the remainder for high-grade land.

[i] Sun Ching-chih, 1958, pp. 407 and 409.

TABLE G 6. RICE YIELDS (HUNAN) (C)

Area	PERIOD 1500–1599	1600–1699	1700–1799	1800–1899	1900–1960 (Catties per Mou)
	(*Shih* per *Mou*—Unhusked Rice)				
Hunan (whole province)	—	—	1.0–2.0[a]	—	341–426[b]
Ch'ang-sha Fu	—	0.7[c]	—	—	—
Ch'ang-sha *hsien*	—	—	—	2.8 (10)*[d]	5.0[e]
Hsiang-t'an *hsien*[f]	—	—	—	5.0 (2)	—
Hsiang-t'an *hsien*[g]	—	—	—	2.9 (4)*	—
Liu-yang *hsien*[h]	—	1.6	2.6 (2)	—	—
Liu-yang *hsien*[i]	—	—	1.1*	2.6 (3)*	—
I-yang *hsien*[j]	2.8*	—	1.6*	2.6 (5)*	—
Hsiang-yin *hsien*[k]	2.6*	—	2.5 (2)*	—	—
Ning-hsiang *hsien*[l]	—	—	—	4.2 (3)*	—
Heng-chou Fu[m]	—	—	2.6 (4)*	—	—
Ch'i-yang *hsien*[n]	2.4*	—	2.3*	3.6 (6)*	—
Heng-shan *hsien*[o]	—	—	2.0 +	—	—
Ch'a-ling chou[p]	—	2.0	—	—	—
Yu *hsien*	0.5[q]	—	—	3.5*[r]	—
Ling-ling *hsien*[s]	—	—	—	2.2*	—
Ling *hsien*[t]	—	—	—	4.0*	—
Kuei-yang *hsien*[u]	—	—	—	4.0	—
Kuei-t'ung *hsien*[v]	—	—	—	3.2 (3)*	—
Shao-yang *hsien*[w]	—	—	—	4.0 (2)*	—
Shan-hua *hsien*[x]	—	—	2.2 (2)*	2.8 (3)*	—
Ch'en-chou[y]	—	—	—	3.6	—
Tz'u-li *hsien*[z]	—	—	—	—	5.8
Yung-sui *hsien*[aa]	—	—	—	—	5.0
Li-chou[bb]	—	—	1.8*	—	—
T'ao-chou[cc]	—	—	—	4.0*	—
Hsiang-hsiang *hsien*[dd]	—	—	—	3.0*	—
Hui-t'ung *hsien*[ee]	—	—	—	3.0*	—
Lan-shen *hsien*[ff]	—	—	—	3.3*	—
	1.8 (7)				
Average	2.1 (4)	1.4 (3)	2.2 (16)	3.2 (50)	341–426[b]
Average (yield only)	—	—	2.2 (4)	4.4 (4)	—
Average (rent only)	—	—	2.2 (12)	3.1 (46)	—

These data were collected by Mr. Yeh-chien Wang and also appear in his unpublished paper, "Agricultural Development and Peasant Economy in Hunan during the Ch'ing Period (1644–1911)".

* These estimates are derived from rent data on the assumption that rent constituted half of the total yield.

( ) Figures in parentheses are the number of observations.

[a] *Hunan wen-cheng* (1871) 9.10b. The higher figure is for a good year, the lower an ordinary year in the middle of the eighteenth century.

[b] Sun Ching-chih, 1958, pp. 264 and 269. The lower figure is the yield per *mou* of sown acreage. The higher figure is the yield per *mou* of cultivated acreage.

[c] *Hsiang-t'an hsien chih* (1818) 17.24a. This is stated to be the yield in a good year in the early part of the seventeenth century.

ᵈ These rent data (× 2) are for school land, land for maintaining a charity ferry, and land for maintaining prisoners. These data are mainly for the years 1810–1867. *Ch'ang-sha hsien chih* (1810) 5.4a–9a, 8.103a–105a, 10.69, 10.75b–80a, and *Ch'ang-sha hsien chih* (1867) 11.43.

ᵉ Nihon Gaimusho Tsushokyoku *Shinkoku Jijo*, vol. II, p. 321.

ᶠ These are yield figures for 1869 and 1889, the latter being on medium-grade land. Wang K'ai-yun, *Hsiang-ch'i-lou jih chi* (1927) 1.3a, and *Hsiang-t'an hsien chih* (1889) 6.15a.

ᵍ These rent data are for private land (medium-grade) in 1818 and 1889 (2.0 × 2 in both cases) and for academy and temple land in 1818. *Hsiang-t'an hsien chih* (1818) 12.5a, 12.15a–22, and 39.3b and *Hsiang-t'an hsien chih* (1889) 6.15a.

ʰ *Liu-yang hsien chih* (1818) 36.65a, 39.9a; and *Liu-yang hsien chih* (1873) 6.28a. These yield data are for 1632, 1736 (stated to be a good year), and 1791.

ⁱ *Liu-yang hsien chih* (1873) 6.28a, 4.8a, 7.17a, 8.25a. The 1736 figure is on private land. The 1873 data are for a school orphanage and granary.

ʲ The 1568 figure is on land used to subsidize poor students. The other data are for 1757 (school land), 1803 (academy land), 1856 (school land) and 3 in 1874 (various charities' land). *I-yang hsien chih* (1874) 6.2a, 8.61a, 6.17b–19b, and 6.24, and *Hunan t'ung chih* (1757) 44.9b.

ᵏ These data are for 1556 (school land), 1755 (clan land) and 1756 (temple land). *Hsiang-yin hsien t'u chih* (1880), 30.50b, 30.61b–62b.

ˡ These figures are for private land in 1816 and temple land in 1867. *Ning-hsiang hsien chih* (1867) 7.7a, 13.83b–107b, 24.7a–8b.

ᵐ These data are for academy land in 1763. *Heng-chou fu chih* (compiled in 1763, published in 1875) 16.48b–55a.

ⁿ These data are for 1564 (good school land), 1737 (school land), 1812, 1868 and 1870 (all academy land), and, 1865 (orphanage land). *Ch'i-yang hsien chih* (1870) 23.27b, 10.2a–9b, 21.30b, 19.41a.

ᵒ *Hunan wen-cheng* (1871), 46.7a.

ᵖ This figure is for high-grade land in 1695. *Ch'a-ling chou chih* (1695) 8.1a.

ᑫ This figure is the yield on military land in the Ming period (date not given). *Yu hsien chih* (1871) 20.6.

ʳ This figure is for academy land in 1871. *Yu hsien chih* (1871) 15.12b–17a.

ˢ This figure is for school land in 1876. *Ling-ling hsien chih* (1876) 5.8a–9a.

ᵗ This figure is land for a charity granary (1873). *Ling hsien chih* (1873) 6.24b.

ᵘ *Kuei-yang chou chih* (1868) 5.18b.

ᵛ These data are for low-, medium-, and high-grade school land in 1866. *Kuei-t'ung hsien chih* (1866) 5.50b–53a.

ʷ This figure is for school land. *Shao-yang hsien chih* (1877), 4.7b.

ˣ These data are for 1746 (private land), 1747 (academy land), and 1877 (**sacrifice**, temple, and ferry land). *Shan-hua hsien chih* (1877) 16.10b, 6.3a–4a, 11.65b–66a, and *Ch'ang-sha fu chih* (1747) 13.34b.

ʸ *Ch'en-chou fu i-t'ien tsung-chi* (1845) vol. I, 7b.

ᶻ This figure is the average of a range (5.0–6.5) for the year 1923. *Tz'u-li hsien chih* (1923) 6.2a.

ᵃᵃ This figure is the average of a range (4.0–6.0) for 1909. *Yung-sui-ting chih* (1909) 15.33.

ᵇᵇ This figure is for school land in 1757. *Hunan t'ung chih* (1757) 43.32b.

ᶜᶜ This figure is for academy land in 1830. *T'ao chou chih* (1877) 5.35a.

ᵈᵈ This figure is for average land in 1872. *Hsiang-hsiang hsien chih* (1874) Last vol., 17b.

ᵉᵉ This figure is for rent on asylum land (× 2). *Hui-t'ung hsien chih* (1876) 3.25b.

ᶠᶠ This figure is for academy land in 1867. *Lan-shan hsien chih* (1867) 7.92a–93b.

TABLE G.7. RICE YIELDS (HUPEI) (C)

Hsien Name	Pre-1500[a]	1500-1599[b]	1600-1699[b] (Shih per Mou)	1700-1799[b] —Unhusked	Pre-1800[b]	1800-1899[b]	1930's[c] 1957[d] (Shih Catties per Shih Mou)	
Chiang-hsia	—	1.68 (3)*	1.47 (2)*	—	—	—	—	—
Wu-ch'ang	—	—	—	—	1.46*	—	300	—
Pu-chi	—	—	—	—	1.31 (5)*	—	267	—
Hsien-ning	—	—	—	—	1.40*	—	257	—
Chung-yang	—	1.38 (2)*	1.78*	—	2.38 (2)*	—	346	—
T'ung-ch'eng	—	—	1.16*	—	—	—	375	—
Ta-yeh	—	—	—	—	1.87 (2)*	—	300	—
Han-yang	—	—	—	—	2.62 (6)*	—	300	—
Han-ch'uan	—	—	2.0*	—	—	—	348	—
Hsiao-kan	—	—	—	—	1.64*	—	300	—
Huang-kang	2.50 (2)	—	2.18*	2.4 (2)	—	—	300	—
Ao-chou	—	—	0.43 (2)*	—	—	—	400	—
Lo-t'ien	—	—	4.0*	3.2 (3)	—	—	343	—
Huang-mei	—	—	—	—	1.12*	—	325	—
Ying-ch'eng	—	—	—	—	—	—	367	—
Ying-shan	—	—	—	—	1.16*	—	200	—
Ching-shan	—	—	—	—	1.21*	—	316	—
Hsiang-yang	—	—	1.25*	0.62 (7)	—	—	200	—
Tsao-yang	—	—	—	—	—	—	222	—
Nan-chang	—	—	—	2.75 (2)	3.52*	—	333	—
Chu-shan	—	—	—	—	—	—	300	—
Tang-yang	—	—	—	—	—	6.0*	292	—
Chien-li	—	—	—	1.3 (2)	—	—	400	—
Sung-tzu	—	—	—	—	—	1.6*	375	—
Kung-an	—	—	—	1.98 (3)	—	—	400	—
Average	2.50 (2)	1.56 (5)	1.62 (10)	1.73 (19)	1.92 (22)	3.8 (2)	319	517

( ) The figure in parentheses is the number of observations.

[a] Amano Gennosuke, 1962, pp. 255-56. These yield figures were originally in husked rice and were converted to unhusked rice by multiplying by two.

[b] These are all rent figures on school land that have been multiplied by two to convert them to yield estimates. One or two *hsien* may have had school land that was planted to crops other than rice, but most of the *hsien* are in the rich rice areas of southeast and southwest Hupei. Source of all data is the *Hupei t'ung chih* (1921), pp. 1,597-1,638.   [c] *Hupei sheng nien chien* (no. 1), pp. 162-69.

[d] The 1957 rice yield on sown acreage was 465 catties per *mou*. About 3,300,000 *mou* were double-cropped so that yield per cultivated *mou* was 517 catties. Yield on the double-cropped land by itself was 660 catties per *mou*. (Source: Sun Ching-chih, 1958, pp. 77-82.)

TABLE G 8. RICE YIELDS (KWANGTUNG) (SE)

Area	PERIOD				1900–1960[a] (Catties per *Mou*)
	1500–1599	1600–1699	1700–1799	1800–1899	
	(*Shih* per *Mou*—Unhusked Rice)				
Kwangtung					
Chao-chou Fu	—	4.2*[b]	—	—	—
Nan-hsiung	—	—	—	6.1 (5)*[c]	—
Yang-shan[d]	2.9 (2)*	—	3.5	—	—
Weng-yuan[e]	—	—	2.2	—	—
Weng-yuan[e]	—	—	3.8*	—	—
Swatow Area					
	—	—	—	640–1,280[f]	900 +
Chieh-yang[g]	2.9 (2)*	3.2 (6)*	3.2 (4)*	—	—
Chao-yang[h]	3.8*	2.5 (2)*	2.2 (3)*	8.9 (6)*	—
Feng-shun[i]	—	—	4.6 (4)*	—	—
Chao-an	—	—	—	—	—
Nan-ao[j]	—	—	2.2*	—	—
Canton Area					
(Pearl River Delta)	—	—	—	—	500
Ching-yuan[k]	2.6*	—	—	3.7	—
Shih-cheng[l]	4.0*	—	2.0 (2)*	—	—
San-shui[m]	—	—	—	3.6	—
En-p'ing[n]	—	—	2.9	—	—
Kuang-ning[o]	—	3.2 (2)*	—	8.9 (3)*	—
Fan-yu[p]	—	—	—	6.8 (2)	—
Hui-chou[q]	1.0	—	—	—	—
Nan-hai[r]	2.1*	—	—	—	—
Hua[s]	—	—	—	400–500	—
Southwest and Hainan					
Chiung-chou fu[t]	—	—	3.0 (14)	—	—
Chin-chou[u]	—	—	—	3.6	—
Hsiang-shan[v]	—	—	3.7	—	—
Yang-chun[w]	2.6 (2)*	—	—	—	—
Hai-yang[x]	4.0*	—	2.9 (3)*	—	—
Kuei-shan[y]	1.2 (2)*	—	—	—	—
Wan-chou[z]	—	—	1.7*	—	—
Range	1.0–5.0	2.5–4.2	2.0–4.6	3.6–8.9	—
Average	2.6	3.2	3.03	7.1	455
Average (rent data only)	2.7 (13)	3.2 (11)	3.06 (19)	7.9 (14)	—
Average (Yield data only)	1.0 (1)	— (0)	2.99 (18)	4.9 (5)	—

* These estimates are derived from rent data on the assumption that rent constituted half of the total yield.

( ) Figures in parentheses are the number of observations.

[a] Sun Ching-chih, 1959b, 954, pp. 65–66. These yields are per cultivated *mou* and are derived from data in this source.

[b] *Chao-chou fu chih* (1873) 17.1b. The rent figure is on school land in 1636.

[c] *Nan-hsiung chou chih* (1824) 14.27a–29a. These data are for 1808.

[d] *Yang-shan hsien chih* (1823) 3.12b, 3.17b. The 1739 figure is the yield on sacrifice land (emperor's fields). The rent data (for 1523) are for sacrifice land (*chi* rather than *chieh*).

[e] *Weng-yuan hsien chih* (1819) 6.9b–10b. The yield figure (1727) is on emperor's sacrifice land. The rent figure is on school land (1751).

[f] George Jamieson, "Tenure of Land in China and the Condition of the Rural Population," in *Chinese Economic and Social Life*, vol. 2, p. 113. This figure is in catties per *mou*.

[g] *Chieh-yang hsien chih* (1779) 2.28b–31a. These data are for the year 1578, 1592, 1602, 1609, 1622, 1628, 1629, 1712, and 1720.

[h] *Chao-yang hsien chih* (1884) 6.1b, 7.5a–b, and 7.14b–15b. The 1625 and 1635 figures are for high- and middle-grade land (slightly more of the latter) as is the 1596 figure. The 1752 figures are for school land and newly enclosed land while the 1795 figure is for high-grade land. The 1802 figure is on high-grade land whereas those for 1812, 1873, and 1874 are on medium-grade land.

[i] *Feng-shun hsien chih* (1746) 2.13a–b. These figures are rents on school land.

[j] *Nan-ao hsien chih* (1783) 6.15b. This figure was based on the rent on school land.

[k] *Ching-yuan hsien chih* (1880) 6.2b, 6.18a. The 1596 figure is on school land, the 1880 figure on sacrifice land.

[l] *Shih-cheng hsien chih* (1819) 2.4a and *Chung-hsiu Shih-cheng hsien chih* (1892) 4.34a. The 1545 figure is on school land as is the 1712 figure.

[m] *San-shui hsien chih* (1819) 4.19a. This figure is for emperor's sacrifice land.

[n] *En-p'ing hsien chih* (1766) 2.36b. This figure is for emperor's sacrifice land (1749).

[o] *Kuang-ning hsien chih* (1824) 15.12b–15a and 23a–24a. These figures are all for school land (1684–91 and 19th century).

[p] *Fan-yu hsien hsü chih* (1869–1911) 12.2a. The yield for two crops in rocky soil is stated to be 5 *shih*, that on rich soil, 8–9 *shih*.

[q] *Hui-chou fu chih* (1595), 6.13b. This is the yield in a good harvest on poor land.

[r] *Nan-hai hsien chih* (1835) 11.44b. This was the rent (× 2) on 403 mou of temple and school land in 1591.

[s] *Hua hsien chih* (1924) 6.8a. This is the yield on the best irrigated rice land.

[t] *Chiung-shan hsien chih* (1853) 7.18a–b and *Chiung chou fu chih* (1890) 13.9b–10a. This was the yield on emperor's sacrifice land in 1787 and 1735.

[u] *Chin-chou chih* (1834) 4.10a. This was the yield on emperor's sacrifice land in 1750.

[v] *Hsiang-shan hsien chih* (1827) 3.45a. This was the yield on emperor's sacrifice land in 1750.

[w] *Yang-chun hsien chih* (1820) 5.9a–b. These were the rents (× 2) on school land in 1571 and 1585.

[x] *Hai-yang hsien chih* (1898) 19.34b–35a and 20.3a. These rents (× 2) were on temple land (1573–1619 and 1723), emperor's sacrifice land (1726), and temple land (1730).

[y] *Kuei-shan hsien chih pu* (1783) 1.18b. These data are for temple land (1592).

[z] *Wan chou chih* (1828) 6.22b–23a. This figure is for school land in 1783.

TABLE G.9. RICE YIELDS (KWANGSI) (SE)

Area	1465–1487	1680–1740	c. 1780–1800	1900–1960 (Catties per *Shih* Mou—Unhusked)	
		(Unhusked Rice—*Shih* per *Mou*)			
Kwangsi[a]					
Nan-ning Fu	under 2.0[b]	—	3.3 (6)*	—	—
Kwei-lin Fu	—	—	3.0 (9)*	295[c]	—
Lin-kuei *hsien*	—	1.3 (2)*	2.0*	—	—
Hsing-an *hsien*	—	—	2.2*	—	—
Ch'uan *hsien*	—	—	2.0*	—	—
T'ai-ping Fu	—	—	1.3 (5)*	—	—
Shang-szu chou	—	0.6 (3)*	—	—	—
Hsin-chou Fu	—	—	4.0 (4)*	230[c]	—
Kuei-p'ing *hsien*	—	—	0.4*	—	—
P'ing-nan	—	—	2.9*	—	—
Chen-an Fu	—	—	3.4 (8)*	—	—
Wu-chou Fu	—	—	4.0 (5)*	—	—
P'ing-lo Fu	—	—	3.6 (7)*	—	—
Szu-en Fu	—	—	3.2 (4)*	—	—
Liu-chou Fu	—	—	2.9 (8)*	257[c]	—
Szu-ch'eng Fu	—	—	4.0 (5)*	—	—
Average (sacrifice land)	—	3.2 (63)		—	—
Average (school land)	—	1.4 (10)		—	—
Average	2.0	3.0		238[c]	400[d]

* These estimates are derived from rent data on the assumption that rent constituted half of the total yield.

( ) Figures in parentheses are the number of observations.

[a] All Kwangsi data were taken from the *Kwangsi t'ung-chih* (1801), 164.12b–16a, 166.11b–23b. These data are not dated, but presumably they are figures obtained shortly prior to the publication of the *T'ung-chih*. The figures are for school land and emperor's sacrifice lands. The latter are not explicitly said to be rents, but presumably are.

[b] The source states that two *shih* (unhusked rice) was the highest yield ever achieved in the area. This figure is in the *Kwangsi t'ung chih* (1801) vol. 87.

[c] Chang P'ei-kang, *Kwangsi shih-liang wen-t'i* (Changsha: 1938) p. 23. This is presumably the yield per sown *mou*.

[d] Sun Ching-chih, 1959b, pp. 247 and 252 gives data on paddy acreage, sown acreage in rice, and the yield per *mou* on the sown acreage. The figure in the table is the yield on cultivated acreage.

TABLE G.IO. RICE YIELDS (SZECHWAN) (SW)

Area	Sung	PERIOD 1500–1599	1700–1799	1800–1899	1900–1960 (Catties per *Mou*)
		(*Shih* per *Mou*—Unhusked)			
Szechwan	1.75[a]	—	—	—	—
Hsin-tou *hsien*[b]					
—irrigated	—	—	—	2.4 (3)*	—
—dry land	—	—	—	1.4 (1)*	—
—unspecified	—	—	—	1.6 (8)*	—
Mien-chou[c]	—	—	—	1.8 (3)*	—
Te-yang[d]	—	—	—	6–7	—
Average	1.75 (1)	—	—	1.8 (15)	641[e]

* These estimates are derived from rent data on the assumption that rent constituted half of the total yield.

( ) Figures in parentheses are the number of observations.

[a] This figure is based on the amount received (*sui-shou*) from military colonists' land in 1137. *Szechwan t'ung chih* (1816), 87.2a–10a. The amount was 150,000 *shih* from 85,400 *mou* of land. It is not absolutely clear that this figure represents yield as contrasted to a rent or a tax.

[b] These data are based on school-land rents expressed in terms of unhusked rice for the years 1812, 1813, 1826, 1827, and 1838. *Hsin-tou hsien chih* (1929 revised ed.) 23.28b.

[c] *Mien chou chih li chou chih* (1873) 16.63a. These are based on rents on school land.

[d] *CKNY*, Vol. I, p. 619. This figure is unhusked rice in the year 1874.

[e] Sun Ching-chih, 1960, p. 522 and Chen, 1967, pp. 314 and 361. These yields are for the cultivated area and not the sown area. For the amount of double-cropped rice acreage see Table III.2.

TABLE G.11. RICE YIELDS (YUNNAN) (SW)

	YEAR			
	1581	*1681–1739*[a]	*1800–1899*	*1957* Catties per
Area	*(Shih* per *Mou*—Unhusked)			*Shih Mou*
K'un-ming *hsien*	—	1.8*	—	—
Fu-min *hsien*	—	3.3 (3)*	—	—
Lo-tz'u *hsien*	—	1.6*	—	—
Chin-ning chou	—	3.3 (3)*	—	—
Ch'eng-kung *hsien*	—	2.3 (2)*[b]	—	—
An-ning chou	—	3.0 (7)*	—	—
K'un-yang chou	—	8.9 (5)*	—	—
Sung-ming chou	—	3.4 (11)*	—	—
Ta-li *hsien*	—	4.1 (5)*	—	—
Ta-li *hsien*[c]	2.55 (4)*	3.0 (16)*	2.82 (6)*	—
Yuan-nan *hsien*	—	1.9 (6)*	—	—
Lang-ch'iung *hsien*	—	0.8*[d]	—	—
Chien-shui *hsien*	—	2.0 (3)*	—	—
A-mi chou	—	1.9*	—	—
Ho-hsi *hsien*	—	1.1*	—	—
Ch'u-hsiung *hsien*	—	1.5 (2)*	—	—
Chen-nan chou	—	1.3 (2)*	—	—
Ting-yüan *hsien*	—	1.4*	—	—
Chiang-ch'uan *hsien*	—	2.9*	—	—
Shun-ning *hsien*	—	2.1*	—	—
Nan-ning *hsien*	—	0.9 (2)*	—	—
Chan-i chou	—	1.7 (5)*	—	—
Ma-lung chou	—	0.3*	—	—
P'ing-i *hsien*	—	4.0*	—	—
Hsuan-wei chou	—	0.5*	—	—
Hou-ch'ing chou	—	3.7 (3)*	—	—
Wei-hsi t'ing	—	4.1 (3)*	—	—
T'eng-yüeh t'ing	—	1.9 (2)*	—	—
Yung-p'ing *hsien*	—	2.1*	—	—
Hui-che *hsien*	—	0.9 (7)*	—	—
Ch'iao-chia t'ing	—	1.8 (2)*[e]	1.5 (2)*[e]	—
Chen-hsiung chou	—	0.8 (2)*	—	—
Ta-kuan t'ing	—	1.0 (2)*	—	—
Lu-tien t'ing	—	0.4*	—	—
Ching-tung chih-li t'ing	—	1.7 (12)*	—	—
Meng-hua chih-li t'ing	—	1.3*	—	—
Yung-pei chih-li t'ing	—	1.9*	—	—
Chen-yüan chih-li t'ing	—	1.4 (2)*	—	—
En-lo *hsien*	—	3.7*	—	—
Mi-le *hsien*	—	1.9 (4)*	—	—
Lu-ch'üan *hsien*	—	2.8*	—	—
Hsin-p'ing *hsien*	—	3.3 (2)*	—	—
Average	—	2.6 (130)	—	447

* These estimates were derived from rent data on the assumption that rent constituted half of the total yield.   ( ) Figures in parentheses are the number of observations.

^a *Yunnan t'ung chih* (1894) 82.4a, 40a–41a, 46a; 83.1b–32b; 84.2a–31b; 85.3a–28b; 86.9a–30b; 87.3b–22a. These figures are all rents on school land given explicitly in *ching* (capital) *shih* which I assume to be the "standard" *shih* of Peking. Figures given in unhusked rice I have multiplied by 2 to obtain yields. Figures given in husked rice have been multiplied by 4. These figures all fall between the years 1681 and 1739 except where noted below.

^b One of these two figures (2.1) is for the year 1785, the other is for 1734.

^c *Ta-li hsien chih kao* (1916) 29.6b–7b, 18a–19b. The sixteenth-century figures are for sacrifice land in 1581. The eighteenth- and nineteenth-century figures are for school land in 1778 and 1849.

^d This figure is for the year 1753.

^e These figures are for the years 1775, 1795, 1875 and 1879. The latter two are given in terms of *shih* (market) *shih* rather than *ching shih*.

TABLE G.12. GRAIN YIELDS (SHANTUNG) (N)

Area	1600–1699	1700–1799	1800–1899	1900–1960[a] millet kaoliang (Catties per Mou)	
	(*Shih* per *Mou*—Unhusked Grain)				
Shantung					
Pen-lai *hsien*	0.27 (3)*[b]	—	—	160	175
Huang *hsien*	0.12 (2)*[c]	—	—	300	346
Tsou-p'ing *hsien*	1.1[d]	—	—	115	100
Fu-shan *hsien*	—	0.14[e]	—	112	224

* These estimates are derived from rent data on the assumption that rent constituted half of the total yield.

( ) Figures in parentheses are the number of observations.

^a *Chung-kuo shih-yeh chih* (*Shantung Sheng*), pp. E, 38–46, 64–71. These figures are for the early 1930's.

^b *Pen-lai hsien chih* (1839) 3.7a–b. These data are for school land in 1604, 1607, and 1616. School land data are usually rents, but this source does not so state.

^c *Huang hsien chih* (1755) 3.43b. These data are for school land in 1616 and 1672. The latter figure is explicitly stated to be rent, the former is not.

^d *Tsou-p'ing hsien chih* (1836) 5.21b. This is the income in millet in a good harvest in 1696. The yield is given in terms of *hu* (nominally equal to ten *tou*). This conversion factor may be wrong.

^e *Fu-shan hsien chih* (1763) 2.10b. A part of the rent on this school land was paid in silver and I have converted this to grain at the rate of one *liang* of silver equals one *shih* of grain.

TABLE G.I3. GRAIN YIELDS (SHENSI) (NW)

			PERIOD		
Area	Pre-1600	1600–1699	1700–1799 (*Shih* per *Mou*—Unhusked Rice)	1800–1899	1900–1960
Shensi					
Ch'ien chou	—	(w) 0.68*a	—	—	—
An-sai *hsien*	—	—	—	—	0.16b
Lan-t'ien *hsien*c	—	0.48 (4)*	—	—	—
Lan-t'ien *hsien*c	—	(w) 0.34 (2)*	—	—	—
Lan-t'ien *hsien*c	—	(M) 0.46*	—	—	—
Lan-t'ien *hsien*c	—	(R) 0.8*	—	—	—
Ta-li *hsien*d	—	—	0.12*	—	—
Hua choue	—	—	—	(w) 0.2–0.3	—
Hua-yin *hsien*f	—	(w&M) 1.2*	—	—	—
Lung choug	—	—	0.9	—	—
Feng-hsiang *hsien*h	—	—	(w) 0.29 (2)*	—	—
Feng-hsiang *hsien*h	—	—	(M) 0.5 (2)*	—	—
Lin-t'ung *hsien*i	—	—	(w) 0.2 (2)*	—	—
Lin-t'ung *hsien*i	—	—	(M) 0.15 (2)*	—	—
Mei *hsien*j	3.0	(M) 0.6*	(M) 0.6*	—	—
T'ung-kuan *hsien*k	—	—	—	—	0.26 (4)
Fu-p'ing *hsien*l	—	—	—	(w) 0.4*	—
Yang *hsien*m	—	—	—	(w) 1.2	—
Yang *hsien*m	—	—	—	0.75	—
Han-yin t'ingn	—	—	—	(c) 0.36*	—
Ning-ch'iang chouo	2.0*	—	—	—	—
Wei-nan *hsien*p	—	—	—	2.0–3.0	—
Kao-ling *hsien*q	—	—	—	0.26 (6)*	—
San-shui *hsien*r	—	—	(w) 0.08*	—	—
	—	—	(M) 0.08*	—	—
Southwest Shensis	—	—	—	(R) 1.18 (4)*	—
Southwest Shensis	—	—	—	(M) 1.1*	—
Southwest Shensis	—	—	—	(c) 0.24 (3)*	—
Southwest Shensis	—	—	—	(w) 0.22*	—
			0.39 (25)		
Average	2.5 (2)	0.53 (12)	0.31 (13)	0.51 (21)	—
	—	(w) 0.44 (3)	(w) 0.21 (5)	(w) 0.52 (4)	(w) 197t
	—	(R) 0.8 (1)	—	(R) 1.18 (4)	(R) 330u
	—	(M) 0.53 (2)	(M) 0.33 (6)	—	} 119t
	—	(c) —	—	(c) 0.27 (4)	
Average (rent data only)	—	0.53 (12)	0.26 (12)	0.37 (17)	—
Average (yield data only)	—	—	0.9 (1)	1.18 (4)	—

* These estimates are derived from rent data on the assumption that rent constituted half of the total yield.

( ) Figures in parentheses are the number of observations.

(w) Wheat (M) Millet (R) Rice (c) Corn

ᵃ *Ch'ien chou chih* (1633) shang, 22b. This figure is based on the rent on school land (wheat-planted).

ᵇ *An-sai hsien chih* (1914) 6.2a. This is a yield figure for poor land.

ᶜ *Lan-t'ien hsien chih* (1796) 6.2a. These estimates are based on rent data on school land (in 1599). The rice figure is for irrigated land.

ᵈ *Ta-li hsien chih* (1844) 9.9a. This estimate is based on the rent on school land in 1769.

ᵉ *San hsü Hua chou chih* (1882) 4.4a. It is stated that yields of two to three *tou* are attained on only 10 per cent of the land.

ᶠ *Hua-yin hsien chih* (1715) 4.5a. This rent figure (× 2) for 1602 is based on two crops, not just one.

ᵍ *Lung chou hsü chih* (1766) 4.2a. This figure was the yield on sacrifice land in unhusked grain in 1727.

ʰ *Feng-hsiang hsien chih* (1767) 3.21a–b. These data are stated to be the annual collections (*sui cheng*) on school land.

ⁱ *Lin-t'ung hsien chih* (1776) 4.23. These data are what was received (*shou*) from school land in wheat and barley (w) and unhusked grain (millet).

ʲ *Mei hsien chih* (1733) 7.13a and *Mei hsien chih* (1778) 4.11a. These yields for 1619 and 1778 are on school land and are in unhusked millet. The 1567 figure is for wheat or barley plus beans.

ᵏ *T'ung-kuan hsien chih* (1944) 10.5a and 9a. These data apparently refer to the twentieth century. The area is stated to be very poor with no possibility of irrigation. One figure (0.2) is the average yield on poor mountainous land, while another (0.3) is stated to be the yield in a good harvest.

ˡ *Fu-p'ing hsien chih* (1891) 2.16a. This figure is based on the rent on school land in 1842.

ᵐ *Yang hsien chih* (1897) 4.2a. The higher figure is the yield of wheat or barley on high-grade land. The lower figure is the fall harvest of miscellaneous grains.

ⁿ *Han-yin t'ing chih* (1817) 4.15b. This is rent in corn (*pao-ku*) on hilly land (school land) in 1816. The area is given in *tuan* (1 *tuan* = 24 *mou*).

ᵒ *Ning-ch'iang chou chih* (1577) 4.2a. This figure is based on the rent on school land and is given in terms of *ts'ang tou* (granary peck). According to the *Hsun yang hsien chih* (1783), 11.14a, one *ts'ang tou* is less than one-half of a *shih tou*.

ᵖ *Hsin hsü Wei-nan hsien chih* (1892) 11.16a. This was stated to be the yield in the excellent fall harvest in 1878.

ᑫ *Kao-ling hsien hsü chih* (1884) 2.16b. These figures are based on collections (*cheng*) from high-, middle- and low-grade school land (on high-grade the yield was 0.28, low-grade 0.23 *shih*).

ʳ *San-shui hsien chih* (1785) 6.4a. These figures are based on the rents on school land.

ˢ *Hsü hsiu Shensi t'ung chih* (1934) 47.8b–10b. These are figures of rents or amounts received on *ying-t'ien* (military land ?) for the years 1806–1810.

ᵗ Chen, 1967, p. 323. The 119 catty figure is the yield per *mou* of all coarse grains, not just corn and millet, although these two crops were the major component of coarse grains in Shensi.

ᵘ Buck, 1937 (Statistical Volume) p. 210. This is the rice yield in one village of one *hsien* only.

TABLE G.I4. GRAIN YIELDS (LIAONING, HONAN)
(NE AND N)

Area	Pre-1900 (Unhusked Grain)	1957 (Unhusked Grain) (Catties per *Mou*)
	(A.D. 1640's)	
Liaoning	0.54 *shih*[a]	220[b]
	(A.D. 1262)	
Honan	1.0 *shih*[c]	—
(converted)	100 + catties[d]	180[e] (150)

[a] *Shen-yang chuang ch'i* (1641), p. 630. This yield comes from an account of his stay in China by a Korean hostage. The total amount of land involved in calculating these yields was 4,700 *mou*.

[b] Sun Ching-chih, 1959a, p. 90. This is the yield per *mou* of sown area, but there was little double cropping in Liaoning so that the yield per unit of cultivated area was approximately the same.

[c] *Hsü wen-hsien t'ung-k'ao*, p. 2778. This was the yield on 96,000,000 *mou* of cultivated land in Honan province during the Chin dynasty. High-grade land yielded 1.2 *shih*, middle-grade 1.0 *shih*, and poor land 0.8 *shih*. The source states that one-tenth of the annual output was 9,600,000 *shih*.

[d] To convert, I have assumed that Chin weights and measures were the same as those of the Sung and that the weight per *shih* of the grains of Honan was the same as unhusked rice (130 catties per *shih*).

[e] This figure was obtained by taking average annual Honan grain production (1931–1937) and dividing by 90 per cent of the cultivated acreage (see Appendix B). The figure in parentheses is the yield on the 1931–1937 average sown acreage. (SOURCE: Chinese Ministry of Information, *China Handbook, 1937–43*, pp. 559–74.)

Water-Control Data

Chinese gazetteers generally devote one or more volumes to water-control data. These compilations list each project by name and group the projects by *hsien* and prefecture. In many instances no further information is provided. Often, however, the listing includes the dates when the project was started and when it underwent major repairs, statistics pertaining to the size of the project, and information whether construction was initiated by officials (*kuan*) or by private individuals or groups (*min*).

In a study published in the 1930's, Chi Ch'ao-ting (1936) counted all the dated projects in the provincial gazetteers available to him and listed the totals by province and by dynasty. Although a pioneering work, a great many key questions remain concerning the extent to which simply counting the number of projects accurately reflects real trends in the level of water-control construction.

Another problem with Chi's data is that eight of the provincial gazetteers he used were published in the first half of the eighteenth century. Thus projects undertaken during the almost two centuries until the collapse of the Ch'ing dynasty in 1911 are not included. Even more serious, the projects are listed only by dynasty. Thus for each province there is one total for the entire period 1368 to 1644 and another for the years from 1644 to 1911. Such a listing obscures many important fluctuations that took place within these periods of nearly three centuries each. An understanding of the nature of these fluctuations is crucial if one is to understand the relationship between water-control activities and population growth.

Because of these shortcomings in the Chi data, I had my research assistants,

TABLE H.I. WATER CONTROL PROJECTS
(Total Number—Excluding Repairs and Projects no Longer in Use)

Province	Total	Pre-T'ang (before A.D. 618)	T'ang (618–907)	10th	11th	12th	13th	14th	15th	16th	17th	18th	19th
N													
Hopei	488	9	12	2	18	1	14	23	44	119	50	171	28
Shantung	51	1	3	0	1	1	5	5	6	15	4	4	0
Shansi	194	3	15		12	6	11	25	15	66	30	11	0
NW													
Shensi	234	1	5		12		1	2	9	28	6	78	92
E													
Anhwei	203	10	15	1	3	11	2	9	14	37	28	64	9
Kiangsu	463	32	23	6	26	57	15	30	67	81	126	*	*
Chekiang	1,257	14	74	6	90	115	76	409	76	196	137	64	—
C													
Kiangsi	432	2	23	1	11	12	11	18	54	118	56	26	100
Hupei	253	3	7	2	1	14	10	8	21	56	21	80	30
Hunan	284	2	13	9	8	4	0	26	16	187	8	10	1
SE													
Fukien	641	4	22		324		25	22	52	52	38	98	4
Kwangtung	279	1	0	3	14	12	18	84	49	36	15	17	30
SW													
Szechwan	176	0	15	1	8	1	3	0	11	12	14	76	35
Yunnan	330	3	1	0	0	0	3	5	20	71	47	119	61
Total	5,285	85	228		792		194	666	454	1,074	580	818	394

Gazetteers used in compiling the water-control data appearing in this appendix are:

Hopei: *Chi-fu t'ung chih* (1884 edition), vols. 86–87.

Shantung: *Shantung t'ung chih* (1910 edition), vols. 28–33.

Shansi: *Shansi t'ung chih* (1890 edition), vols. 29–33.

Shensi: *Shensi t'ung chih* (1735 edition), vols. 39–40, and *Hsü Shensi t'ung chih* (1931 edition), vols. 57–61.

Anhwei: *Anhwei t'ung chih* (1821–1850 edition), vols. 46–49.

Kiansu: *Kiang-nan t'ung chih* (1736 edition), vols. 61–64; *Hsu-chou fu chih* (1862–1874 edition), vols. 11–13; and *Ch'ang-chao ho chih kao* (1889 edition), vol. 9.

Chekiang: *Chekiang t'ung chih* (1736 edition, reprinted in 1946), pp. 1,095–1,218.

Kiangsi: *Kiangsi t'ung chih* (1875 edition), vols. 62–64.

Hupei: *Hupei t'ung chih* (1795–1803 edition), vol. 25 and *Hupei t'ung chih* (1910–1921 edition), vols. 39–40.

Hunan: *Hunan t'ung chih* (1885 edition), vols. 12–28, 46–47.

Fukien: *Fukien t'ung chih* (1871 edition), vols. 33–37.

Kwangtung: *Kwangtung t'ung chih* (1822 edition), vols. 115–119.

Kwangsi: *Kwangsi t'ung chih* (1801 edition), vols. 117–119.

Szechwan: (a) *Szechwan t'ung chih* (1816 edition), vol. 23.
    (b) *Chung-hsiu mien-chou chih-li chou chih* (1873 edition), vol. 10.
    (c) *Ch'iung-chou chih-li chou chih* (1818 edition), vol. 13.
    (d) *Chih hsien chih* (1931 edition), vol. 2, 23b.
    (e) *Hua-yang hsien chih* (1816 and 1934 editions), vol. 9 and vol. 2, 2a.
    (f) *Chang-ming hsien chih* (1874 edition), vol. 7.
    (g) *Hsu-chou fu chih* (1895 edition), vol. 6, 40a–51b.
    (h) *Jen-shou hsien chih* (1866 edition), vol. 1, 43a.
    (i) *T'ung-ch'uan fu chih* (1897 edition), vol. 4, 22a.
    (j) *Pao-ning fu chih* (1821 edition), vol. 9, 10b, and
    (k) *Hsin-fan hsien chih* (1876 edition), vol. 3.

Yunnan: *Yunnan t'ung chih* (1835 edition), vols. 52–54.

Kweichow and Honan: Provincial and local gazetteers for these provinces were looked at, but their lists of water-control projects were very incomplete and even fewer were dated.

Miss Ming Su and Mrs. Hsiao, recalculate these figures. All projects for which a date or other useful information (e.g., the area irrigated by the project) was given were written down. In the case of several provinces, all projects, dated or not, were recorded. As there were over 5,000 dated projects and several times that number of undated ones, the task of recording these items was rather laborious. When the recording was completed, I then compiled the data in accordance with various criteria. The more interesting and useful results so obtained appear in the tables in this appendix.

For five of the eight provinces for which Chi used eighteenth-century gazetteers, the Harvard-Yenching library had nineteenth century gazetteers which could be used in their stead. The problem of dating the projects by century rather than by dynasty presented no difficulty because most projects were dated by year or reign period rather than simply by dynasty.

Representativeness of Data

The most difficult issue to deal with is whether simply counting the number of projects accurately reflects fluctuations in the level of water-control construction. The figures whose reliability we are attempting to establish appear in Table H.1.

The first step in the analysis is to compare the results of this study with those obtained by Chi Ch'ao-ting. It is apparent from Table H.2 that Chi's totals are generally higher than those in this study even when the gazetteers he uses are for an earlier period. Generally the difference between the two results is greatest for the Ch'ing period. Part of this discrepancy is accounted for by the fact that Chi counted major repairs as well as new projects, whereas I only counted the latter. The principal use of water-control data in this study is as an indication of the expansion of irrigated acreage, hence a figure net of depreciation is desirable. It would also appear, however, that Chi was somewhat freer in assigning dates to projects than was the case in this study. Finally, some of the earlier gazetteers apparently included more dated projects for the late seventeenth–early eighteenth centuries than did later gazetteers. That such was the case is not surprising, and it must be kept in mind when using the data in this study. (For less significant differences in the two tables, refer to the notes to Table H.2).

Consistency between the data in this study and those of Chi, however, proves little. The key issue is whether dated projects are a representative sample of the changes over time in a universe consisting of all water-control construction. This issue in turn depends on:
1. The size of the sample relative to the size of the universe.
2. The variance in the size of projects included in the sample, and whether that variance declines as the sample size increases.
3. Biases in the sample such as:
   a. The possibility that most dated projects are those carried out by officials and hence represent official activity rather than that of both officials and private individuals.
   b. the possibility that dates are assigned only to large projects.

TABLE H.2. COMPARISON BETWEEN CHI AND THIS STUDY (TS)
(Number of Projects)

	GAZETTEER USED		PRE-MING	PRE-14TH	MING	14TH–16TH	CH'ING	17TH–19TH	TOTAL	
	Chi	TS	Chi	TS	Chi	TS	Chi	TS	Chi	TS
N										
Hopei	1884	1884	71	53	228	186	542	249	841	488
Shansi	1734	1890	111	47	97	106	156	41	364	194
NW										
Shensi	1735	1735/[a] 1931	102	19	48	39	38	176	188	234
Anhwei	1877	1821–1850	40	42	30	60	41	101	111	203
E										
Kiangsu	1736	1736	183	177[b]	234	239[b]	62	47[b]	479	463
Chekiang	1736	1736	459	403[b]	480	671[b]	175	183[b]	1114	1257
C										
Kiangsi	1732	1875	93	60	287	190	222	182	602	432
Hupei	1921	1800/ 1921	36	37	143	85	528	131	707	253
Hunan	1885	1885	20	36	51	229 (95)	183	19	254	284
SE										
Fukien	1754	1871	461	375	212	126	219	140	892	641
Kwangtung	1822	1822	79	48	302	169	165	62	546	279
SW										
Szechwan	1815	1815[a]	24	28	5	23	19	125	48	176
Yunnan	1736	1835	10	7	110	96	292	227	408	330

[a] Shensi and Szechwan data are also taken from several *hsien* gazetteers.

[b] The Kiangsu and Chekiang data were recalculated so that seventeenth-century Ming data are included in the fourteenth–sixteenth-century category and fourteenth-century Yuan data were transferred to the pre-fourteenth category. These steps make the two sets of data more comparable.

Causes and Nature of Discrepancies:

1. This study's totals for Szechwan and Shensi in the seventeenth–nineteenth centuries are considerably above those of Chi. This situation results from the inclusion of data culled from *hsien* gazetteers in this study (for these two provinces only).
2. This study's low figure for Shensi in the pre-fourteenth–century period results from my decision not to include projects built in that era but which since have become defunct.
3. The fourteenth–sixteenth-century figures for Hunan include 134 observations from a single *hsien* built by one particular prefect. Chi's Hunan figures for the Ch'ing period are probably made up primarily of repairs which I have excluded from my totals. There were a great many projects repaired in Hunan in the late seventeenth and eighteenth centuries.

c. The possibility that the median size of a project in one period differs markedly from that in another.

d. The possibility that gazetteers more faithfully recorded recent projects than projects of an earlier period.

e. The possibility of within- and between-province geographic biases.

These questions will be taken up below.

From the data in Table H.3, it is clear that the size of the sample varies considerably among provinces. The Kwangsi sample is too small to be of much use. The Kweichow sample (fifteen dated observations) is even smaller. Data from

TABLE H.3. COVERAGE OF DATED WATER CONTROL PROJECTS

Province	Total Number of Projects	Dated Projects	Percentage
NW			
Shensi	1,100	234	21
N			
Shantung	950	51	5
E			
Anhwei	4,020	203	5
Chekiang	5,000 –	1,257	25
C			
Kiangsi	17,000 +	432	2.5
Hunan	6,970	284	4
SE			
Fukien	4,100 +	641	16
Kwangtung	2,500	279	11
Kwangsi	1,000 +	20	2
SW			
Yunnan	1,100	330	30

these two provinces, therefore, were not used in the analysis in the text. Dated projects in the 1815 Szechwan gazetteer are comparably scarce but in this case these data could be supplemented by material in *hsien* snd prefecture gazetteers. The amount of time consumed in recording and counting undated projects prevented me from including all the provinces in Table H.3. The sample size for provinces not included in Table H.3 can be obtained from Table H.1 (although the size of the universe cannot be so obtained).

A more serious difficulty concerns the variation in the size of individual projects. It is possible, for example, that if all water-control projects in the nineteenth century were very large while those in the eighteenth century were small, the conclusion based on just the number of projects that water-control activity in the eighteenth century was significantly higher than in the nineteenth century could be reversed. Data relevant to these issues are given in Tables H.4–H.6.

TABLE H.4. AVERAGE IRRIGATED AREA PER PROJECT

	PERIOD OR CENTURY									
	Pre-T'ang	*T'ang*	*10th–12th*	*13th*	*14th*	*15th*	*16th*	*17th*	*18th*	*19th*
Chekiang (E)										
Dated Projects of Which:	14	74	211	76	409	76	196	137	64	—
Irrigated Area Given	3	12	21	7	10	6	16	9	3	—
Average Area (1,000) *mou*)	337	111	274	94	25	18	77	21	138	—
Eliminating Largest Observation	55	84	108	43	17	5	35	14	8	—
Fukien (SE)										
Dated Projects of Which:	4	22	324	25	22	52	52	38	98	4
Irrigated Area Given	3	10	38	5	3	15	11	0	6	1
Average Area (1,000 *mou*)	61	32	221	400	37	5	1	0	24	100
Kwangtung (SE)										
Dated Projects of Which:	1	0	29	18	84	49	36	15	17	30
Irrigated Area Given	0	0	21	3	57	33	18	6	7	27
Average Area (1,000 *mou*)	—	—	275	12	9	15	10	4	13	2
Shensi (NW)										
Dated Projects of Which:	1	5	12	1	2	9	28	6	78	92
Irrigated Area Given	5	6	2	0	2	6	5	7	18	15
Average Area (1,000 *mou*)	1,490	112	150	—	21	17	7	7	8	5
Shansi (N)										
Dated Projects Of Which:	3	15	18	11	25	15	66	30	11	—
Irrigated Area Given	3	3	6	7	9	8	24	14	1	—
Average Area (1,000 *mou*)	99	458	17	7	39	17	9	3	5	—
Anhwei (E)										
Dated Projects of Which:	10	15	15	2	9	14	37	28	64	9
Irrigated Area Given	8	9	4	1	2	2	2	5	0	3
Average Area (1,000 *mou*)	695	40	431	0.3	16	0.6	2	287	—	148

TABLE H.5. LENGTH OF DIKE CONSTRUCTION

	Before 10th	10th–12th	13th	14th	15th	16th	17th	18th	19th
				CENTURY					
Hopei (N)									
Dated Projects									
of Which:	21	18	14	23	44	119	50	171	28
Length Given	1	5		2	12	31	12	70	19
Average Length									
(*li*)	10	2		4	41	15	23	23	39
Hupei (C)									
Dated Projects									
of Which:	10	17	10	8	21	56	21	80	30
Length Given	0	4	1	7	6	12	7	49	11
Average Length									
(*li*)	—	75	100	57	18	48	21	13	40
Szechwan (four *hsien* and two *fu* only) (SW)									
Dated Projects									
of Which:	15	10	3		23		14	76	35
Length Given	2	2	0		5		3	30	19
Average Length									
(*li*)	2	4	—		21		0.4	4	7
Fukien (SE)									
Dated Projects									
of Which:	26	324	25	22	52	52	38	98	4
Length Given	11	24	1	1	8	10	9	15	2
Average Length									
(*li*)	10	6	0.6	11	14	11	8	11	7
Anhwei (E)									
Dated Projects									
of Which:	25	15	2	9	14	37	28	64	9
Length Given	0	2	0	0	3	1	3	22	2
Average Length									
(*li*)	—	93	—	—	2	0.2	6	19	13
Kiangsi (C)									
Dated Projects									
of Which:	25	24	11	18	54	118	56	26	100
Length Given	1	7	2	0	10	21	12	4	13
Average Length									
(*li*)	0.6	7	2	—	9	7	3	6	5
Kiangsu (E)									
Dated Projects									
of Which:	55	89	15	30	67	81	126	16	—
Length Given	3	10	1	3	12	6	56	4	—
Average Length									
(*li*)	61	64	38	25	29	49	21	37	—

One *li* = approximately 0.36 of a mile.

	Dated No. of Projects	Projects Avg. Acreage (mou)	Undated No. of Projects	Projects Avg. Acreage (mou)
		(14th–19th centuries Only)		
Fukien (SE)	42	51,000	1081	1000
Kwangtung (SE)	148	9,400	1776	8000
Kiangsi (C)	32	65,000	827	980
Shensi (NW)	213	2,100	668	460

To test whether the mean size of water-control projects varied from one century to another, I did an analysis of variance on the data in Tables H.4 and H.5. For the irrigated acreage data in Table H.4, the hypotheses that there are no significant differences in the means of water-control projects between centuries and between provinces must both be rejected at a 95 per cent level of confidence.[1] The problems are all with the pre-fourteenth–century acreage data. An analysis of variance on just the fourteenth through nineteenth century data leads one to accept the hypothesis of no difference in means between centuries or between provinces even at the 99 per cent level of confidence and higher.[2] As for the data on dikes in Table H.5, the hypotheses that there are no significant differences in the mean size of projects either between centuries or between provinces can both be accepted at a 95 per cent level of confidence even with the inclusion of pre-fourteenth–century data.[3] Thus the principal problem is with the pre-fourteenth–century figures, but even with these only one set of data indicate that the means in that period differed significantly from the means of a later period. In neither set of data is there any reason for becoming suspicious of the fourteenth- to nineteenth-century estimates.

Even without doing an analysis of variance, it is apparent from statistics in Table H.4 that the average irrigated acreage per project was much greater in periods prior to the thirteenth or fourteenth century. My own opinion is that simply counting the number of projects recorded in provincial gazetteers for the T'ang and Sung periods does understate the amount of water-control construction in those periods relative to later periods, but not by as much as the averages in Table H.4 indicate. Chinese tend to use the words for 10,000 (*wan*) and 1,000 (*ch'ien*) simply to indicate that the number is large. Hence the term "*wan-ch'ing*" which translates to "1,000,000 *mow*" may in fact refer to a number which if measured precisely would be much smaller. The frequency of such vague references is rare from the fourteenth century on and is not as frequent as I expected in earlier periods, but it does not take many "*wan-ch'ing's*" to raise the

1. For the differences between provinces, $F=0.256$ (F.95 [5,513] $=0.229$) and for the differences between centuries, $F=0.596$ (F.95 [9,513] $=0.369$).
2. For the differences between provinces, $F=0.076$ (F.99 [5,340] $=0.111$) and for the differences between centuries, $F=0.0310$ (F.99 [5,340] $=0.111$).
3. For the differences between provinces, $F=0.258$ (F.95 [6,574] $=0.273$) and for the differences between centuries, $F=0.109$ (F.99 [8,574] $=0.206$).

averages. Interestingly, there is no real difference in the average length of dikes for the periods before and after the fourteenth century (Table H.5).

In the *Sung hui-yao chi-kao* there are water-control construction data for projects completed during the reform period of Wang An-shih (1070's). These figures are presented in Table H.7 and compared to data from gazetteers (from Table H.1). The much larger number of projects in the earlier source and their smaller average size would appear to further bear out the contention that the provincial gazetteers understate the size of water control activity in the Sung. But it also appears to be the case that figures for the 1070's in the *Sung hui-yao*

TABLE H.7. WATER CONTROL PROJECTS IN THE SUNG PERIOD
(11th Century A.D.)

	NUMBER OF PROJECTS		AVERAGE AREA IRRIGATED (100 *mou*)	
	SHY	*TS*	*SHY*	*TS* (*10th–12th Cent.*)
N				
Hopei	45	6*	1,324.9	—
Shantung	177	1	146.6	—
Shansi	114	12	41.4	170
NW				
Shensi	132	4*	37.7	1,500
E				
Anhwei ⎱ Kiangsu ⎰	2,794	29	30.6	4,310
Chekiang	1,980	90	52.4	2,740
C				
Kiangsi	997	26	4.7	—
Hupei	233	1	37.5	—
Hunan	1,473	8	0.8	—
SE				
Kwangtung	407	14	1.5	2,750
Fukien	212	108*	14.3	2,210
Kwangsi	879	—	3.1	—
SW		—		
Szechwan	315	8	14.8	—
Total	9,758	307	318.9	—

SOURCE: Wada Sei, 1960, vol. I, pp. 97–99. I am indebted to Professor Robert Hartwell for pointing these materials and their relevance out to me. The original source of these figures is the *Sung hui-yao chi-kao* (Wada Sei's work is a translation into Japanese).

   * Data for these three provinces are only available for the Sung period as a whole. I have divided the figures in Table H.1 by 3 to obtain the estimates used here.

chi-kao were recorded in great detail with all projects in effect dated, no matter how small and whether they were new or simply repairs of older systems. Still, if the principal concern is with estimating the relative amounts of activity over time within a particular province, the Sung figures—particularly for the provinces of Kiangsu, Chekiang, Hupei, Hunan, and Szechwan—must be revised upward.

From data in Table H.6 it is apparent that in the several provinces for which statistics were available there may be another source of bias arising from the fact that the average size of dated projects appears to be somewhat larger than for undated projects. But the differences are not great, particularly when one takes into account the fact that the comparatively small number of projects in Kiangsu and Fukien that are both dated and for which irrigated acreage figures are available probably exaggerates the average acreage of dated projects. Whatever the case, this bias does not reduce the usefulness of the data. In fact the value of the dated projects as indicating changes over time in water-control construction is enhanced if they generally represent the larger projects.

Another possible source of bias arises from the fact that officials may have been more diligent in recording the dates and other details of projects which directly concerned them or in some way redounded to their credit. I, for one, originally thought this probably to be the case. Perhaps so, but it is clear from data in Table H.8 that the gazetteers do record the dates of a large number of privately sponsored projects. To estimate the bias, if any, one would have to know what was the proportion of total official to total private projects. This

TABLE H.8. OFFICIAL AND PRIVATE WATER CONTROL
CONSTRUCTION
(Number of Projects)

	KWANGTUNG (SE)		YUNNAN (SW)	
	Official	*Private*	*Official*	*Private*
No dates	7	44	2	24
T'ang and Before	0	1	0	0
9th–12th Centuries	15	8	0	0
13th	9	5	1	0
14th	20	40	4	2
15th	23	12	12	3
16th	13	12	14	5
17th	6	4	20	7
18th	9	4	38	16
19th	30	0	6	16
Total	132	130	97	73

information is not available. But even if there is a bias in favor of official projects, it does not follow that the value of the period totals is necessarily reduced. Officials and private individuals may have responded to the same kinds of considerations and hence fluctuations in official and private series may have moved together. This seems generally to have been the case for Yunnan and Kwangtung (except for nineteenth-century Kwangtung, but in nineteenth-century Kwangtung, 28 of 30 observations are from a single *hsien*).

Geographical biases of the kind appearing in nineteenth-century Kwangtung are not very frequent. Other examples are found in Fukien where 241 of 324 observations during the tenth–twelfth centuries are from two *hsien* and 58 of 98 observations during the eighteenth century are from a single *hsien*, and in Hunan where 134 of 187 observations in the sixteenth century are from a single *hsien* and were built by one particular prefect. Generally, however, the geographic coverage within each province is broad and probably not a source of significant bias.

Geographic biases between provinces, however, are more serious. From the various tables in this appendix it is clear that data for some provinces are much more detailed than for others. These differences do not present problems as long as the data are used to explain the timing of water-control construction efforts within a particular province. They do, however, make it necessary to exercise caution in comparing the level of activity in one province with that in another. One cannot, for example, determine from the data in Table H.1 that water-control activity in Chekiang was more vigorous than in Kiangsu simply because there are many more dated projects for Chekiang. One must also be careful in drawing conclusions from total figures for all provinces lumped together for any particular century.

But for provinces with a sufficient number of dated projects, the possible biases in the data do not appear serious enough to negate their use, provided they are used with care. Further, as was shown in Chapter III, the timing of water-control construction in the various provinces forms a plausible pattern given what else we know of developments in these provinces. It is circular reasoning, however, to argue that the data are reliable because they tell a plausible story and then to turn around and use those data as evidence in support of that story. The detailed analysis in this appendix was undertaken in order to independently establish the rough reliability of the figures.

The Size
of Interprovince Trade

The quality of Chinese commercial data for the mid-1950's varies considerably. The government statistical bureau probably had only a general notion of the size of local free-market trade, but a reasonably thorough understanding of the size of trade in commodities over which the state exercised tight control, such as grain, cotton, and a number of major cash crops (see Perkins, 1966, Appendices A and D).

As one moves back in time, the quality of the data deteriorates. Foreign trade figures remain reliable and are much more accessible than those for the 1950's. But the overall size of rural commerce can only be surmised from a few sample surveys that indicate the percentage of farm produce marketed. For the years prior to the 1920's and 1930's, even such surveys are not available.

For late nineteenth- and early twentieth-century China, however, there are two kinds of data which can be used to estimate the size of a portion of internal commerce. The first set of figures are the *likin* tax revenues, the second, the internal trade data collected by the Imperial Maritime Customs. Both sets of data were a byproduct of a system of taxes or tariffs on internal trade.

If these figures are to be used to indicate the size and nature of China's internal commerce, two basic issues must be dealt with. First, there is the question of the reliability of the figures. Were they collected with care and concern for accuracy? Second, what portion of China's internal commerce do these figures represent? What were the kinds of trade (or taxes) reported? Was the *likin* or maritime customs definition of trade an inclusive one?

THE ACCURACY OF TRADE DATA

Ignoring for the moment the question of the coverage of the *likin* and customs definitions of internal trade, do *likin* and customs figures accurately reflect trade as they define it? The figures of the China maritime customs are probably quite reliable in this sense. The customs administration was run by foreigners who used European procedures and who were isolated from the numerous irregularities and forms of corruption that characterized many activities under the unfettered control of the Chinese government. Personnel of the customs were generally well trained, the most notable exception of relevance to this study being the several years after 1902 when "Native Customs" offices were put under "Maritime Customs" control with the procedures and personnel of the former only gradually altered to meet the standards of the latter (see S. F. Wright, 1938, pp. 391–97).

No similar degree of confidence can be placed in the *likin* data. Most important, the *likin* figures are tax revenue, not trade, data. For several provinces, we do not even have the actual revenue figures, but only the estimates of Lo Yü-tung (1936). Whether Lo's estimates or the reported figures for the other provinces are reliable remains an issue.

The more serious difficulty comes when one attempts to convert tax data into estimates of trade. In theory, the *likin* tax was a percentage of the value of goods passing a particular tax station. Thus, once one knows the relevant percentage, it is a simple matter to derive the value of trade passing that station. The reality is more complicated.

First, each province charged a different rate and in some cases several different rates were used within a single province. The former problem can be dealt with by using a different rate for each province when estimating trade, but the latter problem can only be handled by guessing what share of the trade paid which rate. Further, there were a variety of special rates for such commodities as tea, sugar, wine, tobacco, opium, and others. Those special rates are applied in some provinces, but not others. Occasionally the revenue figures are broken down to show how much revenue was obtained from a particular tax, more often they are not. I have not made any attempt to deal with these different rates, but have simply applied the general rate (see Table I.1) to the total *likin* revenue figure. This procedure introduces some error into the trade estimate, but I doubt if it is a major source of error.

It is much more difficult to dismiss the problem that arises because a single commodity might be taxed at several tax stations, each time paying the rate set for that province. Lo Yü-tung has taken some of this multiple taxation into account in calculating the rates in Table I.1, but not all. When one looks at the revenue data, it is difficult to see how a single commodity could have paid the going rate many times. Such high rates would lead to improbably low estimates of internal trade. Estimates of the tea trade would seem to indicate that tea paid the tax only once (see Table I.2). Provinces such as Kiangsu and Honan, for example, give a very small figure for tea. This small figure accurately reflects these provinces' contribution to tea production, but certainly not their level of tea consumption, indicating that tea presumably only paid the tax at its point of origin. But then tea may have been a special case.

	General Rate	Other Selected Rates	
Kiangsu	5	—	
Chekiang	5.5, 10	4.5, 9	(before 1864)
Fukien	10	0.6	(in 1850's)
Hupei	2	—	
Kwangtung	7.5	6	(before 1890)
Hunan	6	5	(before 1894)
Kiangsi	10	5	(short hauls)
Kwangsi	2	5	(after 1904)
Anhwei	2	6	(past 3 stations)
Kansu	1, 2	5	(after 1906)
Shensi	4	0.45	(early)
Shansi	1.5	—	
Honan	1.625	1.25	(before 1902)
Shantung	2	—	
Szechwan	4	—	
Hopei, Yunnan, Kweichow	1.25, 5, ?	—	
Manchuria	1, 1, 2	—	

TABLE I.I. LIKIN TAX RATES (PERCENTAGE)

SOURCE: Lo Yü-tung, 1936.

Other potential sources of error are the numerous irregularities that characterized many Chinese administrative activities. Extortion and bribery were not rare and both could and to some extent did obscure the relationship between revenue and the value of trade. According to Edwin Beal, however, "a study of the Chinese documents relating to these matters reveals that the Ch'ing government, from the beginning of the operation of the *likin*, was well informed of the difficulties and abuses which were springing up, and that it tried to reduce and eradicate these abuses by removing guilty officials and by attempting to establish an adequate system for reporting the handling of funds" (1958, p. 46).

For many kinds of tax revenue, there has been a tendency throughout Chinese history for unchanging tax quotas to be submitted for rates calculated as a percentage of goods in transit or other similar rates. The administrative convenience of using quotas rather than rates is obvious, but where such procedures are used trade data cannot be derived from revenue data. Quotas were a common feature of the tax system of the Ming dynasty and of the Ch'ing land tax. But they do not appear to have been used to a significant degree in connection with the *likin* tax.

In 1899, the viceroy of Kwangtung, Li Hung-chang, did establish a quota for that province as a substitute for direct *likin* collections on trade,[1] but revenue

1. At least this is stated to be the case in Parker, 1901, p. 239. Many of Parker's statements must be used with care. Some of his "facts" are contradicted by material in Lo Yü-tung who had access to much more detailed and reliable information.

TABLE I.2. TEA PRODUCTION AND TAXES (LIKIN)

Province	Year	Likin *Tax* (taels)	Tax Rate (taels *per* picul *or* %)	Estimated Production (piculs)	1914–1918 Production (piculs)
Fukien	1861–1865	548,100	2.35	230,000	—
Fukien	1898	341,207	1.91	180,000	181,000
Chekiang	1860's	90,000	1.05	90,000	436,000
Kiangsi	1889–1894	177,000	1.25	140,000	210,000
Anhwei	1890–1899	52,000	0.2	260,000	436,000
Anhwei	1890–1899	52,000	1.3	40,000	436,000
Hunan	1890–1899	54,000	7.5%	36,000	2,300,000
Kiangsu	1890–1899	504	9%(?)	280	6,000
Honan	1890–1899	2,265	1.25%	9,000	1,000
Shantung	1890–1899	2,725	2%	7,000	1,000

SOURCE: All data are from Lo Yü-tung, 1936. The years selected are ones for which both tax rate and revenue data are available. I have used an average price per *picul* of 20 *taels* in estimating production for provinces where only a percentage tax rate is given.

Fukien: See pp. 325–30 and 562–63.

Chekiang: pp. 254 and 509. The rate on chest (*hsiang*) tea was 1.4 *liang*, while that on basket (*lou*) tea was 0.7 *liang* per 100 catties. I have averaged these two figures.

Kiangsi: pp. 288 and 533.

Anhwei: p. 276. The proper tax rate to use is impossible to calculate. The transport tax on tea is five or more times the regular tax, but it is unclear to me whether that tax was normally paid or not.

Hunan: pp. 312 and 548–49.

Kiangsu: pp. 236 and 487. The tax on tea is said to be higher than the rate on other commodities (which was 7.5) because of a 20 per cent surcharge.

Honan: pp. 376 and 599. It is not clear whether tea prior to 1900 paid the same rate as other commodities. I have assumed it did.

Shantung: pp. 371–72 and 594. The tax figure excludes the 20 per cent surcharge added in 1895. I have assumed the tea tax rate was the same as on other commodities.

data for subsequent years would seem to indicate that this quota system never went into effect. Generally when quotas are used, revenue figures remain unchanged or virtually unchanged for many years. Available *likin* revenue figures in Lo Yü-tung, however, change in every year in each province. Further, as the discussion in a subsequent section will indicate, many of the changes in revenue seem to reflect the gradual inflation in prices that occurred in the 1890's and 1900's.

Perhaps most important, there is a great deal of direct evidence from foreign visitors and residents and many others that *likin* stations did collect duties on actual goods in transit.[2] Some of these same sources also indicate that smuggling designed to avoid these tax stations was not on a large scale in most areas.

It is impossible to estimate the precise net margin of error introduced by the various sources of error analyzed in this section. If taxes were charged on a single commodity many different times en route, or if the use of the general tax rate to

2. Virtually every traveller to China who went inland had comments to make about the numerous *likin* tax stations.

derive the value of all commodities including special commodities such as salt, tea, and opium exaggerates the value of these special commodities, then the *likin*-derived trade estimates overstate the true size of trade passing the *likin* stations. If smuggling and bribery of tax officials were more serious, the trade figures are underestimates. Perhaps a more detailed analysis of *likin* procedures than that done here (or that by Lo Yü-tung) could arrive at a more precise notion of the direction and degree of error.

THE COVERAGE OF THE DATA

The maritime customs trade figures and the *likin* revenue and derived trade figures are presented in Tables I.3, I.4, and I.5. Assuming that errors of one sort or another do not make these data wholly unreliable, just what is it that the figures represent?

TABLE I.3. MARITIME CUSTOMS TRADE STATISTICS
(Annual Averages in 1,000 hk. *Taels*)

	FOREIGN TRADE		DOMESTIC INTERPORT TRADE		TRADE IN CHINESE GOODS
	Imports (1)	*Exports* (2)	*Imports* (3)	*Exports* (4)	(2) + (3)
1880–1889	99,190	77,140	58,040	47,290	135,180
1890–1899	183,360	132,810	88,730	66,620	221,540
1900–1909	364,100	234,110	153,660	127,400	387,770
1910–1919	526,590	436,850	230,490	217,080	667,340
1920–1929	1,016,210	788,880	548,650	579,140	1,337,530
1930–1936*	936,100	550,800	919,570	890,640	1,470,370

SOURCE: All figures are derived from data appearing in the annual reports of the China Maritime Customs.
  * After 1931 the trade of Manchuria was not included in the customs report for China.

The maritime customs figures include all of China's trade with foreign countries and that part of internal trade that took place between "treaty ports" and in foreign ships or Chinese ships registered with the customs administration. It is clear from the outset, therefore, that these trade figures do not include any local commerce within rural market towns or any of the trade that supplied China's cities with food and raw materials from areas near the particular city being supplied. Vegetables for urban residents would not be recorded since they generally came from farms within a few miles of the city. Cotton grown in Hupei and shipped to Hankow would only be recorded if it were shipped on from Hankow to Shanghai or some other "treaty port" city.

The only question that remains, therefore, is whether these figures do include most long-distance trade as defined in Chapter VI. This question can be further broken down into, first, whether trade between treaty ports did account for most internal long distance trade, and, second, whether most of that trade was carried in ships that registered with the maritime customs administration.

TABLE I.4. LIKIN REVENUE
(Annual Averages in 1,000 *Taels*)

	1870–1879	1880–1889	1890–1899	1900–1908
Kiangsu	2,478	2,250	2,527	3,666
Chekiang	2,012	1,988	2,080	2,169
Fukien	2,158	2,074	1,852	981
Hupei	1,466	1,466	1,570	1,893
Kwangtung	1,011	1,172	1,576	1,695
Hunan	1,217	1,259	1,277	1,351
Kiangsi	1,205	1,105	1,192	1,669
Kwangsi	685	687	573	676
Anhwei	511	481	446	543
Kansu	365	383	266	387
Shensi	262	336	470	532
Shansi	110	133	65	178
Honan	80	84	81	155
Shantung	64	55	84	148
Szechwan	519	489	410	470
Chihli, Yunnan, Kweichow	410–580	464–720	500–800	500–800
Manchuria	15,046	15,104	15,683	18,120

SOURCE: Lo Yü-tung, 1936.

A glance at Map I.1 (p. 352) suggests an answer to the first question. Virtually all major ports along the China coast or the Yangtze river were by the late nineteenth century classified as "treaty ports." Commodities that were first shipped to a nearby large port and then transhipped to another large port thus would have been included in the figures. Goods shipped directly from a rural area to some distant large port would not be included. In addition, trade between interior points, one of which was not on the Yangtze, would not be reported in the interport customs publications. There were no "treaty ports" on the north China plain (except along the coast) and only a limited number in the southwest, and those were designed primarily to control foreign trade with Indo-China.

As for the second issue, a large number of ships carrying goods between treaty ports did not register with the maritime customs until after 1903. Prior to 1904, all steamships, whether foreign or Chinese-owned, did clear with the maritime customs when entering or leaving a treaty port, but only a small number of junks did so (see Table I.6). After that time, the placing of the "Native Customs" stations within 50 *li* of treaty ports under the maritime customs

TABLE I.5. INTERPROVINCE TRADE (*likin* ESTIMATE)
(Annual Averages in 1,000 *Taels*)

	1870–1879	1880–1889	1890–1899	1900–1908
Kiangsu	49,560	45,000	50,540	73,320
Chekiang	25,150	24,850	26,000	27,110
Fukien	21,580	20,740	18,520	9,810
Hupei	73,300	73,300	78,500	94,650
Kwangtung	16,850	19,530	21,010	22,600
Hunan	24,340	25,180	21,280	22,520
Szechwan (excl. salt)	12,980	12,230	10,250	11,750
Kiangsi	12,050	11,050	11,920	16,690
Kwangsi	34,250	34,350	28,650	33,800
Anhwei	25,550	24,050	22,300	27,150
Kansu	18,250	19,150	13,300	19,350
Shensi	6,550	8,400	11,750	13,300
Shansi	7,330	8,870	4,330	11,870
Honan	6,400	6,730	6,480	9,540
Shantung	3,200	2,750	4,200	7,400
Chihli, Yunnan, Kweichow	40,000	47,000	52,000	52,000
Manchuria	30,000	37,000	39,000	64,000
Total	407,340	420,180	420,030	516,860

SOURCE: These figures were derived using the general tax rates in Table I.1 and the revenue data in Table I.4. For Chihli, etc., I have used 1.25 per cent and for Manchuria, 1.5 per cent.

resulted in most junks involved in treaty port trade entering and clearing with the maritime customs administration.

Thus from 1904, on the customs data probably include most intertreaty-port trade. Even before that date, the reports are more inclusive than one would assume by simply counting numbers of vessels. By the 1890's the bulk of interport trade was being carried on steamships and hence was recorded. Thus there was some increase in interport trade in the years 1904–1909 that could not be attributed to a rise in prices, but the increase was not dramatic. The further one goes back in time, the larger was the percentage of goods in long-distance trade that was carried on junks, and hence the greater the discrepancy between reported and actual intertreaty-port trade.

In the 1910's and thereafter the coverage of the customs figures for internal trade again declines as railroads began to carry an increasingly large proportion

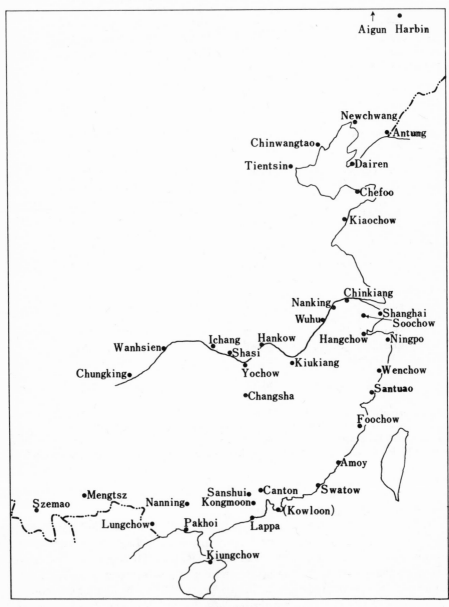

Map I. 1
Chinese Treaty Ports
(circa 1900)

TABLE I.6. VESSELS ENTERING AND CLEARING TREATY PORTS

	STEAMSHIPS		JUNKS	
	Number (1,000)	Tonnage (1,000)	Number (1,000)	Tonnage (1,000)
1890–1899 average	33	30,095	9	1,136
1900	58	39,556	12	1,251
1901	53	47,255	12	1,162
1902	58	52,806	11	1,184
1903	63	55,930	14	1,360
1904	75	57.652	148	6,122
1905	88	66,373	136	6,383
1906	88	70.118	121	5,702
1907	91	74,130	127	5,979
1908	87	77,956	121	6,036
1909	88	80,614	121	6,158
1910	96	82,337	124	6,439
1911	90	80,238	104	5,691
1912	93	82,389	90	5,174
1913	101	87,614	90	5,721
1914	108	91,126	112	6,858
1915	104	84,641	103	6,022
1916	105	82,382	97	5,639
1917	105	80,267	109	6,640
1918	98	74,201	95	6,046
1919	113	89,844	97	5,882
1920	121	99,642	89	4,624
1921	125	109,320	89	5,300
1922	123	119,355	63	4,776
1923	122	127,279	60	4,026
1924	132	136,830	54	4,603
1925	120	124,516	48	3,686
1926	117	132,249	42	2,410
1927	107	112,048	48	4,163
1928	141	148,261	46	4,369
1929	141	150,203	46	4,464
1930	135	151,700	46	3,906
1931	138	155,332	44	4,673

SOURCE: These figures are from the annual maritime customs reports. Those for the years up through 1928 can also be found in National Research Institute of Social Sciences, Academia Sinica, *Statistics of China's Foreign Trade During the Last Sixty-Five Years* (1931), p. 132. After 1931, junk and steamship figures are only separated for one year (1936).

of the goods in long-distance commerce. The relative position of the various modes of transport in the 1950's and the late 1930's and 1940's is presented in Table I.7. The dominance of the railroad in the 1930's or 1940's (the pre-1949 peak period) is clear from these figures. But in the 1900–1909 period railroad construction was just getting underway and the volume of goods carried was negligible.

TABLE I.7. TRANSPORT TONNAGE

	Railroad	Steamship	Junk	Truck
		(*1,000 tons originated*)		
Pre-1949 high[a]	136,650	12,640	—	8,190
1952	132,170	14,320	—	22,100
1954	192,880	28,750	96,000[b]	43,030
1957	274,200	53,770	—	83,730
		(*1,000,000 ton kilometers*)		
Pre-1949 high[a]	40,400	12,830	—	460
1952	60,160	10,610	—	770
1954	93,240	18,640	12,430[b]	1,940
1957	134,590	34,390	—	3,940

SOURCE: *TGY*, pp. 146–48 except where otherwise noted.

[a] I do not know how these figures were arrived at, but most such data are derived from official materials for the 1930's and 1940's. The Chinese national railways in 1936 carried only 34,360,000 tons, while Manchurian railways in 1939 carried 50,734,000 tons (*Manchoukuo Yearbook 1942*, pp. 587–90) and this figure was probably surpassed in the 1940's. If the Communist pre-1949 estimate is correct, other railroads must have carried 50 or 60,000,000 tons.

[b] According to one source (Wang Shou-tao, 1955, p. 220), junks in 1954 carried 77 per cent of all freight on inland waterways and accounted for 40 per cent of freight turnover (ton kilometers).

Thus the years when the maritime customs coverage is most complete (least incomplete) are those between 1900 and 1909.

In principle and to some degree in reality, the coverage of the *likin* figures is much greater than the maritime customs data. *Likin* tax stations were numerous and located in every province and region of the empire. Local market-town trade did not pay *likin* duties, and some of the goods supplied to urban areas such as vegetables were not taxed. But a much greater proportion of these urban supplies paid *likin* than entered into the reports of the maritime customs. Further, the *likin* tax caught all commodities entering long-distance trade, including those that did not pass through two treaty ports. Finally, the *likin* tax was applied to virtually all commodities of any significance.

In practice, the coverage of the *likin* tax was less complete than indicated by these remarks. Hunan, for example, according to one source (Sun Ching-chih, 1958, p. 217), exported 630,000 *piculs* of tea in the 1890's, yet the tax data indicate a trade of only 36,000 *piculs* (see Table I.2). Lesser but significant discrepancies can be found for other provinces and other commodities. Part of the explanation for these discrepancies may lie in the widespread abuses of the transit-pass system. The transit-pass was designed to enable foreign imports and Chinese exports to foreign countries to pass through the numerous *likin* barriers without payment. These goods, however, were supposed to pay a transit tax when they reached their destination (this discussion is based on S. F. Wright, 1938, pp. 324–33). Thus all foreign imports and many exports abroad did not pay the *likin* tax. The amount of exports formally exempted under this procedure, however, does not appear to have been large. In Shanghai, for example, only 6.4 million *taels* of goods were brought from the interior under transit pass (in 1908). Total exports of Chinese goods abroad from Shanghai in that year came to 82.5 million *taels*. (The figures are from the maritime customs reports for 1908).

A greater loss of *likin* revenue probably resulted from abuses of the transit pass. These passes were illegally sold or cavalierly issued so that many Chinese goods destined for domestic consumption passed through the *likin* barriers without payment. How large a loss resulted from these practices is unclear. The hostility of local officials toward transit passes in general, and those held by Chinese in particular, however, probably kept most traders from using such methods.

Thus both the maritime customs data and *likin* estimates included much of the long-distance trade, but not all. Neither included any local commerce, but the *likin* figures did contain some trade, principally long-distance trade that did not involve treaty ports, and was not recorded by the maritime customs administration. On the other hand, the *likin* figures did not include goods moving under transit passes. Given the degree of overlap, however, the two sets of data can be usefully compared.

The nationwide totals are compared in Table I.8; provincial breakdowns for three years are in Table I.9. In Table I.9, all recorded domestic interport trade,

TABLE I.8. LONG DISTANCE TRADE—CHINESE
GOODS (CURRENT PRICES)
(1,000 *Taels*)

	MARITIME CUSTOMS DATA[a] (EXCLUDING FOREIGN-MADE GOODS)		LIKIN ESTIMATE[b]
		(Annual Averages)	
	(1)	*(2)*	*(3)*
1870–1879	—	—	417,340
1880–1889	135,180	182,470	420,180
1890–1899	221,540	288,150	420,030
1900–1908	—	—	516,860
1900–1909	387,770	515,170	—
1910–1919	667,340	884,420	—
1920–1929	1,337,530	1,916,670	—
1930–1936	1,470,370	2,316,010	—

SOURCE: All data are from the annual reports of the China Maritime Customs. For 1908, "domestic trade" is the difference between "total exports originated" and foreign exports, whereas for 1928 "domestic trade" is the "net Chinese imports into Chinese ports." The concepts are almost, but not quite identical.

(1) Foreign exports plus interport trade in domestic goods, imports only.

(2) Foreign exports plus interport trade in domestic goods, both exports and imports.

[a] Included in these totals are net exports to both foreign and Chinese ports, together with net imports from Chinese ports only. See Table I.3.   [b] See Table I.5.

both imports and exports, are included, whereas in Table I.8 the national totals are presented net of domestic exports (1) as well as with exports included (2). Adding in both domestic exports and imports in effect double-counts domestic trade since the export of one port is the import of another. If one is interested in the volume of trade passing through a particular province, this double-counting is generally perfectly proper, but it exaggerates the total volume of nation-wide long-distance commerce as recorded by the customs administration.

If one assumes that the *likin* tax was levied both at the province of origin of a particular good and at that good's destination, then the proper comparison is between *likin* estimates and total customs trade, both imports and exports. This is the comparison made in Table I.9. The two estimates do not give identical results, but for many provinces, particularly those along the Yangtze (the first seven provinces in the table), the figures are quite close.[3] The only exception is Hunan, but both the *likin* and customs estimates for that province are of dubious validity. Neither, for example, includes much tea.

TABLE I.9. PROVINCIAL BREAKDOWN OF TRADE ESTIMATES
(1,000 *Taels* or Haikwan *Taels*)

	1896		1906		1908	
	Likin	*Customs*	*Likin*	*Customs*	*Likin*	*Customs*
Kiangsu	67,490	62,890	76,680	118,250	77,540	124,890
Anhwei	19,200	7,370	29,150	14,610	26,040	19,050
Chekiang	26,180	8,700	31,770	22,660	28,100	34,690
Kiangsi	11,880	8,410	18,890	14,750	17,810	19,770
Fukien	19,230	10,680	9,460	19,600	7,910	21,010
Hupei	79,560	31,760	85,830	64,920	80,760	85,040
Hunan	20,420	—	22,000	3,000	22,690	7,270
Szechwan	11,500	6,200	10,960	14,170	16,430	17,290
Kwangsi	27,360	—	30,310	4,080	48,410	5,870
Kwangtung	23,380	61,410	18,190	123,730	36,980	132,000
Shantung	5,380	9,750	4,890	33,510	7,150	34,030
Manchuria	35,800	14,660	68,400	30,760	113,330	43,080
Liaoning	15,800	—	—	—	—	—
Total	363,180	221,830	406,530	464,040	483,150	543,990

SOURCES: Annual reports of the China maritime customs and Lo Yü-tung, 1936, pp. 464–469. The percentages used to convert *likin* revenues to trade estimates are those in Table I.1. Provinces for which estimates are available from only one of the two sources are not included.

For the southeast (Kwangtung, Kwangsi, and Fukien), the discrepancies are very large. These provinces, particularly Kwangtung, have always been famous for their independence of Peking and resulting tax irregularities. In addition, the number of treaty ports in Kwangtung was very large (see Map I.1) and much trade of a local nature may have been recorded by customs officials. The Fukien figures are quite close if one compares the 1896 *likin* estimate with customs data

3. The large size of Kiangsu trade as recorded by the customs administration as compared to the *likin* estimate can probably be explained by the fact that many goods exported abroad from Shanghai were produced in the city or its immediate environs and hence never paid a *likin* tax. Transit passes account for a discrepancy of another 10 million *taels*.

in 1906 and 1908. In 1903 the procedures for reporting the Fukien *likin* tax were changed and tax revenue dropped by over 40 per cent.

For north China, we are handicapped by the lack of customs data for the interior. In Manchuria, for example, the customs data include little or no trade within this large region. Thus the customs data really only reflect trade in the southernmost Manchurian province, Liaoning (compare the two figures for 1896, the only year for which official Liaoning [i.e., Feng-t'ien] data are available).

As for Shantung, the explanation of the discrepancy would appear to be that the *likin* tax was not systematically collected (that is the opinion of Parker, 1901, pp. 234, 240). In both Shantung and Honan, the terrain may have made avoidance of tax stations a rather simple matter and, hence, systematic tax collection was too difficult to be worth the effort.

Although there is no customs data for north China's interior, a Japanese estimate (*CKNY*, II, p. 251) of the import trade of Shensi province is available for the year 1914. From these figures one can derive a total domestic trade estimate for 1914 of 12.5 million *taels*, which is close to the *likin* figure for 1900–1908 of 13.3 million taels.[4] Shensi was a province with well-defined trade routes where *likin* taxes appear to have been systematically collected.[5]

If the above analysis is generally correct, then it is possible to reconstruct some notion of the size of China's long-distance trade from these two sets of data. Starting with the maritime customs data for 1908, then adding the *likin* figures for north China and northern Manchuria plus those for the southwest, and making allowance for underestimation in the Honan, Shantung, Hunan, and Kwangsi figures, one arrives at a figure of between 800 and 900 million *taels* for total trade excluding foreign imports. Eliminating double counting of commodities, the result is a total of 600 to 700 million *taels*. The inclusion of foreign imports raises the total to over one billion *taels*.

A Third Estimate of Long-Distance Trade

The low quality of the *likin* estimates and the limited coverage of the domestic maritime customs figures makes it desirable to attempt to test these figures against other independent data. The procedure followed is to start with data for the 1950's and attempt to work back in time to 1900 with aid of a number of assumptions. The data for the 1950's are presented in Tables I.10 and I.11.

From these figures and from the commodity data from the maritime customs reports (Table I.12), it is clear that internal long-distance trade around 1900 must have been dominated by a fairly small number of commodities: silk, tea, cotton and cotton textiles, oils and oil seeds, tobacco and tobacco products, grain, sugar, and salt. Items such as coal and steel were of little or no significance

4. The 1914 estimate for domestic trade was arrived at by assuming total exports equalled total imports and adding the two together. Then foreign imports were subtracted out.

5. See, for example, "Inland Communications in China," *Chinese Economic and Social Life*, vol. 2, pp. 30–36.

TABLE I.IO. RETAIL SALES IN RURAL AREAS
(1,000,000 *Yuan*, Current Prices)

	1953	1954	1955	1956
Rural Retail Sales—Total[a]	17,520	20,080	21,340	24,570
Grain[b]	—	4,840	4,960	4,940
Cotton cloth[c]	3,150	3,100	3,230	4,300
Producer goods[d]	1,920	2,500	2,820	3,700
Edible Oils[e]	—	—	800	—
Salt[f]	380	570	590	—
Sugar[f]	—	—	500	—
Kerosene[g]	—	—	440	—
Free Market[h]	9,974	7,020	6,804	7,500
Total[i]	—	—	20,144	(22,700)[j]

[a] These figures are the official estimate (1956) or derived from an officially estimated index (1953–1955). For sources, see Chen, 1967, p. 394.

[b] Grain sales figures for rural areas are given for grain years, not calendar years. I have taken the average of two grain years (e.g., 1954–55 and 1955–56) to estimate calendar-year sales (e.g., for 1955). (SOURCE: *T'ung-chi kung-tso* data office, "The Basic Situation with Respect to Our Country's Unified Purchase and Sale of Grain," *Hsin-hua pan-yueh-k'an*, November 25, 1957, pp. 171–72). I assumed that the average sales price was 12 *yuan* per *picul* based on a perusal of miscellaneous local price data. This assumption is somewhat arbitrary, but the error introduced is not likely to be over 10 per cent in either direction.

[c] Data on cotton cloth sales in rural areas can be found in *Wo-kuo-te kang-t'ieh, tien-li, mei-tan, chi-chieh, fang-chih, tsao-chih kung-yeh-te chin-hsi*, p. 185. The average price of cotton cloth per bolt in 1955 was 35.7 *yuan* (Huang K'o, "How We May Settle the Disequilibrium," in *Extracts from China Mainland Magazines*, No. 119, p. 33). Cotton textile prices did not change during this period.

[d] *TGY*, p. 170.

[e] Supply and marketing cooperatives, which are primarily in rural areas, sold 669,000 tons of edible oils in 1955 (Chen, 1967, p. 400). It is unlikely that significant amounts of edible oils were sold outside the coops. The price of peanut oil in 1955 in Tientsin was 1,200 *yuan* per ton, Shanghai 1,220 *yuan*. I have used the Tientsin figure. The source of these price data can be found in Perkins, 1966, p. 238.

[f] These estimates are based on sales by supply and marketing coops together with Tientsin and Shanghai prices. For sources of these data, see note e.

[g] There are no good figures on kerosene sales, but two sample surveys of rural consumption indicate that rural per capita consumption in 1955 in Honan was about two catties per year (Office of the Supply and Marketing Cooperatives of Honan Province, "The Changes in Purchasing Power and the Volume of Sales of the Peasantry after Agricultural Collectivization," *Ching-chi yen-chiu*, No. 4, 1956, pp. 63–65). One can obtain a similar figure for Inner Mongolia in 1958 (Chen, 1967, p. 398). The price of kerosene per catty in Shanghai in 1955 was 1.67 *yuan* (*Shanghai chieh-fang ch'ien-hou wu-chia tzu-liao hui-pien*, p. 503).

[h] These figures are official Chinese estimates of the free market in agricultural products (for source, see Chen, 1967, p. 393).

[i] Some small portion of the commodities listed individually was sold on the free market. Thus adding up these figures exaggerates the coverage of the items listed. In addition, part of the free market sales of agricultural products was in urban areas.

[j] This figure was obtained by assuming that oils, salt, sugar, and kerosene sales were the same in 1956 as in 1955.

in 1900. If one excluded grain, cotton, and oil seeds and products derived from them; the gross value output of the remaining items in 1933 (in 1933 prices) was about 1.3 billion *yuan* (Liu and Yeh, 1965, pp. 142–43, 513). Thus if 70 per cent of these items entered long-distance trade, the value of such trade would be 900 million *yuan* or, in 1900–1909 prices, perhaps something over 300 million *taels*.[6] In the maritime customs data, a much smaller proportion of the output of these items was recorded, but these are probably underestimates (see Table I.13).[7]

The gross value output of factory and handicraft production of cotton textiles and edible oils was 2.4 billion *yuan* in 1933 (in 1933 prices) (Liu and Yeh, 1965, pp. 142–43, 513). By the 1920's and 1930's, a substantial portion of both cotton textiles, cotton, oil seeds, and oils entered long-distance trade as the result of the concentration of modern processing industries in a few large cities such as Shanghai, Hankow, and Tientsin. But in 1900–1909 these industries were much more spread out. I have no way of estimating what percentage of output entered long-distance trade, but one can assume it was 30 per cent and make calculations accordingly.[8] This estimate would result in a figure of 720 million *yuan* to which one would have to add another 500 million *yuan* to account for the value of raw materials that had to be shipped to the cities to make the finished product.[9] These two items together would amount to perhaps 400 million *taels* in the prices of 1900–1909.

The remaining steps are to add the value of the grain trade (70 million *taels*) and miscellaneous items, perhaps 30 per cent of total trade in domestic products if Table I.12 is a proper guide.[10] The result is an estimate of total trade of 1.1 billion *taels* (excluding foreign imports). This figure cannot be taken very seriously but it does appear to indicate two things. First, the *likin* and maritime customs trade figures are underestimates, but, second, that they do give some notion of the size of interprovince trade. If I had used a 15 or 20 per cent figure for cotton textiles and oil output entering long-distance trade, the resulting total would have been well under one billion *taels*.

6. See discussion of prices in the next section of this appendix. One half of 900 million is 450 million *yuan*, or 300 million *taels*.

7. The coverage of long-distance trade in cotton and cotton products is probably fairly complete and such a large part of tea and silk output was sent abroad that a significant portion of the trade in these items was recorded. The most difficult figure to understand is that for the sugar trade. Sugar was mainly produced in provinces with numerous treaty ports (i.e., Kwangtung and Fukien), yet little sugar seems to have been shipped to other treaty ports.

8. The pre-modern textile industry was probably much more concentrated than the pre-modern oil-seed processing. Southern Kiangsu, for example, has for centuries been a major producer of cotton and cotton textiles.

9. A high percentage of the gross value of cotton textiles and vegetable oils comes from the value of the raw materials used. Because cotton was often grown in the immediate neighborhood of large cities (e.g., Shanghai), it would not be recorded by the customs administration, but I have not reduced the estimate to take this fact into account but rather have treated local cotton shipments as long-distance trade.

10. For the size of the grain trade, see Chapter VII. The 30 per cent figure is somewhat arbitrary. In 1908, according to Table I.12, these items accounted for over 40 per cent of maritime customs interport trade (foreign plus domestic exports). But maritime customs data for 1908 includes only a small amount of cotton and cotton textiles, whereas I have made allowances for a much larger quantity.

TABLE I.11. SALES BY AGRICULTURE (INCLUDING DIRECT TAXES)
(1,000,000 *Yuan*, Current Prices)

	1952	1953	1954	1955	1956	1957
Sales[a]	12,970	15,320	17,360	17,800	18,400	20,280
Ag. Tax[b]	2,704	2,711	3,278	3,054	2,965	2,970
Total	15,674	18,031	20,638	20,854	21,365	23,250
Grain[c]	—	5,700	7,930	7,040	6,100	—
Soybeans[d]	—	1,690	1,560	1,520	1,540	—
Cotton[e]	1,660	1,440	1,270	2,010	1,780	—
Edible Oils[d]	—	510	570	590	620	—
Subtotals	—	9,150[f]	10,930[f]	—	—	—
	—	(9,340)	(11,330)	(11,160)	(10,040)	—
Tea[g]	—	—	130	180	230	210
Sugar[h]	—	—	180	190	200	—
Tobacco[i]	—	—	110	140	240	—
Silkworm[j] (cocoon)	130	90	140	160	170	150
Hemp, Ramie, Jute[k]	—	—	(50)	(100)	100	120
Subtotal	—	—	610	770	940	—
Free Market[l]	—	9,974	7,020	6,804	7,500	—
Total	—	—	18,560	18,734	18,480	—

[a] *TGY*, p. 168.   [b] Chen, 1967, p. 441.

[c] The sources of official calendar-year grain purchase and collection data can be found in my *Market Control and Planning in Communist China*, p. 248–49. An estimate of the average purchase price for grain was obtained by dividing the official agricultural tax data given in value terms by the agricultural tax data given in fine grain equivalents (*ibid.*).

[d] These are the estimates of R. Hsia, "Government Acquisition of Agricultural Output in Mainland China, 1953–56," p. 34. Hsia's estimates are based on official percentages of the amount of oil-bearing crops purchased together with official purchase price data.

[e] The percentage of the cotton crop that is marketed can be found in Tseng Ling, 1956, p. 13. Hsia applies the official cotton–grain price ratio to grain-purchase prices to obtain the cotton price. Chinese cotton-price data, however, indicate that it is the grain sales price to which the ratio should be applied. I have taken an unweighted average of the official cotton-purchase prices for various regions and used the figures so obtained (85, 77, 81, 81, and 81 *yuan* for the years 1952–1956) to derive the estimates in the table. Price data sources are, *Jen-min jih-pao* August 4, 1952; Shanghai *Chieh-fang jih-pao* August 10, 1952; "Regulating this Year's and Next's Cotton Seasonal Price Differential," *Hsin-hua yueh-pao*, September 1953, p. 165; and the Tientsin *Ta kung pao*, December 4, 1954.

[f] These figures can be derived from data in *T'ung-chi Kung-tso*, no. 11, 1957, p. 29.

[g] Official tea-purchase data can be obtained in (or derived from data in) Chen, 1967, p. 403 and Hsia, 1958, p. 39. The tea–grain price ratio can be obtained from *T'ung-chi Kung-tso*, no. 3, 1957, p. 33. These ratios should be applied to grain-sales prices, not purchase prices. A national average grain-sales price of 12 *yuan* per *picul* (or 95 *yuan* per *picul* of tea in 1955) yields the results presented in the table. A tea price of 95 *yuan* is consistent with figures of 82 *yuan* for Hunan in 1955 (*Hsin Hunan Pao*, October 5, 1956) and 100 *yuan* for Chekiang in 1955 (Tientsin *Ta Kung Pao*, July 3, 1955, and Hangchow *Tang-tai Jih-pao*, July 4, 1955), the two major tea-producing provinces. I have assumed tea prices in 1957 were the same as in 1956.

[h] I have assumed that 85 per cent of sugar cane and beet were marketed, and applied the official national average price of 1.12 *yuan* per *picul* (for source, see Hsia, 1958, p. 42) to obtain the estimates in the table.

[i] The official marketed percentage for tobacco can be found in Chen, 1967, p. 405. For lack

of a better alternative, I have followed Hsia, 1958, p. 41, in using the purchase price for tobacco in Kwangtung Province and assumed it to represent the national average.

ʲ Silk-price data can be obtained in or derived from figures given in a report on the silk industry appearing in *Chung-hua jen-min kung-ho-kuo fa-kuei hui-pien*, no. 8, pp. 225–32. When combined with production data (*TGY*, p. 125) one arrives at the figures in the table.

ᵏ Official purchase data for hemp, ramie, and jute can be found in Chen, 1967, p. 403. Applying a price of 16.5 *yuan* per *picul* (R. Hsia, 1958, p. 37), one obtains the figures in the table. The 1954 estimate is a guess based on the fact that jute and hemp production (no ramie data) in that year was 2.74 million *piculs* (as against 5.16 and 6.02 million *piculs* in 1956 and 1957).

ˡ These figures are official Chinese estimates of the free market in agricultural products (see Chen, 1967, p. 393).

TABLE I.12. MARITIME CUSTOMS TRADE—COMMODITY BREAKDOWN
(1,000,000 Hk. *Taels*)

	1908		1928	
	Exports Abroad	*Domestic Trade*	*Exports Abroad*	*Domestic Trade*
Silk	83.0	14.1	187.6	7.7
Cotton textiles	2.6	3.4	38.8	176.0
Cotton, raw	10.3	2.0	34.2	82.4
Tea	32.8	4.1	37.1	19.7
Grain and Flour	—	23.9	37.4	88.7
Beans	9.1	8.6	145.3	25.3
Beancake	14.3	6.6	56.0	15.5
Oils	5.4	7.4	16.1	12.1
Wood oil			23.3	8.1
Sesamum seed	9.2	0.7	8.2	1.4
Peanuts	0.5	3.0	10.8	7.1
Tobacco	2.4	4.3	5.1	17.5
Cigarettes	0.3	2.2	20.2	53.0
Sugar	1.4	5.2	0.3	2.6
Opium	0.9	11.7	—	—
Salt	—	—	1.8	28.7
Medicines	2.6	3.6	5.7	5.8
Paper	3.4	3.8	5.1	10.7
Coal and coke	0.2	2.7	28.4	23.4
Subtotal	178.4	107.3	661.4	585.7
Total	276.7	162.1	991.4	688.6

The crux of the problem of arriving at a reliable estimate by this method is to obtain a clearer picture of the share of rural handicrafts in the output of cotton textiles and vegetable oils. If the *likin* and maritime customs figures are any indication, the proportion of such products processed in large urban centers must have been very small. To attempt to arrive at a precise figure, however, would take us well beyond the boundaries laid down for this study.

In Chapter VI, I have assumed that long-distance trade in the years 1900–1909 was about 800 to 1,000 million *taels* per year, 1.2 to 1.4 billion *taels* if foreign imports are included.

TABLE I.13. THE SHARE OF MARITIME TRADE IN OUTPUT

		1908		1928	
	1931–1937 Output	*Export Abroad*	*Domestic Trade*	*Export Abroad*	*Domestic Trade*
Tea	3,992	1,576	108	904	744
Silk[a]	322	152	22	213	10
Cotton	19,600	650	130	1,256	2,659
Tobacco	18,300	150	332	190	727
Sugar[b]	18,720	274	1,006	23	339
Cotton yarn[c]	10,000	—	—	350	2,281

SOURCE: Maritime Customs reports and Appendix D.

[a] Quantity figures given in terms of cocoons have been converted to silk using the ratio 1/13.

[b] Cane quantity figures have been converted to sugar using the ratio 1/10.

[c] Much of the yarn produced was converted into cotton textiles before being shipped to other ports. The value of textiles shipped was over 200 million *taels* (Table I.12) in 1928 as compared to the total value of yarn which was 158 million *taels*. Thus the amount of yarn shipped in the form of cloth must have been another 2.5 million *piculs*. Cotton yarn output in 1957 was 3.6 million bales which at 3 6 *piculs* of yarn per bale is 16.9 million *piculs*. If output of yarn in the 1930's was in the same proportion to 1957 as the output of raw cotton, then yarn output in the 1930's would be 10 million *piculs*.

DEFLATING WITH PRICE INDEXES

There are three kinds of data that can be used to construct a price index for deflating domestic trade data so that one can arrive at a picture of the real increases in internal trade. For the 1930's and before there are the indexes of prices paid or received by farmers computed by Buck (1937) and the foreign-trade import and export price indexes computed by Nankai University. These two sets of data are presented in Table I.14. Given the predominance of agricultural and processed agricultural products in foreign trade, one would expect the two indexes to be similar, and on the whole they are. Although similar, however, they are not identical. If one averages the indexes for 1930–1936 and those of 1900–1909, the latter is exactly 50 per cent of the former. For lack of anything better, I have used that percentage in converting data from the prices of one period to those of the other. In making these conversions, one must also be careful to take into account that one *tael* was equivalent to about 1.5 *yuan*.

From the foreign-trade price indexes, it also seems probable that most of the increase in *likin* receipts in the 1890's and early 1900's was due to the rise in prices, not to any real increase in trade. The relevant *likin* data and price indexes are presented in Tables I.15 and I.16. Kiangsu Province is presented separately because the foreign-trade price indexes probably best reflect price movements in that province.

For the 1950's we have government estimates of the changes in prices paid and received by farmers as compared to the 1930's. These estimates are presented in Table I.17. I have argued at length elsewhere (1966, Appendix B) that price indexes calculated by the Chinese State Statistical Bureau for the 1950's

TABLE I.14. PRICE INDEXES

	Export Price Index (Nankai)[a]	Prices Received by Farmers (Buck)[b]	Import Price Index (Nankai)[a]	Prices Paid by Farmers (Buck)[b]
		(1926 = 100)		
1870–1879	33.9	—	23.1	—
1880–1889	31.5	—	23.2	—
1890–1899	42.4	40	32.4	—
1900–1905	57.8	38	50.8	—
1906	59.2	39	50.0	—
1907	63.8	46	54.5	58
1908	61.5	49	63.2	57
1909	59.2	50	63.1	54
1910	60.0	53	68 0	57
1911	59.8	56	67.8	61
1912	57.9	55	66.3	65
1913	65.4	58	66.3	65
1914	68.9	59	72.2	64
1915	70.5	61	74.9	68
1916	76.5	65	81.2	71
1917	69.4	69	86.9	76
1918	74.8	69	97.5	79
1919	73.2	69	99.6	82
1920	73.1	80	116.5	85
1921	76.9	90	111.0	88
1922	81.5	92	97.3	91
1923	89.1	98	98.6	95
1924	92.3	97	98.7	101
1925	95.4	102	100.1	101
1926	100.0	100	100.0	100
1927	97.3	95	107.2	103
1928	103.5	106	105.5	109
1929	111.0	127	104.8	118
1930	111.4	125	115.8	126
1931	108.7	116	127.9	135
1932	91.5	103	119.5	127
1933	79.3	71	114.8	104
1934	72.9	—	100.7	—
1935	73.5	—	91.6	—
1936	91.0	—	101.0	—

[a] The original Nankai index numbers use 1912 as the base year. I have recomputed these figures to make 1926 the base year to make them comparable to Buck. For 1870–1879, 1880–1889, 1890–1899, etc., I have averaged the Nankai figures and then converted them to the 1926 base. This method of computing an index for the decade is not entirely proper, but any error introduced by this method is likely to be negligible. The source of these figures is Hou, 1965, pp. 231–32.

[b] Buck, 1937, (Statistical Volume) pp. 149–50. The Buck data for 1890–1899 and 1900–1905 are for only four areas. In computing the averages for these early periods, I eliminated two observations which clearly reflected local famine conditions.

TABLE I.15. PRICE CHANGES AND LIKIN RECEIPTS

Annual Averages	Likin Receipts[a] (*1,000* Taels)	INDEXES		EXPORT PRICE INDEXES[b]	
		1870–1879 =100	*1890–1899 =100*	*1870–1879 =100*	*1890–1899 =100*
1870–1879	15,046	100	—	100	—
1880–1889	15,104	100	—	93	—
1890–1899	15,683	104	100	125	100
1900–1905	17,582	117	112	171	136
1906	18,792	125	120	175	140
1907	19,934	132	127	188	150
1908	21,414	142	136	181	145

[a] These data are the estimates of Lo Yü-tung, 1936, p. 469.
[b] Derived from data in Table I.14.

TABLE I.16. KIANGSU LIKIN DATA

	KIANGSU LIKIN RECEIPTS		
Annual Average	(*1,000* Taels)[a]	Index	Export Price Index[b]
1870–1879	2,478	100	100
1880–1889	2,250	91	93
1890–1897	2,797	113	125
1900–1908	3,666	147	174

[a] See Lo Yü-tung, 1936, p. 464. The years 1898 and 1899 were not included because they were unusually low (1.87 and 1.02 million *taels*, respectively).
[b] Derived from data in Table I.14.

TABLE I.17. FARM PURCHASE PRICE INDEXES AND RURAL RETAIL PRICE INDEXES

	PURCHASE PRICE INDEXES		Retail Prices of Industrial Production in Rural Areas
	1930–1936 = 100	*1933 = 100*	*1930–1936 = 100*
1930–1936	100	—	100
1933	—	100	—
1950	188	213	—
1951	221	251	—
1952	225	255	—
1953	248	281	—
1954	256	290	—
1955	255	289	—
1956	262	297	280
1957	275	312	—
1958	281	319	—

SOURCE: For the sources of these figures see Chen, 1967, p. 425 and *TGY*, p. 173.

appear to reliably reflect the movement in prices of most major commodities. Free-market prices are less reliably reflected in these indexes, but even there the difference between free-market and controlled prices in 1957 was not pronounced. In any case, free-market goods did not generally enter into long-distance trade. Many, for example, were perishables. The indexes in Table I.17 indicate that prices in 1957 were about 200 per cent above the levels of the 1930's, and that is the figure I have used in deflating data for the 1950's.

References Cited

BOOKS AND ARTICLES IN CHINESE

CHANG, HSIAO-MEI (comp.), 1939. *Kweichow ching-chi* (Kweichow economy). Shanghai, Kunming, Kweiyang and Chungking: China National Economics Research Office.

CHANG, HSIAO-MEI (comp.), 1939. *Szechwan ching-chi tsan-k'ao tzu-liao* (Reference materials on the Szechwan economy). Shanghai: Chinese National Economic Research Office.

CHANG, P'EI-KANG and CHANG CHIH-I, 1940. *Chekiang sheng shih-liang chih yun-hsiao* (The Grain Market in Chekiang Province). Changsha: Commercial Press.

CHANG, P'EI-KANG, 1938. *Kwangsi shih-liang wen-t'i* (The Kwangsi Grain Problem). Changsha: Commercial Press.

CHAO, CHING-HSIN, 1956. "Seasonal Variations of Our Market after Agricultural Cooperation," *Ching-chi yen-chiu*, No. 5, 1956, pp. 19–38.

CHAO, CHING-WEN, 1957. *Hsin Chung-kuo-te kung-yeh* (New China's Industry). Peking: Statistics Press.

CH'EN, CHEN-HAN, 1958. "Agricultural Labor Productivity, Land Rent and Land Concentration in China in Late Ming and Early Ch'ing," in *Chung-kuo tzu-pen-chu-i ming-ya wen-t'i t'ao-lun chi*, pp. 272–94.

CH'EN, HENG-LI, 1958. *Fu nung shu yen-chiu*. Peking: Chung-hua Publishers.

CH'EN, HOU, *Ming chi*.

CHEN, TSU-KUEI, 1958. *Tao* (Rice) Vol. I. Peking.

CH'EN, TZU-LUNG, HSÜ FU-YUAN, and SUNG HUI-PI (comps.), 1964. *Huang-ming ching-shih wen-pien* (Collected essays on statecraft in the Ming dynasty). Taipei: reprint of the Kuolien Book Co.

Chieh-fang jih-pao (Shanghai), Aug. 10, 1952.

CHIN, CH'AO, 1957. "The Grain Situation in Hupei after a good Harvest," *Hsin-hua pan-yueh-k'an*, Feb. 25, 1957, pp. 99–100.

CHIN, SHAN-PAO, 1961, *Chung-kuo hsiao-mai tsai-pei hsüeh* (A study of wheat growing in China). Peking: Agricultural Press.

Chinese Cotton Statistics Association, 1935, *Chung-kuo mien-ch'an t'ung-chi* (Chinese cotton output statistics). Shanghai: Chinese Cotton Statistics Association.

Ch'ing shih-lu (Veritable records of the Ch'ing dynasty).

CHU, MEI-YU, 1937. *Chung-kuo ch'a-yeh* (Tea in China). Shanghai: Shanghai Book Publishers.

Chu p'i-yü che (1738 preface).

CH'UAN, HAN-SHENG. "The Rice Trade of Soochow during the Mid-Ch'ing Period" (forthcoming paper).

CH'UAN, HAN-SHENG and WANG, YEH-CHIEN, 1959. "Rice Prices during the Yung-cheng Period (1723–1735)," in *Chung-yang yen-chiu-so chi-kan*, Vol. 30 (1959), pp. 157–85.

Cotton Research Office of the China Agricultural Science Institute, 1959. *Chung-kuo mien-hua tsai-pei hsüeh* (A Study of Cotton Raising in China). Shanghai: Shanghai Science and Technology Press.

FANG, CHUEH-HUI (comp.), 1940. *Ming t'ai-tsu ko-ming wu-kung chi* (A history of the revolutionary military success of Ming T'ai-tsu) (1940 preface).

FU, I-LING, 1961. *Ming Ch'ing nung-ts'un she-hui ching-chi* (The rural society and economy of Ming and Ch'ing). Peking: San-lien bookstore.

HO, CHANG-LING, 1963. *Huang chao ching shih wen pien* (Essays on statecraft in the Ch'ing dynasty) (reprinted in 1963 in Taipei).

HO, CHI-LI, 1958. "Water Conservancy is the Life's Pulse of Agriculture," in *1956–1967 nien ch'uan-kuo nung-yeh fa-chan kang-yao (hsiu-cheng tsao-an) chiang-hua* (Speeches on the draft 12-year agricultural development plan). Peking: China Youth Press.

HO, KANG-TE, 1908. *Fu chün nung ch'an k'ao lüeh* (1903 preface).

Hsin Hunan pao, Oct. 5, 1956.

HSÜ, KUANG-CH'I, 1628. *Nung-cheng ch'üan-shu*.

HSÜ, TUNG, 1848. *Pao-chia shu* (1848).

Hsü wen-hsien t'ung-k'ao (Encyclopedia of historical records, continued). Commercial Press edition, 1936.

HUNG, CHOU (comp.), 1956. *Shou-shih t'ung-k'ao* (Encyclopedia of agriculture) (1742, reprinted in 1956).

Hupei nien chien (No. 1) (Hupei yearbook), 1937. Hupei: Statistical Office of the Secretariat of the Hupei Provincial Government.

HWANG, NAI-LUNG, 1963. *Chung-kuo nung-yeh fa-chan shih (ku-tai chih-pu)* (A history of agricultural development in China [ancient section]). Taipei: Cheng-chung Bookstore.

HWANG YÜ-CHIA, 1940. "Tenant Agriculture and Living Conditions in Sung and Yuan," *Shuo-wen yueh-k'an*, Vol. 2, No. 2, 1940, pp. 1–14, and No. 3, pp. 5–10.

International Trade Office of the Ministry of Industry, 1940. *Chu-ma* (Hemp). Changsha: Commercial Press.

International Trade Office of the Ministry of Industry, 1933. *Chung-kuo shih-yeh chih (Chekiang sheng)* (A record of the economy of Chekiang). Shanghai: International Trade Office of the Ministry of Industry.

International Trade Office of the Ministry of Industry, 1933. *Chung-kuo shih-yeh chih (Kiangsu sheng)* (A record of the Kiangsu economy). Shanghai: International Trade Office of the Ministry of Industry.

International Trade Office of the Ministry of Industry. 1934. *Chung-kuo shih-yeh chih (Shantung sheng)* (A record of the economy of Shantung). Shanghai: International Trade Office of the Ministry of Industry.

International Trade Office of the Ministry of Industry, 1935. *Chung-kuo shih-yeh chih (Hunan sheng)* (A record of the Hunan economy). Shanghai: International Trade Office of the Ministry of Industry.

International Trade Office of the Ministry of Industry, 1940. *Hua-sheng* (Peanuts). Changsha: Commercial Press.

International Trade Office of the Ministry of Industry, 1940. *Yen-yeh* (Tobacco). Changsha: Commercial Press.

Jen-min jih-pao, Aug. 4, 1952.

Jen-min jih-pao, 1957. Editorial, "Basically Settle the Vegetable Supply Question," *Hsin-hua pan-yueh-k'an*, July 10, 1957, pp. 149–50.

Jen-min jih-pao, 1959. Editorial, "A Great Effort to Organize Transport Properly," *Hsin-hua pan-yueh-k'an*, Mar. 25, 1959, pp. 72–73.

Kiangsi Government Statistical Office, 1936. *Kiangsi nien-chien* (Kiangsi Yearbook). Kiangsi: Statistical Office of the Kiangsi Provincial Government.

KU YEN-WU. *Jih-chih-lu chi-shih* (A comprehensive commentary on the *jih chih-lu*).

Kung-ho-kuo fen-shang ti-t'u, 1953. Shanghai: Map Press.

Land Committee, 1937. *Ch'uan-kuo t'u-ti t'iao-ch'a pao-kao kang-yao*. Nanking.

LI, WEN-CHIH, 1963. "A Discussion of Land Ownership Relations in the Early Ch'ing Period," *Li-shih yen-chiu*, No. 5, 1963, pp. 75–108.

LI, WEN-CHIH, 1957. "Land Rent, Commercial Capital, High Interest Rates, and the Peasants' Standard of Living in the Ch'ing Period Prior to the Opium War," *Chung-kuo tz'u-pen-chu-i ming-ya wen-t'i t'ao-lun chi* (Peking: Sanlien), pp. 609–56.

LI, WEN-CHIH, and CHANG, YOU-I, editors, *Chung-kuo chin-tai nung-yeh shih tz'u-liao* (Historical materials on agriculture in modern China), 3 volumes (Peking: San-lien book company, 1957).

LI, YEN-CHANG. *Jun ching t'ang tzu-chih kuan shu.*

LIANG, FANG-CHUNG, 1935. "Ming Population, Land and Land Tax Statistics," *Chung-kuo chin-tai ching-chi shih yen-chiu chi-kan*, Vol. 3, No. 1, pp. 75–129.

LIEN, CHÜN, 1931. *Tung-san-sheng ching-chi shih k'uang lang-yao*. Shanghai: People's Knowledge Press.

LIU, HUNG-CHU, 1956. *Wo-kuo-te ma* (Our country's hemp). Peking: Financial and Economic Press.

LO, YÜ-TUNG, 1936. *Chung-kuo li-chin shih* (A history of *likin* in China), 2 vols. Shanghai: Commercial Press.

LU, JUNG. *Shu-yuan tsa-chi* (Miscellaneous notes).

LÜ, P'ING-TENG (ed.), 1936. *Szechwan nung-ts'un ching-chi* (The rural economy of Szechwan) Shanghai: Commercial Press.

LU, SHIH-I. *Su Sung fou-liang k'ao* (Studies on excessive land taxation in Soochow and Sung chiang).

MA, TUAN-LIN. *Wen-hsien t'ung-k'ao* (Yuan period).

MA, YIN-CH'U, 1957. "A New Population Theory," *Hsien-hua pan-yueh-k'an*, Aug. 10, 1957, pp. 34–41.

Ministry of Agriculture and Commerce, 1914, 1915, 1917, 1918. *Nung-shang t'ung-chi piao*, (NSTCP) (Tables of Agricultural and Commercial Statistics) No. 3, 1914; No. 4, 1915; No. 6, 1917; and No. 7, 1918. Peking: Ministries of Agriculture and Commerce (1916–1922).

Ministry of Communications, 1956. *Shui-yun-chia hui-pien* (Handbook of water freight rates). Peking: People's Communications Press.

Ministries of Agriculture, Foreign Trade, Textile Industries, Forestry and Second Commerce. "Report on the Silk Production Conference," *Chung-hua jen-min kung-ho-kuo fa-kuei hui-pien*, No. 8, 1958, pp. 225–32.

Ministries of Light Industry, Local Industry, Commerce and Grain and the General Office of Supply and Marketing Cooperatives. "Plant Oil Processing Methods," *Chung-hua jen-min kung-ho-kuo fa-kuei hui-pien* No. 1, 1955, p. 328.

"Nationwide Industrial and Communications Work Conference," *Jen-min shou-ts'e*, *1963*, p. 365.

Office of the Supply and Marketing Cooperatives of Honan Province, 1956. "The Changes in Purchasing Power and the Volume of Sales of the Peasantry after Agricultural Collectivization," *Ching-chi yen-chiu*, No. 4, 1956, pp. 63–65.

OU, PAO-SAN and CHANG, CHIH-I, 1938. *Fukien sheng shih-liang chih yun-hsiao* (Grain Marketing in Fukien Province). Changsha: Commercial Press.

"Regulating this year's and next's Cotton Seasonal Price Differential," *Hsin-hua yueh-pao*, Sept. 1953, p. 165.

Rural Reconstruction Commission, 1934. *Chekiang sheng nung-ts'un t'iao-ch'a* (An investigation of rural Chekiang Province). Shanghai: Commercial Press.

Rural Reconstruction Commission, 1934. *Honan sheng nung-ts'un t'iao-ch'a* (An investigation of rural Honan Province). Shanghai: Commercial Press.

Rural Reconstruction Commission, 1934. *Kiangsu sheng nung-ts'un t'iao-ch'a* (An investigation of rural Kiangsu Province). Shanghai: Commercial Press.

Rural Reconstruction Commission, 1934. *Shensi sheng nung-ts'un t'iao-ch'a* (An investigation of rural Shensi Province). Shanghai: Commercial Press.

Rural Reconstruction Commission, 1935. *Kwangsi sheng nung-ts'un t'iao-ch'a* (An investigation of rural Kwangsi Province). Shanghai: Commercial Press.

Rural Reconstruction Commission, 1935. *Yunnan sheng nung-ts'un t'iao-ch'a* (An investigation of rural Yunnan Province). Shanghai: Commercial Press.

Shanghai Economic Research Office of the Chinese Institute of Science and the Economic Research Office of the Shanghai Institute of Social Sciences, 1958. *Shanghai chieh-fang ch'ien-hou wu-chia tzu-liao hui-pien* (A compilation of price materials for pre- and post-liberation Shanghai). Shanghai: People's Press.

Shen-yang chuang ch'i (The situation in Shen-yang), 1641.

Shou shih t'ung k'ao (compiled in 1742, reprinted in 1956).

"State Economic Committee Extends the Method of Balancing Grain Distribution," *Hsin-hua pan-yueh-k'an*, Mar. 25, 1959, pp. 73–74.

SUN, CHING-CHIH (ed.), 1957. *Hua-pei ching-chi ti-li* (An Economic Geography of North China). Peking: Science Press.

SUN, KUANG, 1957. "We Must Control Urban Population," *Hsin-hua pan-yueh-k'an*, Dec. 25, 1957, pp. 62–64.

Sung hui-yao chi-kao (Collected documents of the essential institutions of the Sung dynasty).

Ta kung pao (Tientsin), July 3, 1955, and Dec. 4, 1954.

Tang-tai jih-pao (Hangchow), July 4, 1955.

TING, FAN, JAO HSÜEH-CH'ENG, and CHI, HSI-CH'EN, 1957. "Szechwan's Cultivated Area is Small, Why Is its Surplus Grain Large?" *Hsin-hua pan-yueh-k'an*, May 25, 1957, pp. 67–69.

TSENG KUO-FAN, 1902. "Memorials on the Suffering of the People," in *Huang-chao tao hsien t'ung kuang tsou-i*. Shanghai.

TSENG, LING, 1956. "The Rural Market in the Surging Tide of Agricultural Collectivization," *Ching-chi yen-chiu*, No. 2, 1956, pp. 1–29.

T'ung-chi kung-tso data office, 1957. "The Basic Situation with Respect to our Country's Unified Purchase and Sale of Grain," *Hsin-hua pan-yueh-k'an*, Nov. 25, 1957, pp. 171–72.

T'ung-chi kung-tso, No. 3, 1957.

T'ung-chi kung-tso, No. 11, 1957.

T'ung-chi yen-chiu data office, 1958. "Changes in 1957 Market Prices and Their Influence on the People's Standard of Living," *T'ung-chi yen-chiu*, April 23, 1958, pp. 25–26.

WANG, CHENG, 1313. *Nung shu* (1313 edition).

WANG, HUNG-HSÜ (ed.), 1697. *Ming shih kao* (Draft history of the Ming dynasty) (1697 edition).

WANG, K'AI-YUN. *Hsiang-ch'i-lou jih-chi* (Diary of hsiang-ch'i-lou).

WANG, SHIH-YING, 1957. "Completely Transform Nature and Guarantee a Good Harvest," *Hsin-hua pan-yueh-k'an*, Aug. 25, 1957, pp. 73–76.

WANG, SHOU-TAO, 1955. "Do Communications and Transport Well Support the Cooperative Movement," *Hsin-hua yueh-pao*, Dec. 28, 1955, p. 220.

Wen-hsien t'ung-k'ao (Yuan edition).

Wo-kuo kang-t'ieh, tien-li, mei-tan, chi-chieh, fang-chih, tsao-chih kung-yeh-te chin-hsi, 1958. Peking: Statistical Publishing Office.

WU, CH'ENG-LO, 1957. *Chung-kuo tu-liang shih* (A history of Chinese weights and measures). Shanghai: Commercial Press.

WU, CH'UAN-CHÜN, et al., 1956. *Hwang-ho chung-yu hsi-pu ti-ch'u ching-chi ti-li* (An economic geography of the western part of the middle reaches of the Yellow River). Peking: Science Press.

WU, CHÜEH-NUNG and HU HAO-CH'UAN, 1935. *Chung-kuo ch'a-yeh fu-hsing chi-hua* (A plan for the revival of Chinese tea). Shanghai: Commercial Press.

YEH, MENG-CHU, 1935. *Yueh-shih pien* (Notes on practical affairs). Shanghai: Chang-ku ts'ung shu.

YEN, CHUNG-P'ING, 1955. *Chung-kuo chin-tai ching-chi shih t'ung-chi* (Statistics on modern Chinese economic history). Peking: Scientific Press.

Yuan shih (History of the Yuan Dynasty).

LOCAL HISTORIES (PROVINCES) IN CHINESE

Anhwei t'ung chih (1821–1850 edition).
Chekiang t'ung chih (1736 edition, reprinted in Shanghai in 1934).
Chekiang t'ung chih (1899 edition).
Chi-fu t'ung chih (1884 edition).
Chiang-nan t'ung chih (1736 preface).
Chung hsiu Anhwei t'ung chih (1877 edition).
Fukien t'ung chih (1871 edition).
Hsü Shensi t'ung chih (1931 edition).
Hunan t'ung chih (1757 edition).
Hunan t'ung chih (1885 edition).
Hunan wen-cheng (1871 edition).
Hupei t'ung chih (1796–1803 edition).
Hupei t'ung chih (1910–1921 edition).
Kiangsi t'ung chih (1875 edition).
Kwangsi t'ung chih (1801 edition).
Kwangtung t'ung chih (1822 edition).
Shansi t'ung chih (1890 edition).
Shantung t'ung chih (1910 edition).
Shensi t'ung chih (1735 edition).
Shensi t'ung chih (1748 edition).
Szechwan t'ung chih (1816 edition).
Yunnan t'ung chih (1835 edition).

LOCAL HISTORIES (HSIEN, FU, AND CHOU) IN CHINESE

An-sai hsien chih (1914 edition) (Shensi).
Ch'a-ling chou chih (1695 edition) (Hunan).
Ch'ang-chao ho chih kao (1889 edition) (Kiangsu).
Chang-ming hsien chih (1874 edition) (Szechwan).
Ch'ang-sha fu chih (1747 edition) (Hunan).
Ch'ang-sha hsien chih (1810 edition) (Hunan).
Ch'ang-sha hsien chih (1867 edition) (Hunan).
Ch'ang-shou hsien chih (1539 edition) (Kiangsu).
Ch'ang-shou hsien chih (1687 edition) (Kiangsu).
Chao-chou fu chih (1762 edition) (Kwangtung).
Chao-chou fu chih (1873 edition) (Kwangtung).
Chao-yang hsien chih (1884 edition) (Kwangtung).
Ch'en-chou fu i-t'ien tsung-chi (1845 edition) (Hunan).
Chen-tse hsien chih (1842 edition, compiled in 1746) (Kiangsu).
Cheng-hai hsien chih (1814 edition) (Kwangtung).
Cheng-ho hsien chih (1919 edition) (Fukien).
Cheng-ku hsien chih (1717 edition) (Shensi).

Chi-an fu chih (1875 edition) (Kiangsi).
Ch'i-yang hsien chih (1870 edition) (Hunan).
Chia-ying hsien chih (1898 edition) (Kwangtung).
Chiang-shan hsien chih (1873 edition) (Chekiang).
Chiang-yin hsien chih (1640 edition) (Kiangsu).
Chiang-yin hsien chih (1744 edition) (Kiangsu).
Chiang-yin hsien chih (1840 edition) (Kiangsu).
Chiang-yin hsien hsü chih (1920 edition) (Kiangsu).
Chieh-yang hsien chih (1779 edition) (Kwangtung).
Ch'ien chou chih (1633 edition) (Shensi).
Chien-ning hsien chih (1916 edition) (Fukien).
Chih hsien chih (1931 edition) (Szechwan).
Chin-chou chih (1834 edition) (Kwangtung).
Ching-yuan hsien chih (1880 edition) (Kwangtung).
Chiu-chiang fu chih (1873 edition) (Kiangsi).
Ch'iung-chou chih-li chou chih (1818 edition) (Szechwan).
Chiung-chou fu chih (1890 edition) (Kwangtung).
Chiung-shan hsien chih (1853 edition) (Kwangtung).
Chou-chih hsien chih (1785 edition) (Shensi).
Chung hsiu mien-chou chih-li chou chih (1873 edition) (Szechwan).
Chung-hsiu shih-cheng hsien chih (1892 edition) (Kwangtung).
En-p'ing hsien chih (1766 edition) (Kwangtung).
Feng-hsiang hsien chih (1767 edition) (Shensi).
Feng-shun hsien chih (1746 edition) (Kwangtung).
Fu-p'ing hsien chih (1891 edition) (Shensi).
Fu-shan hsien chih (1763 edition) (Shantung).
Hai-yang hsien chih (1898 edition) (Kwangtung).
Han-ying t'ing chih (1817 edition) (Shensi).
Heng-chou fu chih (1763 edition, published in 1875) (Hunan).
Hsia-k'ou hsien chih (1920 edition) (Hupei).
Hsiang-hsiang hsien chih (1874 edition) (Hunan).
Hsiang-shan hsien chih (1827 edition) (Kwangtung).
Hsiang-t'an hsien chih (1818 edition) (Hunan).
Hsiang-t'an hsien chih (1889 edition) (Hunan).
Hsiang-yin hsien t'u chih (1880 edition) (Hunan).
Hsin-fan hsien chih (1876 edition) (Szechwan).
Hsin hsü Wei-nan hsien chih (1892 edition) (Shensi).
Hsin-ning chou chih (1879 edition) (Kwangsi).
Hsin-tou hsien chih (1929 revised edition) (Szechwan).
Hsing-ning hsien chih (1929 edition) (Kwangtung).
Hsü-chou fu chih (1862–1874 edition) (Kiangsu).
Hsü-chou fu chih (1895 edition) (Szechwan).
Hsun-yang hsien chih (1783 edition) (Shensi).
Hua hsien chih (1924 edition) (Kwangtung).
Hua-yang hsien chih (1816 edition) (Szechwan).
Hua-yang hsien chih (1934 edition) (Szechwan).
Hua-yin hsien chih (1715 edition) (Shensi).
Huai-chi hsien chih (1916 edition) (Kwangsi).
Huang hsien chih (1755 edition) (Shantung).
Hui-chou fu chih (1595 edition) (Kwangtung).
Hui-t'ung hsien chih (1876 edition) (Hunan).
I-yang hsien chih (1874 edition) (Hunan).
Jen-shou hsien chih (1866 edition) (Szechwan).
K'ai-p'ing hsien chih (1823 edition) (Kwangtung).

Kao hsien chih (1866 edition) (Szechwan).
Kao-ling hsien hsü chih (1884 edition) (Shensi).
Kao-ming hsien chih (1894 edition) (Kwangtung).
Kao-t'ang chou chih (1835 edition) (Shantung).
Kao-yu chou chih (1843 edition) (Kiangsu).
Ku-shih hsien chih (1786 edition) (Honan).
Kuan hsien chih (1786 preface) (Szechwan).
Kuan hsien chih (1932 edition) (Szechwan).
Kuang chou chih (1770 edition) (Honan).
Kuang-hsin fu chih (1736–1795 edition) (Kiangsi).
Kuang-hsin fu chih (1862–1874 edition) (Kiangsi).
Kuang-ning hsien chih (1824 edition) (Kwangtung).
K'uei-chou fu chih (compiled 1827, reprinted in 1891) (Szechwan).
Kuei-shan hsien chih pu (1783 edition) (Kwangtung).
Kuei-t'ung hsien chih (1866 edition) (Hunan).
Kuei-yang chou chih (1868 edition) (Hunan).
Lan-shan hsien chih (1867 edition) (Hunan).
Lan-t'ien hsien chih (1796 edition) (Shensi).
Li-ling hsien chih (1870 edition) (Hunan).
Lien-chou chih (1870 edition) (Kwangtung).
Lin-chiang fu chih (1871 edition) (Kiangsi).
Lin-t'ung hsien chih (1776 edition) (Shensi).
Ling hsien chih (1873 edition) (Hunan).
Ling-ling hsien chih (1876 edition) (Hunan).
Liu-yang hsien chih (1818 edition) (Hunan).
Liu-yang hsien chih (1873 edition) (Hunan).
Lung chou hsü chih (1766 edition) (Shensi).
Lung-ch'uan hsien chih (1818 edition) (Kwangtung).
Lung-chuan hsien chih (1878 edition) (Chekiang).
Lung-men hsien chih (1851 edition) (Kwangtung).
Mei hsien chih (1733 edition) (Shensi).
Mei hsien chih (1778 edition) (Shensi).
Mien-chou chih-li chou chih (1873 edition) (Szechwan).
Na-nao hsien chih (1783 edition) (Kwangtung).
Nan-ch'ang fu chih (1873 edition) (Kiangsi).
Nan-hai hsien chih (1835 edition) (Kwangtung).
Nan-hsiung chou chih (1824 edition) (Kwangtung).
Nan-k'ang fu chih (1862–1874 edition) (Kiangsi).
Nan-ning fu chih (1743 preface) (Kwangsi).
Ning-ch'iang chou chih (1577 edition) (Shensi).
Ning-hsiang hsien chih (1867 edition) (Hunan).
Ning-po fu chih (1560 edition) (Chekiang).
Pa hsien chih (1820 edition) (Szechwan).
P'an-yu hsien chih (1871 edition) (Kwangtung).
P'an-yu hsü hsien chih (1931 preface) (Kwangtung).
Pao-ning fu chih (1821 edition) (Szechwan).
Pen-lai hsien chih (1839 edition) (Shantung).
Po-pai hsien chih (1832 edition) (Kwangsi).
San hsü Hua chou chih (1882 edition) (Shensi).
San-shui hsien chih (1785 edition) (Shensi).
San-shui hsien chih (1819 edition) (Kwangtung).
Shan-hua hsien chih (1877 edition) (Hunan).
Shao-hsing hsien-chih tzu-liao (1938 edition) (Chekiang).
Shao-yang hsien chih (1877 edition) (Hunan).

Shih-ch'eng hsien chih (1819 preface) (Kwangtung).
Shih-ch'eng hsien chih (1888 edition) (Kwangtung).
Shun-te hsien hsü chih (1929 edition) (Kwangtung).
Sung-chiang fu chih (1662–1722 edition) (Kiangsu).
Ta-li hsien chih (1844 edition) (Shensi).
Ta-li hsien chih kao (1916 edition) (Yunnan).
T'ao chou chih (1877 edition) (Hunan).
Tseng-ch'eng hsien chih (1921 edition) (Kwangtung).
Tseng-hsiu Kuan hsien chih (1886 edition) (Szechwan).
Tsou-p'ing hsien chih (1836 edition) (Shantung).
T'ung-ch'uan fu chih (1897 edition) (Szechwan).
Tung-kuan hsien chih (1798 edition) (Kwangtung).
Tung-kuan hsien chih (1911 edition) (Kwangtung).
T'ung-kuan hsien chih (1944 edition) (Shensi).
Tz'u-li hsien chih (1923 edition) (Hunan).
Wan chou chih (1828 edition) (Kwangtung).
Weng-yuan hsien chih (1819 edition) (Kwangtung).
Wu-chiang hsien chih (1747 edition) (Kiangsu).
Wu-hsing chih (1878 edition) (Chekiang).
Wu-hu hsien chih (1919 edition) (Anhwei).
Wu-shan hsien chih (1893 edition) (Szechwan).
Yang-chiang hsien chih (1822 edition) (Kwangtung).
Yang-chun hsien chih (1820 edition) (Kwangtung).
Yang hsien chih (1897 edition) (Shensi).
Yang-shan hsien chih (1823 edition) (Kwangtung).
Yin hsien chih (1877 edition) (Chekiang).
Yin hsien t'ung chih (1935 edition) (Chekiang).
Ying-te hsien chih (1843 edition) (Kwangtung).
Yu hsien chih (1871 edition) (Hunan).
Yuan-chou fu chih (1874 edition) (Kiangsi).
Yuan-ho hsien chih (1761 edition) (Kiangsu).
Yung-sui-ting chih (1909 edition) (Hunan).

BOOKS AND ARTICLES IN JAPANESE

ABE, TAKEO, 1957. "A Study of the Supply and Demand for Grain in the Yung-cheng Period," *Tōyōshi kenkyū*, Vol. XV, No. 4, Mar. 1957, pp. 120–213.

AMANO, Gennosuke, 1962. *Chugoku nōgyō shi kenkyū* (Research on the History of Chinese Agriculture). Tokyo: ochya no sui shobo.

FUJII, HIROSHI, 1943, 1944, 1947. "A Critical Examination of Cultivated Acreage Statistics in the Ming Dynasty," *Tōyō gakuho*, 30, 3–4, 31–1, Aug., 1943; Aug., 1944; and Feb., 1947.

KATO, SHIGESHI, 1953. "The Totals of Landowning and Tenant Households in the Sung Dynasty," *Shina kezai shi kōshō*, Vol. II (Tokyo: Toyo Bunko, 1953), pp. 338–70.

Kosei beikoku unsha chosa (An investigation of Rice Marketing in Kiangsi), 1940. Tokyo: Tetsuson Taini.

Mainichi (Tokyo), Jan. 28, 1967.

NIHON GAIMUSHO TSUSHOKYOKU. *Shinkoku jijo* (Affairs of the Ch'ing empire).

NISHIYAMA, T., 1950. "An Investigation of Landlords in Chiang-nan in the Ming Period," *Nōgyō sōgō kenkyū*, Vol. 4, special, Mar. 1950, pp. 243–51.

Noka kezai chosa hokoku (*Hokushi kezai shiryo No. 5*) (Feng-jun *hsien* village survey), 1939. Dairen: South Manchurian Railway.

Noson gaikyo chosa hokoku (*Hokushi chosa shiryo No. 15*) (T'ai-an *hsien* village survey), 1940. Dairen: South Manchurian Railway.

Noson gaikyo chosa hokoku (*Hokushi: chosa shiryo No. 17*) (Wei *hsien* village survey), 1940. Dairen: South Manchurian Railway.

Noson jittai chosa hokoku (*Hokushi kezai shiryo No. 37*), Vol. 1 (Ts'un-hua *hsien* village survey), 1936. Dairen: Manchurian Japanese Daily News.

Noson jittai chosa hokoku (*Hokushi kezai shiryo No. 39*), Vol. 3 (Mi-yun and Hsiang-ho *hsiens* village surveys), 1936. Dairen: Manchurian Japanese Daily News.

Noson jittai chosa hokoku (*Hokushi chosa shiryo No. 7*) (Tsingtao village survey), 1939. Peking: South Manchurian Railway.

Noson jittai chosa hokoku (*Shanghai man-tetsu chosa shiryo No. 34*) (Chang-shou *hsien* village survey), 1940. Shanghai: South Manchurian Railway.

Noson jittai chosa hokoku (*Shanghai man-tetsu chosa shiryo No. 35*) (Tai-tsang *hsien* village survey), 1940. Shanghai: South Manchurian Railway.

Noson jittai chosa hokoku sho (*Shanghai man-tetsu chosa shiryo No. 48*) (Sung-chiang *hsien* village survey), 1940. Shanghai: South Manchurian Railway.

Noson jittai chosa hokoku sho (*Shanghai man-tetsu chosa shiryo No. 50*) (Wu-hsi *hsien* village survey), 1941. Shanghai: South Manchurian Railway.

Noson jittai chosa hokoku (*Shanghai man-tetsu chosa shiryo No. 51*) (Nan-t'ung *hsien* village survey), 1941. Shanghai: South Manchurian Railway.

SHIGETA, ATSUSHI, 1960. "Landlordism in Hunan at the Beginning of the Ch'ing Dynasty According to the *Hunan Sheng-li Ch'eng-an*," *Oriental Studies Presented to Sei* (*Kiyoshi*) *Wada* (Tokyo: Kodansha), pp. 461–75.

SHIMIZU, TAIJI, 1942. "A Study of Land Detection by Chang Chu-cheng in the Latter Half of the 16th Century," *Tōyō gakuho*, May 1942, 29.2, pp. 1–32.

SHIMIZU, TAIJI, 1942. "On the Total Land Acreage Under the Ming," *Shakai kezai shigaku*, Mar. 1942, pp. 114–30.

SHIMIZU, TAIJI, 1942. "The Relationship Between Land Statistics and Land Taxes During the Ming Dynasty," *Shi-cho*, Oct. 1942, 12.1, pp. 1–34.

SHIMIZU, TAIJI, 1954. "The Custom of Triple Land Ownership in the Agricultural Economy of Fukien During the Ming Period," *Shigaku zasshi*, July 1954, pp. 1–21.

SUDO, YOSHIYUKI, 1954. *Chugoku tochi-seido-shi kenkyū* (Research on the history of China's land system). Tokyo: Tokyo University Toyo Bunka Research Office.

SUDO, YOSHIYUKI, 1962. *So-dai kezai shi kenkyū* (Research on the economic history of the Sung). Tokyo: Tokyo University.

SUDO, YOSHIYUKI, 1965. *To-so shakai kezai shi kenkyū* (Research on the social and economic history of Tang and Sung). Tokyo: Tokyo University Press.

TERADA, TAKANOBU, 1957. "On the Agricultural Economy of the Soochow Plain Under the Ming," *Tōyō shi kenkyū*, Vol. XVI, No. 1 (1957), pp. 1–25.

Toya Dobunkai, 1912. *Shina nenkan* (China yearbook). Tokyo: Toya Dobunkai.

Toya Dobunkai, 1920. *Shina nenkan* (China yearbook). Tokyo: Toya Dobunkai.

Toya Kenkyū So, 1943. *Shina nōgyō koso tokei shiryo*, No. 1 (Chinese Agricultural Statistics). Tokyo: Toya kenkyū so.

WADA SEI (ed.), 1960. *Soshi shokkashi yakuchu* (Translation of the *shih huo chih* section of the Sung history). Tokyo: Toyo Bunko.

BOOKS, ARTICLES, DISSERTATIONS, AND MONOGRAPHS IN WESTERN LANGUAGES (OR TRANSLATED INTO WESTERN LANGUAGES)

AFANAS'YESKIY, YE A., 1962. *Szechwan*, translated in JPRS No. 15, 308, 17 September 1962.

AIRD, JOHN S., 1968. "Population Growth in Mainland China," in A. Eckstein, W. Galenson and T. C. Liu (eds.), *Economic Trends in Communist China*. Chicago: Aldine Publishing Company.

ARNOLD, JULEAN, 1926. *China, A Commercial and Industrial Handbook.* Washington: Government Printing Office.

BALAZS, ETIENNE, 1957. "Une Carte des Centres Commerciaux de la Chine," *Annales: Economies, Societies, Civilizations*, Oct.–Dec., 1957. Vol, 12, No. 4, pp. 587–93.

BALAZS, ETIENNE, 1964. *Chinese Civilization and Bureaucracy.* New Haven: Yale University Press.

BEAL, EDWIN G., 1958. *The Origin of Likin.* Cambridge: East Asian Studies.

BIELENSTEIN, HANS, "The Census of China During the Period 2–742 A.D.," *Bulletin of the Museum of Far Eastern Antiquities*, Stockholm, No. 19, 1947, pp. 125–63.

BISHOP, J. F., 1899. *The Yangtze Valley and Beyond.* London: Murray.

BOSERUP, ESTER, 1965. *The Conditions of Agricultural Growth: The Economics of Agrarian Change under Population Pressure.* Chicago: Aldine Publishing Company.

BUCK, JOHN L., 1937. *Land Utilization in China.* Nanking: University of Nanking.

BUCK, JOHN L., 1930. *China's Farm Economy.* Chicago: University of Chicago Press.

BURGESS, ALAN, 1957. *The Inn of the Sixth Happiness.* New York: Dutton.

CARLSON, ELLSWORTH C., 1957. *The Kaiping Mines, 1877–1912.* Cambridge: Harvard East Asian Research Center.

CHANG, CHUNG-LI, 1962. *The Income of the Chinese Gentry.* Seattle: University of Washington Press.

CHANG, JOHN K., 1967. "Industrial Development of Mainland China, 1912–1949," *The Journal of Economic History*, Mar. 1967, pp. 56–81.

CHAO, KANG, 1965. *The Rate and Pattern of Industrial Growth in Communist China.* Ann Arbor: The University of Michigan Press.

CHEN, NAI-RUENN, 1967. *Chinese Economic Statistics.* Chicago: Aldine Publishing Company.

CHENG, CHU-YUAN, 1967. "The Cultural Revolution and China's Economy," *Current History*, Sept. 1967, pp. 148–54 and 176–77.

CHI, CH'AO-TING, 1936. *Key Economic Areas in Chinese History.* London: Allen and Unwin.

China Handbook, 1955–1956, 1955. Taipei: China Publishing Co.

Chinese Ministry of Information, 1943. *China Handbook, 1937–1943.* New York: Macmillan.

CHONG TWANMO, 1956. "Production of Food Crops in Mainland China: Prewar and Postwar," Rand Research Memorandum No. 16959. Santa Monica: Rand Corporation.

CHOU, LI-PO, 1961. *Great Changes in a Mountain Village.* Peking: Foreign Languages Press.

CH'UAN, HAN-SHENG, 1956. "Production and Distribution of Rice in Southern Sung," in E-tu Zen Sun, ed., *Chinese Social History* (Washington: American Council of Learned Studies), pp. 222–33.

COULING, SAMUEL, 1917. *The Encyclopedia Sinica.* Shanghai: Kelly and Walsh.

DAWSON, O. L., 1966. "China's Cotton Outlook," *The China Mainland Review*, Dec. 1966.

DAWSON, O. L., 1965. "China's Two-pronged Agricultural Dilemma," *Current Scene*, vol. III, No. 20.

DERNBERGER, ROBERT F., 1965. "Foreign Trade and Capital Movements of Communist China, 1949–1962." (Unpublished doctoral dissertation, Harvard University.)

DURAND, JOHN D., 1960. "The Population Statistics of China, A.D. 2–1953," *Population Studies*, Vol. XIII, No. 2, Mar. 1960, pp. 209–56.

D'OHSSON, M. LEBAYSON C., 1834. *Histoire des Mongols.* Amsterdam: Les Freres Van Cleef.

DONNITHORNE, AUDREY, 1967. *China's Economic System.* New York: Praeger.

East Asiatic Economic Investigation Bureau, 1932. *The Manchuria Year Book, 1932–1933.* Tokyo: East Asiatic Economic Investigation Bureau.

ECKSTEIN, ALEXANDER, 1966. *Communist China's Economic Growth and Foreign Trade.* New York: McGraw-Hill.

ECKSTEIN, ALEXANDER, 1961. *The National Income of Communist China.* Glencoe: Free Press.

Editor, 1964. "Agriculture in China: 1963," *Current Scene*, Vol. II, No. 27, Jan. 15, 1964.

Editor, 1965. "Decision for an Upsurge," *Current Scene*, Vol. III, No. 17, April 15, 1965.

Editor, 1966. "And Now There are Four," *Current Scene*, Vol. IV, No. 20, Nov. 10, 1966.

ELIASSEN, SIGURD, 1957. *Dragon Wang's River.* New York: Day.

ENDACOTT, G. B., 1958. *A History of Hong Kong.* London: Oxford University Press.

ERISMAN, ALVA LEWIS, 1967. "Potential Costs of and Benefits from Diverting River Flow for Irrigation in the North China Plain" (Unpublished doctoral dissertation, University of Maryland.)

FANG, CHUNG, 1965. "New Achievements in China's Economic Construction," *Peking Review,* No. 39, Sept. 24, 1965, pp. 17–20.

FEI, HSIAO-TUNG, 1946, *Peasant Life in China.* New York: Oxford University Press.

FEI, HSIAO-TUNG and CHANG CHIH-I, 1948. *Earthbound China.* London: Routledge and Kegan Paul.

FEUERWERKER, ALBERT, 1958. *China's Early Industrialization.* Cambridge: Harvard University Press.

FIELD, ROBERT MICHAEL, 1967. "Chinese Communist Industrial Production," in Joint Economic Committee, *An Economic Profile of Mainland China* (Washington: U.S. Government Printing Office), pp. 269–95.

Food and Agriculture Organization of the United Nations, 1949. *Food Balance Sheets.* Washington.

Food and Agriculture Organization of the United Nations, 1963. *Food Balance Sheets 1957–1959 Average.* Rome.

Foreign Documents Division of CIA, "Agricultural Statistics," *Weekly Reports on Communist China,* Nos. 5, 9, 13, 17, 21 and 26; Dec. 18, 1959–May 20, 1960.

FUTRELL, R. F., 1961. *The U.S. Air Force in Korea, 1950–1953.* New York: Duell, Sloan and Pearce.

GAMBLE, SIDNEY D., 1963. *North China Villages.* Berkeley and Los Angeles: University of California Press.

GERNET, JACQUES, 1962. *Daily Life in China.* London: George Allen and Unwin.

GRILLICHES, ZVI, 1964. "Research Expenditures, Education, and the Aggregate Agricultural Production Function," *American Economic Review,* LIV, No. 6, Dec. 1964, pp. 961–74.

GUILLAIN, ROBERT, 1966. *When China Wakes.* New York: Walker.

HARTWELL, ROBERT, 1967. "A Cycle of Economic Change in Imperial China: Coal and Iron in Northeast China, 750–1350," *Journal of the Economic and Social History of the Orient,* Vol. X, Part I, July 1967, pp. 102–59.

HEADY, EARL O., and DILLON, JOHN L., 1961. *Agricultural Production Functions.* Ames: Iowa State University Press.

HERRMANN, ALBERT, 1966. *Historical and Commercial Atlas of China.* Chicago: Aldine Publishing Company.

HO, PING-TI, 1959. *Studies on the Population of China, 1368–1953.* Cambridge: Harvard University Press.

HO, PING-TI, 1962. *The Ladder of Success in Imperial China.* New York: Columbia University Press.

Hong Kong, Report for the Year, 1961, 1962. Hong Kong: Government Press.

HOSHINO, T., 1920. *Economic History of Manchuria.* Seoul: Bank of Chosen.

HOU, CHI-MING, 1965. *Foreign Investment and Economic Development in China, 1840–1937.* Cambridge: Harvard University Press.

HSIA, RONALD, 1958. "Government Acquisition of Agricultural Output in Mainland China, 1953–1956," Rand Research Memorandum No. AD 211940. Santa Monica: Rand Corporation.

HSIAO, KUNG-CHUAN, 1960. *Rural China: Imperial Control in the Nineteenth Century.* Seattle: University of Washington Press.

HSUEH, MU-CHIAO, *et al.,* 1960. *The Socialist Transformation of the National Economy of China.* Peking: Foreign Languages Press.

HU, CHI, 1964. "How Industry Helps Agriculture," *Peking Review,* No. 50, Dec. 11, 1964, reprinted in *Extracts from China Mainland Magazines,* No. 449, pp. 24–28.

HUC, M., 1855. *Travels in the Chinese Empire,* 2 vols. New York: Harper and Bros.

HUNTER, HOLLAND, 1965. "Transport in Soviet and Chinese Development," *Economic Development and Cultural Change*, Oct. 1965.

Imperial Maritime Customs, *Annual Reports and Returns of Trade*.

India, 1960, 1960. Delhi: Government of India.

Institute for Stragetic Studies, 1964. *The Military Balance, 1964–1965*. London: Institute for Strategic Studies.

ISHIKAWA, SHIGERU, 1965. *National Income and Capital Formation in Mainland China*. Tokyo: Institute of Asian Economic Affairs.

ISHIKAWA, SHIGERU, 1967. "Resource Flow between Agriculture and Industry: The Chinese Experience," *The Developing Economies*, Mar. 1967, Vol. V, No. 1, pp. 3–49.

JAMES, H. E. M., 1888. *The Long White Mountain*. London: Longmans Green.

JAMIESON, GEORGE, 1890. "Tenure of Land in China and the Condition of the Rural Population," *Chinese Economic and Social Life*, Vol. 2, pp. 59–183.

KAO, KUANG-CHIEN, 1964. "Chemical Fertilizer Industry Flourishes," *Peking Review*, Sept. 18, 1964, p. 25.

KAO, KUANG-CHIEN, 1965. "Great Stride Forward in Fertilizers," *China Reconstructs*, No. 2, Feb. 1965, reprinted in *Extracts from China Mainland Magazines*, No. 458, pp. 39–41.

KING, F. H., 1912. "The Wonderful Canals of China," *The National Geographic Magazine*, Oct. 1912, Vol. XXIII, No. 10, pp. 931–58.

KRAUS, RICHARD. "Cotton in China, 1918–1936" (Unpublished doctoral dissertation, Harvard University, 1968).

KUNG, H. O., 1937. "The Growth of Population in Six Large Chinese Cities," *Chinese Economic Journal*, Mar. 1937, pp. 301–14.

KUO, TUNG-TS'AI, 1964. "From Nothing to Something, From Scarcity to Plenty: A Brilliant Record," *Nung-yeh chi-hsieh chi-shu*, No. 9, Sept. 13, 1964, translated in *Extracts from China Mainland Magazines*, No. 442, pp. 15–19.

LI, CHOH-MING, 1962. *The Statistical System of Communist China*. Berkeley: University of California Press.

LIEU, D. K., 1941, *The Silk Industry of China*. Shanghai: Kelly and Walsh.

LINDSAY, T. J., 1958. "Water Conservancy and Hydroelectric Schemes in China," *Contemporary China*, Vol. II, pp. 36–51, Vol. III, pp. 163–80.

LIU, JUNG-CHAO, 1965. "Fertilizer Supply and Grain Production in Communist China," *Journal of Farm Economics*, Nov. 1965, pp. 915–32.

LIU, TA-CHUNG and YEH, KUNG-CHIA, 1965. *The Economy of the Chinese Mainland: National Income and Economic Development, 1933–1959*. Princeton: Princeton University Press.

LOCKWOOD, WILLIAM W., *The State and Economic Enterprise in Japan*. Princeton: Princeton University Press.

MACDOUGALL, COLINA, 1964. "Eight Plants for Peking," *Far Eastern Economic Review*, Jan. 23, 1964, p. 156.

MALLORY, WALTER H., 1926. *China: Land of Famine*. New York: American Geographical Society.

Manchoukuo Yearbook 1942, 1942. Hsinking: Manchoukuo Yearbook Co.

MARGARY, AUGUSTUS, R., 1876. *The Journey of Augustus Raymond Margary (from his journals and letters)*. London: Macmillan.

MARGLIN, STEPHEN A. "Industrial Development in the Labor Surplus Economy: An Essay in the Theory of Optimal Growth" (unpublished paper).

MARTIN, H. D., 1950. *Chinghis Khan and His Conquest of North China*. Baltimore: Johns Hopkins Press.

MARTIN, R. MONTGOMERY, 1847. *China: Political, Commercial, and Social*, 2 vols. London: James Madden.

MESKILL, JOHN (trans.), 1965. *Ch'oe Pu's Diary: A Record of Drifting Across the Sea*. Tuscon: Association for Asian Studies.

MORSE, H. B., 1889. "Currency and Measures in China," in *Chinese Economic and Social Life* (1889) Vol. 2, pp. 46–107.

MURAMATSU, YUJI, 1966. "A Documentary Study of Chinese Landlordism in Late Ch'ing and Early Republican Kiangnan," *Bulletin of the School of Oriental and African Studies*, Vol. XXIX, No. 33 (1966), pp. 566–99.

MURPHEY, RHOADS, 1953. *Shanghai: Key to Modern China.* Cambridge: Harvard University Press.

MYERS, RAMON, 1968. *The Chinese Peasant Economy: Development in Hopei and Shantung Between 1890 and 1949.*

MYRDAL, JAN, 1965. *Report from a Chinese Village.* New York: Pantheon.

NAKAMURA, JAMES, I., 1966. *Agricultural Production and the Economic Development of Japan 1873–1922.* Princeton: Princeton University Press.

National Research Institute of Social Sciences, Academia Sinica, 1931. *Statistics of China's Foreign Trade During the Last Sixty-Five Years.*

NICHOLS, FRANCIS H., 1902. *Through Hidden Shensi.* New York: Scribners.

OGURA, TAKEKAZU (ed.), 1963. *Agricultural Development in Modern Japan.* Tokyo: Japan FAO Association.

OHKAWA, K., 1957. *The Growth Rate of the Japanese Economy since 1878.* Tokyo: Kinokuniya Bookstore.

PARKER, E. H., 1890. "The Financial Capacity of China," *Chinese Economic and Social Life*, Vol. 1, pp. 74–141.

PARKER, E. H., 1901. *China: Her History, Diplomacy and Commerce.* New York: E. P. Dutton.

PARSONS, JAMES B., 1956. "A Case History of Revolt in China, The Late Ming Rebellion of Chang Hsien-chung," *Oriens Extremus*, July 1956, pp. 81–93.

PERKINS, DWIGHT H., 1966. *Market Control and Planning in Communist China.* Cambridge: Harvard University Press.

PERKINS, DWIGHT H., 1967. "Economic Growth in China and the Cultural Revolution," *The China Quarterly*, April–June 1967, pp. 33–48.

PIRENNE, HENRI, 1936. *Economic and Social History of Medieval Europe.* New York: Harcourt, Brace.

PRAWDIN, MICHAEL, 1940. *The Mongol Empire, Its Rise and Legacy.* London: George Allen and Unwin.

REISCHAUER, EDWIN O., and FAIRBANK, JOHN K., 1958. *East Asia: The Great Tradition.* Boston: Houghton Mifflin.

RICHARDS, L., 1908. *Comprehensive Geography of the Chinese Empire.* Shanghai: T'u se wei Press.

ROCKHILL, W. W., 1922. "An Inquiry into the Population of China," in C. F. Remer (ed.), *Readings in Economics for China* (Shanghai: Commercial Press), pp. 463–95.

ROSOVSKY, HENRY, 1968. "Rumbles in the Ricefields: Professor Nakamura vs. the Official Statistics," *Journal of Asian Studies*, Feb. 1968.

Royal Asiatic Society, 1890. "Inland Communications in China," in *Chinese Economic and Social Life*, Vol. 2, pp. 1–213.

SAKAKIDA, EVELYN, 1967. "Fukien in the Mid-Sixteenth Century: A Socio-Economic Study." (Unpublished doctoral dissertation, Harvard University.)

SCHULTZ, THEODORE W., 1964. *Transforming Traditional Agriculture.* New Haven: Yale University Press.

SCHURMANN, H. F., 1956. *Economic Structure of the Yuan Dynasty.* Cambridge: Harvard Yenching Institute Studies.

SHABAD, THEODORE, 1956, *China's Changing Map.* New York: Praeger.

SHEN, THEODORE H., 1951. *Agricultural Resources of China.* Ithaca: Cornell University Press.

SKINNER, G. WILLIAM, 1964–1965. "Marketing and Social Structure in Rural China," Parts I–III, *Journal of Asian Studies*, Vol. XXIV, Numbers 1–3, Nov. 1964, pp. 3–44; Feb. 1965, pp. 195–228; May 1965, pp. 363–400.

SMITH, THOMAS C., 1959. *The Agrarian Origins of Modern Japan.* Stanford: Stanford University Press.

SOLOW, ROBERT, 1957. "Technical Change and the Aggregate Production Function," *The Review of Economics and Statistics*, Vol. 39 (Aug. 1957), pp. 312–20.

State Statistical Bureau, 1960. *Ten Great Years*. Peking: Foreign Languages Press.

STAUNTON, GEORGE, 1799. *Embassy to China*, 2 vols. Philadelphia: Robert Campbell.

Sun, Ching-chih (ed.), 1958. *Hua-chung ti-ch'u ching-chi ti-li* (An economic geography of central China). Peking: Science Press, translated in JPRS No. 2227-N.

Sun, Ching-chih (ed.), 1959a. *Hua-tung ti-ch'u ching-chi ti-li* (An economic geography of east China). Peking: Science Press, translated in JPRS No. 11,438.

Sun, Ching-chih (ed.), 1959b. *Hua-nan ti-ch'u ching-chi ti-li* (An economic geography of south China). Peking: Science Press, translated in JPRS No. 14,954.

Sun, Ching-chih (ed.), 1959c. *Hua-tung-pei ti-ch'u ching-chi ti-li* (An economic geography of the northeast). Peking: Science Press, translated in JPRS No. 15,388.

Sun, Ching-chih (ed.), 1960. *Hua-hsi-nan ti-ch'u ching-chi ti-li* (An economic geography of southwest China). Peking: Science Press, translated in JPRS No. 15,069.

SUNG, YING-HSING, 1966. *T'ien-kung k'ai-wu*, trans. E-tu Zen and Shiou-chuan Sun (University Park and London: Pennsylvania State University Press).

SWANN, NANCY LEE, 1950, *Food and Money in Ancient China*. Princeton: Princeton University Press.

TAEUBER, IRENE B. and WANG, NAI-CHI, 1960. "Population Reports in the Ch'ing Dynasty," *Journal of Asian Studies*, Aug. 1960, pp. 403–17.

TANG, ANTHONY M., 1968. "Policy and Performance in Agriculture," in A. Eckstein, W. Galenson, and T. C. Liu (ed.), *Economic Trends in Mainland China*. Chicago: Aldine Publishing Company.

TAWNEY, R. H., 1932. *Land and Labour in China*. London: George Allen and Unwin.

"The Quiet Revolution: A Call for Action in World Agriculture," 1965. Skokie: International Minerals and Chemicals Corporation.

TS'AO, TING and LIANG, K'UANG-PAI, 1965. "The Role of Communications and Transport in Our National Economy," *Ching-chi yen-chiu* No. 2, Feb. 20, 1965, trans. in *Extracts from China Mainland Magazines*, No. 461, pp. 18–25.

TUMA, ELIAS H., 1965. *Twenty-six Centuries of Agrarian Reform*. Berkeley and Los Angeles: University of California Press.

TUNG, TA-LIN, 1958. *Agricultural Cooperation in China*. Peking: Foreign Languages Press.

TWITCHETT, DENNIS C., 1963. *Financial Administration under the T'ang Dynasty*. Cambridge: Cambridge University Press.

ULLMAN, MORRIS, B., 1961. *Cities of Mainland China, 1953 and 1958*. Washington: Foreign Manpower Research Office.

United Nations, 1963. *Statistical Yearbook, 1962*. New York: United Nations.

WALKER, KENNETH R., 1965. *Planning in Chinese Agriculture*. Chicago: Aldine Publishing Company.

WALKER, KENNETH R., 1968. "Organization for Agricultural Production in China," in A. Eckstein, W. Galenson and T. C. Liu (eds.), *Economic Trends in Mainland China*. Chicago: Aldine Publishing Company.

WANG, YEH-CHIEN, 1965, "The Impact of the Taiping Rebellion on Population in the Southern Part of Kiangsu," *Papers on China*, Vol. 19 (Dec. 1965), pp. 120–58.

WANG, YEH-CHIEN. "Agricultural Development and Peasant Economy in Hunan during the Ch'ing Period." (Unpublished seminar paper.)

WANG, YEH-CHIEN. "China's Land Taxation in the Late Ch'ing." (Draft, unpublished doctoral dissertation, Harvard University.)

"Water Conservancy," *China News Analysis*, No. 579, Sept. 3, 1965.

WELCH, HOLMES, 1967. *The Practice of Chinese Buddhism 1900–1950*. Cambridge: Harvard University Press.

WIENS, THOMAS, 1966. "The British American Tobacco Company and the Nanyang Brothers Tobacco Company." (Unpublished paper.)

WILBUR, C. MARTIN, 1968. "Militarism and the Nationalist Regime: Political Disintegration and Reestablishment of Central Authority," in P. T. Ho and T. Tsou (eds.), *China's Heritage and the Communist Political System* (Chicago: University of Chicago Press).

WITTFOGEL, KARL A., 1957. *Oriental Despotism*. New Haven: Yale University Press.

WRIGHT, MARY, 1957. *The Last Stand of Chinese Conservatism*. Stanford: Stanford University Press.

WRIGHT, STANLEY F., 1938. *China's Struggle for Tariff Autonomy, 1843-1938*. Shanghai: Kelly and Walsh.

WU, YUAN-LI, 1956. *An Economic Survey of Communist China*. New York: Bookman.

WU, YUAN-LI, et al., 1963. *The Economic Potential of Communist China*, 3 vols. Menlo Park: Stanford Research Institute.

YANG, C. K., 1959. *A Chinese Village in Early Communist Transition*. Cambridge: Technology Press.

YANG, LIEN-SHENG, 1961. "Numbers and Units in Chinese Economic History," *Studies in Chinese Institutional History*. Cambridge: Harvard University Press, pp. 75-84.

YANG, MARTIN C., 1945. *A Chinese Village: Taitou, Shantung Province*. New York: Columbia University Press.

YAO, SHAN-YU, 1943. "The Geographical Distribution of Floods and Droughts in Chinese History, 206 B.C.–A.D. 1911," *The Far Eastern Quarterly*, Aug. 1943.

Index